M000308788

3D MODELING IN AUTOCAD

Creating and Using 3D Models in AutoCAD 2000

John E. Wilson

San Francisco

Published by CMP Books

600 Harrison Street, San Francisco, CA 94107

An Imprint of CMP Media, Inc.

Copyright © 1999 by John E. Wilson. All rights reserved. No part of this book covered by copyrights hereon may be reproduced or copied in any manner whatsoever without written permission, except in the case of brief quotations embodied in articles and reviews. For information contact the publishers.

The programs and applications on the accompanying disk have been carefully tested, but are not guaranteed for any particular purpose. The publisher does not offer any warranties and does not guarantee the accuracy, adequacy, or completeness of any information and is not responsible for any errors or omissions or the results obtained from use of such information.

Distributed to the book trade in the U.S. and Canada by

Publishers Group West, 1700 Fourth Street, Berkeley, CA 94710

Cover Design: Visual Group

Interior Design and Composition: Greene Design

Library of Congress Catalog Card Number: 99-041431

ISBN 0-87930-551-7

Printed in the United States of America

  00 01 02 03 04   5 4 3 2

Preface

With mechanical engineering degree in hand, John Wilson cut his CAD teeth in Idaho beginning with AutoCAD 2.5. Joining project teams that numbered 8,000-plus, he designed nuclear reactors for the Department of Energy back in the days before nuclear power developed a less than stellar reputation. Wilson was a member of project teams in charge of designing fuel rods and constructing experiments that would place these rods under severe conditions to determine their meltdown threshold. Talk about the vital application of design principles and the need for high quality—and accurate—design tools!

His Idaho days also saw Wilson designing fuel rods for use in nuclear submarines, but a yearning for city life and independence drew him to Minneapolis where he set up shop as an independent designer. He submitted his first feature to an upstart CAD publication in 1991. His article on fonts that ran in the September issue of *CADENCE* turned into a four-part series. And that became the mark of John Wilson. He soon earned the reputation as a writer who was a master of his material, and one who preferred covering subjects comprehensively.

When AutoCAD with Release 10 introduced 3D capabilities, Wilson went to work mastering them in short order. By Release 11, he had proposed a series of articles on how to plumb Auto-CAD's 3D depths. The June 1993 issue of *CADENCE* debuted Wilson's 3D tips for AutoCAD, and he hasn't missed turning in a column since.

With the current tome, I'll go on record saying that Wilson has written the book on AutoCAD and 3D. This book has everything you could possibly want to know about how to take advantage of AutoCAD's 3D features, including the latest changes introduced with AutoCAD 2000. Wilson jokingly says that the book probably even sports a thing or two about 3D that you'd rather not know. But that's a mark of his infectious self-deprecating humor. You do want to know everything you can about AutoCAD's 3D capabilities, if it's your software of choice. And John Wilson takes you through each 3D feature step-by-step in his usual clear, concise and insightful manner.

If you're an architect, Wilson will show you how to render simple models for your client proposals. And for those of you who belong to the MCAD discipline, Wilson can show you how to achieve about 80 percent of all the solid modeling capabilities you'll ever need for modeling parts and machinery. And you'll find using AutoCAD in this way to be easier in many cases than working with a parametric modeler.

Today John Wilson continues his very successful independent one-person business designing waste-water treatment facilities and working on other environmental projects. A team of one is a bit smaller than one of 8,000, and water treatment doesn't necessarily have the adrenaline-boosting affect of fuel-rod experiments, but Wilson nevertheless sees a challenge in continually working to hone his design skills. In his columns, as in this book, he generously shares insights into 3D gained over years and years of perfecting his craft.

We at CADENCE find him to be one of our top columnists and authors. And we're sure you'll find him to be without parallel in helping you mine the 3D riches of AutoCAD.

—Arnie Williams, Editor in Chief, *CADENCE*

Table of Contents

Introduction

Hard to Use, Impractical, Difficult to learn, Crude, Slow. All of these expressions have been used to describe 3D modeling in AutoCAD. At one time there was some validity in each of them, but as AutoCAD and the computers that run AutoCAD become more and more powerful and sophisticated, the reasons for not using the 3D features of AutoCAD become less and less valid. AutoCAD has good 3D modeling capabilities, most objects in the real world are 3D, and most designs should be done in 3D.

The advantages of designing in 3D are almost self evident. Since you actually construct (in a computer) the object you are designing, rather than draw views of it that are as you imagine it looks, the design is more likely to be correct and accurate. From that model, realistic shaded pictures (renderings) can be produced to show what the design will look like, and dimensioned, multi-view 2D drawings can be made for manufacturing it.

What's in This Book

This book will guide you through all of the AutoCAD commands and techniques for building 3D models. You will discover that most 3D work involves the same commands, and uses the same tools that 2D drafting does. Therefore, to be successful in 3D you should have a good basic knowledge of AutoCAD's commands, along with skill and experience in using those commands.

While this book assumes that you do have a working knowledge of AutoCAD, it makes no assumptions about your knowledge and experience in using its 3D features. Therefore, the all of the concepts and principles of AutoCAD's 3D features will be explained completely, and hands-on exercises will give you experience in using them. Furthermore, detailed descriptions of every AutoCAD command related to 3D are included to serve as a reference. These descriptions go beyond those of AutoCAD's on-screen help, and even beyond the AutoCAD manuals.

AutoCAD, a computer to run AutoCAD, this book, and the CD-ROM that comes with the book are all you need. You do not need to acquire or learn any extra cost external programs. Also, you do not need to know anything about AutoCAD customization or about programming. Although a few AutoLISP programs will be used to enhance some AutoCAD functions, they are included on the CD-ROM, and instructions for using them are given in the book.

The book is divided into five sections, as follows:

- Section 1: Working With 3D Wireframe Models in 3D Space. This section will introduce you to 3D space and to the tools for working in it. Chapters in this section will teach you, among other things, how to specify 3D points, how to view objects in 3D space, and how to control AutoCAD's moveable coordinate system. Although the section's emphasis is on wireframes, you will find its information valuable even if your primary interest is in surface modeling or solid modeling.

- Section 2: Building Surface Models. This section of the book will explain how to build models that represent building and rooms; as well as models that have sculpted free-form shapes, such as those in automobile body parts. It will also show you how to set up perspective views, and how to remove obstructing objects from views.

- Section 3: Solid Modeling. Chapters in this section will tell you how to use the powerful solid modeling capabilities that are built into AutoCAD. You will learn how to build solids from profiles, as well as from primitives, and how to use Boolean operations to make complex solid models.

- Section 4: 2D Output and Paper Space. Even though the objects you design are 3D, most manufacturing and construction operations depend on 2D documentation. Chapters in this section will show you how to make conventional 2D drawings from 3D models.

- Section 5: Renderings From 3D Models. In this section you will find out how to make realistic shaded images from 3D models. You will learn how to install lights, how to make shiny surfaces (and even transparent and reflective surfaces), how to attach images of building materials (such as bricks and shingles) to surfaces, and how to add landscape objects to renderings.

Subjects are arranged in an order that builds upon previous information to systematically lead you through all of AutoCAD's 3D features; beginning with an elementary explanation of coordinate systems, and ending with advanced techniques in rendering.

Ideally therefore, you should read each chapter in order. However, depending upon your level of 3D experience and your areas of interest, you may choose to concentrate on specific sections and chapters. If, for example, if your interests are largely architectural, the subjects you may want to concentrate on will be in sections one, two, and five. On the other hand, if your interests are principally related to mechanical parts, you may want to concentrate on the subjects in sections one, three, and four.

What's on the CD-ROM

Practice and experimentation is the best way—perhaps the only way—to become adept in building 3D models. Therefore, this book contains numerous exercises to give you experience in using the AutoCAD 3D related commands and features. To fully utilize this book, you should do the exercises. Finished versions of the 3D models of most exercises are in AutoCAD drawing files on the CD-ROM that comes with this book. You can then compare the model you built with the corresponding model on the CD-ROM. Also, some exercises start with a model that is in a file on the CD-ROM.

The CD-ROM also contains the script files and the AutoLISP programs that are referred to in the book. As a bonus, numerous bitmap image files suitable for use in rendering materials are on the CD-ROM. See Appendix A for details on the CD-ROM contents.

Working with Wireframe Models in 3D Space

The World Coordinate System and 3D Space

This chapter will help you establish a foundation for working in 3D space. Even though the principles and techniques explained in this chapter are in the book section emphasizing wireframes, they apply equally well to surface models and solid models.

You should at least skim through this chapter even if you are already acquainted with coordinate systems and viewpoints—the chapter contains some details and facts that you may not know. Specifically, this chapter will

- describe AutoCAD's 3D World Coordinate System;
- explain how to interpret and manage AutoCAD's coordinate system icon;
- discuss the proper orientation of models in 3D space;
- show you how to establish viewpoints in 3D space;
- describe techniques in specifying points in 3D space;
- lead you through two exercises in constructing simple 3D wireframe models.

AutoCAD's 3D World Coordinate System

AutoCAD uses three mutually perpendicular lines, which intersect at a point called the *origin*, to identify point locations in 3D space. These three lines are named the *X axis*, the *Y axis*, and the *Z axis*. With them, the location of any point in 3D space can be specified by the point's distance from the origin in the X direction, in the Y direction, and in the Z direction. These three distances, which are called *coordinates*, are usually written together, separated by commas.

A point, for example, having the coordinates of 2.25, 1.75, 2.50 is 2.25 units from the origin in the X direction, 1.75 units from the origin in the Y direction, and 2.50 units from the origin in the Z direction. The coordinates of the origin are 0,0,0. The units used for distance may be inches, millimeters, miles, light-years, or any other measurement system you choose.

AutoCAD displays the current coordinates of the screen cursor in the drawing editor status bar on your computer screen. Beginning with Release 14, all three coordinate values are displayed (the Z coordinate will generally be 0). Previous releases of AutoCAD displayed only the X and Y coordinates.

The X, Y, and Z axes extend an infinite distance in both directions from the origin, with each axis having a positive and a negative direction. A minus sign preceding a coordinate value means that the distance is in the negative direction from the origin. The figure on the lower right shows the point coordinates for selected corners on a 3D solid model. Notice that some of the coordinate values have negative numbers, indicating they are on the negative side of the origin.

AutoCAD refers to this setup for designating point locations as the *World Coordinate System (WCS)*. AutoCAD has a secondary coordinate system, called the *User Coordinate System (UCS)*, that can be moved about within the WCS to make it easier for you to draw objects in 3D space. Since this movable coordinate system is extremely important in building 3D models, we will devote considerable space to the UCS in the next chapter.

Two other terms regarding coordinate systems that you will encounter as you work with AutoCAD are *model space* and *paper space*. Model space is the fully 3D environment that we have just described. It is the space you work in as you build 3D models. Paper space, on the other hand, is a 2D world that has only X and Y axes and is used for making 2D drawings of 3D objects. AutoCAD's **tilemode** system variable determines whether model space or paper space is in effect. We will describe paper space completely and explain how to use it in Section Four.

The X-Y Plane

While the WCS contains an infinite number of planes, the one defined by the X and Y axes is especially important in AutoCAD, because

- A pointing device, whether it is a mouse or a digitizer, can specify points off the X-Y plane only through the use of object snaps on existing objects. (There is one exception that we will cover later in this chapter when we discuss AutoCAD's ELEVATION command.)

- Virtually all 2D drafting is done on the X-Y plane.
- Many AutoCAD objects—including circles, arcs, and 2D polylines—are always drawn either on or parallel to the X-Y plane.
- When AutoCAD's grid is displayed, it is placed on the X-Y plane. (Again, there is one exception that will be covered soon.)
- Most AutoCAD prototype and template drawings start out with a viewpoint that looks straight down on the X-Y plane. This particular viewpoint is often referred to as the *plan view*.

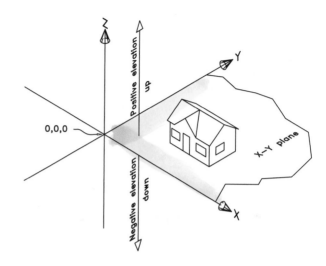

- The X-Y plane is generally considered to be a level, or horizontal, plane. Therefore, most 3D models are based on the X-Y plane. A 3D model house, for instance, is almost always drawn with its floor on, or parallel to, the X-Y plane.

Since the X-Y plane represents a horizontal plane, distance from the X-Y plane in the Z axis direction represents height, or *elevation*. Consequently, the term elevation is often used in Auto-CAD prompts and messages when referring to distance in the Z direction from the X-Y plane, as well as to the value of the Z coordinate. Also, the terms *up*, *down*, *above*, and *below* are commonly relative to the X-Y plane; with up and above referring to the positive side of the X-Y plane, and down and below referring to the negative side.

The Right-Hand Rule

Since the positive end of the Z axis can physically point in either of two directions from the X-Y plane, a convention is needed to consistently establish its positive and negative directions. Autodesk, along with everyone else involved in 3D geometry, follows the *right-hand rule*. While the right-hand rule can be defined by vector mathematics, it is more easily defined and visualized by using your right hand. One method is to mentally extend your right arm along the Y axis toward the origin, with your fingers curled toward the X axis. Your extended thumb will then point in the positive direction of the Z axis.

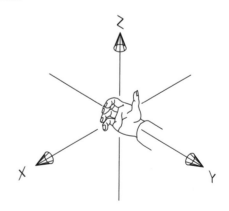

Another technique commonly used in visualizing the right-hand rule is to point the thumb of your right hand in the positive X direction and extend your index finger in the positive Y direction. Then, curl your middle finger 90 degrees from your index finger—it will point in the positive direction of the Z axis.

See if you can spot the right-hand coordinate systems in the figure below.

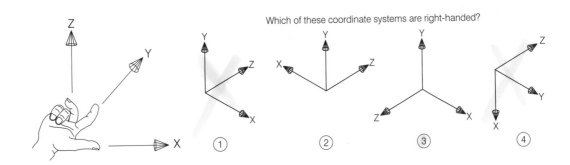

Which of these coordinate systems are right-handed?

The UCS Icon

The coordinate systems numbered 2 and 3 in the figure on the right are right-handed, while the other two are not. To assist you in keeping directions straight as you work in 3D space, AutoCAD has an icon that shows the directions of the X, Y, and Z axes. It is called the *UCS icon* because it indicates the current location and orientation of AutoCAD's supplementary, movable UCS. (We will discuss the UCS in the next chapter.) When no UCS is being used, which will be the case throughout this chapter, the icon shows the direction of the WCS axes.

Even though the icon is relatively simple in appearance, it is packed with information:

- The UCS icon lies on the X-Y plane and has two wide arrows indicating the directions of the X and Y axes.
- When the icon is located on the coordinate system origin, the icon will have a plus-sign-shaped cross at the junction of the X and Y axes.
- When the 3D space viewpoint is one that looks toward the X-Y plane from the positive Z direction, a box will be drawn at the junction of the X and Y axes.
- When no UCS is being used, a W is shown on the Y axis.

If no UCS is being used, this W will be shown.

This arrow points in the Y axis direction.

If you are looking down on the X-Y plane, these lines will be shown.

If the UCS icon is positioned at the origin, this cross will be shown.

This arrow points in the X axis direction.

The UCS icon is managed through AutoCAD's UCSICON command. This command has options for turning the display of the icon on or off, and for causing it to be positioned either on the coordinate system origin or in the lower-left corner of the current viewport. When the option to position the icon on the origin is in effect and the origin is either outside the current viewport or very close to the viewport's edge, the icon will automatically move to the lower-left corner of the viewport.

The figures on the next page show a 3D solid model as it might appear when various UCS icon settings, viewpoints, and coordinate systems are used. Notice the differences in the appearance of the UCS icon.

Similar to AutoCAD's dot grid, the UCS icon is transparent to screen picks and cannot be printed. Although you may prefer to keep the UCS icon turned off while working in 2D, you will want it on as you work in 3D space. Most of the time you will also want it positioned on the coordinate system origin. Occasionally though, especially if you are working close to the origin, it may obscure objects. Then, you may want to temporarily move it to the lower-left corner of the viewport, or perhaps even turn it off for a while.

When your viewpoint in 3D space is one that looks edge-on, or almost edge-on, to the X-Y plane, the UCS icon is replaced by an icon showing a broken pencil. The broken pencil represents a warning that you should not rely on your pointing device to specify points. You can, however, continue to use object snaps with your pointing device to specify points. The figure on the right shows the same solid model shown in the previous figures as it is seen when the viewpoint is parallel to the X-Y plane.

No UCS is in effect.
UCS icon is located at the origin.
The viewpoint looks at the X-Y plane from the positive Z direction.

No UCS is in effect.
UCS icon is located at the origin.
The viewpoint looks at the X-Y plane from the negative Z direction.

No UCS is in effect.
UCS icon is not located at the origin.
The viewpoint looks at the X-Y plane from the positive Z direction.

A UCS is in effect.
UCS icon is located at the origin.
The viewpoint looks at the X-Y plane from the positive Z direction.

The broken pencil icon indicates that the viewpoint is edge-on, or nearly edge-on, with the X-Y plane.

Command: UCSICON

Purpose: This command controls whether or not the UCS icon is displayed and whether or not it is to be positioned at the coordinate system origin.

Initiate with:

- On the command line, enter UCSICON.

- From the View pull-down menu, select Display. Then select UCS Icon.

Options:

The following options are offered in a command line menu:

- ON

This option causes the UCS icon to be displayed.

- OFF

The display of the UCS icon is turned off by this option.

- All

  By default, the ON, OFF, Noorigin, and ORigin options affect only the current viewport. This option, however, causes their settings to affect all viewports. When this option is selected, AutoCAD will reoffer the ON, OFF, Noorigin, and ORigin options on the command line.

- Noorigin

  When this option is in effect, the UCS icon will always be positioned in the lower-left corner of the viewport, regardless of the location of the UCS origin.

- ORigin

  This option causes the UCS icon to be positioned on the UCS origin. When the view is such that the UCS origin is either not in the current viewport or is close to its edge, the UCS icon will be positioned in the viewport's lower-left corner.

Notes:

- In model space, the UCS icon is shaped like two wide arrows. In paper space, it is shaped like a 30- to 60-degree triangle with the short side indicating the direction of the X axis.

- AutoCAD 2000 will display the UCS icon as three mutually perpendicular arrows when the 3D wireframe viewing mode of the SHADEMODE command is in effect. You may prefer this form of the UCS icon, even though it does not give as much information as the standard icon. See the description of the SHADEMODE command in Chapter 7 for more information about the 3D wireframe viewing mode and this alternate UCS icon form.

Related system variable:

- **ucsicon**

  The integer within this system variable controls the UCS icon display in the current viewport. Its value, which can range from 0 to 3, is the sum of the following:

  0   The UCS icon is not displayed.

  1   The UCS icon is displayed.

  2   The UCS icon will be positioned at the UCS origin.

  Thus, when **ucsicon** equals 3, the UCS icon will be displayed and will be positioned at the UCS origin, provided the origin is in the viewport. When **ucsicon** equals 2, the UCS icon will not be displayed. (If it were displayed, however, it would be at the UCS origin.) You must use the SETVAR command to access this system variable because its name duplicates a command name.

UCS icon in model space

UCS icon in paper space

Directions and Model Orientation in 3D Space

As you construct a 3D model, you should orient it so that as many of its straight edges and flat sides as possible are parallel with the X, Y, and Z axes. One reason for this is that eventually you are likely to make an orthographic, multiview drawing of your model, and it will be much easier to set up the views when the model's orientation matches the three principal axes. A second reason is that since viewpoint directions in 3D space are relative to the principal axes, you will find it easier to keep your directions straight when you orient your model with the axes.

Orienting your model with the coordinate system axes

Yes   No   Absolutely no

Although your choices of sides to represent the top and front of your model are often rather arbitrary, especially for mechanical items, AutoCAD has some conventions for directions in its menus, toolbars, and dialog boxes that are based upon model orientation. You should keep these conventions in mind as you construct your model:

- The top of the model is the side seen when you are looking straight down on the X-Y plane from the positive end of the Z axis.
- The front of the model is the side seen when you are looking from the negative Y direction toward the positive Y direction.
- The right side of the model is the side seen when you are looking from the positive X direction toward the negative X direction.

Occasionally AutoCAD menus for view directions use compass directions rather than axes directions. The relationship of compass directions to the principal axes is that north points in the same direction as the positive end of the Y axis, while east points in the same direction as the positive end of the X axis. Thus, a NW isometric view is one that looks at the top, back, left side of the model.

Top view

Front view   Right side view

Setting Viewpoints in 3D Space

Just as you walk around a large physical object, such as an automobile or a chair, to examine features on its various sides, you will move around in 3D space to see, and work on, features on various sides of your 3D model. AutoCAD has three different commands for setting general viewpoints in 3D space—VPOINT, 3DORBIT, and DVIEW. 3D ORBIT, which was introduced in AutoCAD 2000, and DVIEW are more complex than VPOINT, being able to set up perspective views and clip away portions of your 3D model to obtain unobstructed views of a particular section, in addition to setting viewpoints. Since these uses are particularly applicable to surface models, we will not discuss 3DORBIT and DVIEW until Section Two of this book.

Although 3DORBIT will probably become your favorite command for setting viewpoints, you will still find VPOINT to be useful for quickly setting exact viewpoints with minimum effort, and you will often use it even though it is a very old 3D command.

AutoCAD also has a dialog box version of the VPOINT command—DDVPOINT—that you may find useful at times. And, since views looking straight down from the Z axis toward the X-Y plane (and the top of your model) are common, AutoCAD has a specialized command—PLAN—for setting that particular viewpoint.

Screen pull-down menus for 3D viewpoints

Using the VPOINT Command

The most important thing to remember as you use VPOINT is that in spite of the command's name and this book's (as well as AutoCAD's) frequent use of the word *viewpoint*, it sets a viewing direction rather than an observation point in space. Consequently, in using the command you specify just a view direction, rather than establish camera and target points. The command will automatically display your entire 3D model regardless of where it is located in 3D space, doing the equivalent of a Zoom-Extents. Then you can use the ZOOM command to move in closer to your model, or further away from it.

VPOINT offers three different methods for setting a view direction—vector direction coordinates, rotation angles, and a rotating tripod. Of the three methods, you are not likely to find the rotating tripod (which represents the principal axes) with its companion bull's-eye target useful. This method is neither faster nor more convenient to use than the other methods, and you cannot set precise, repeatable view directions with it. You cannot, for instance, set up a viewpoint that looks exactly at the right side of your model. You can come close by carefully positioning the bull's-eye cursor in a certain spot, or by rotating the axes tripod until the X axis is pointing directly out of the screen, but it is unlikely that the resulting view direction will be exactly perpendicular to the X-Y plane.

While direction vector coordinates can be used to set any view direction angle, they are especially convenient for quickly and precisely setting one of the principal orthographic and isometric views. A principal orthographic view is one that looks straight at one of the principal coordinate system planes, while an isometric view is one having a view direction that has the same angle with each principal plane. The following table shows the viewpoint direction coordinates for the six principal orthographic views and the eight isometric views.

View	View Coordinates		
Top (Plan)	0,	0,	1
Bottom	0,	0,	-1
Front	0,	-1,	0
Back	0,	1,	0
Left	-1,	0,	0
Right	1,	0,	0
Top/Front/Left Isometric	-1,	-1,	1
Top/Front/Right Isometric	1,	-1,	1
Top/Back/Right Isometric	1,	1,	1
Top/Back/Left Isometric	-1,	1,	1
Bottom/Front/Left Isometric	-1,	-1,	-1
Bottom/Front/Right Isometric	1,	-1,	-1
Bottom/Back/Right Isometric	1,	1,	-1
Bottom/Back/Left Isometric	-1,	1,	-1

Although at times you may want to set a viewpoint that looks precisely head on at one side of your model, most of the time you are better off working from an isometric-type view, because it is hard to visualize depth in your model when you look at it head on. Furthermore, head-on views will generally have objects stacked on top of other objects, which make point selections by object snaps uncertain.

Consider, for example, the wireframe model of a cube. It will be made of twelve equal-length lines. If you have a view looking straight at one side of this cube, it will look like a square, with the lines of the back edges exactly behind the lines making up the front edges. Moreover, the lines for the side edges will not even be noticeable since only their ends are shown.

An isometric view is better for working in 3D, but it too has visualization problems. Although you can generally see all of the objects in the model, lines that are parallel to one another sometimes appear to run into each other. This causes an isometric view of our 3D cube to look like a 2D hexagon that has been divided into triangles. True isometric views are a carryover from 2D drafting, where they are fairly easy to draw since their scale in the three cardinal directions is equal (hence the name, isometric). They are seldom useful viewpoints in 3D modeling, however.

Same wireframe cube seen from three viewpoints

View coordinates:
0,-1,0

View coordinates:
1,-1,1

View coordinates:
0.4967,-0.7094,0.5000

The best viewpoints for working in 3D space are those that have a different angle to each of the three principal axes, such as the one of the cube shown on the right in the previous figure. The view angles you select will depend upon the shape of your model and upon the orientation of the section of the model you are working on. Although the correct name for views having unequal viewing angles is *trimetric,* that name is seldom recognized or used. Therefore we will refer to them in this book as *isometric-type views.*

While some people are comfortable using VPOINT's direction vector coordinates in setting isometric-type views, most prefer to use rotation angles. The method is easy to implement, and after some practice, you will have no trouble visualizing the results. You simply enter the value of two angles—one for the horizontal angle from the X axis, and one for the vertical angle from the X-Y plane. You can input the angles by pointing, but it is generally easier to type them in.

AutoCAD has no limit on the sizes of angles in VPOINT, although there is no reason for you to specify angles greater than 360 degrees since angles greater than 360 degrees wrap around. Thus, a 385-degree angle is the same as a 25-degree angle. Also, vertical angles (those from the X-Y plane) wrap around after 90 degrees and add 180 degrees to the horizontal angle at the same time. For example: a viewing angle 30 degrees from the X axis and 110 degrees from the X-Y plane is equivalent to one 210 degrees from the X axis and 70 degrees from the X-Y plane.

Resulting view

Positive and negative angle rotation directions are controlled by AutoCAD's **angdir** system variable. The default value of 0 for this variable sets the positive angle rotation direction to be counterclockwise. VPOINT accepts negative angle input to rotate the view direction angle in the opposite direction, and you may prefer to do this for angles that exceed 180 degrees. If, for instance, you wanted to set up a view looking up toward the underside of the X-Y plane while making the model of a boat hull, you could specify the angle from the X-Y plane as minus 35 degrees rather than 325 degrees. Even though these two angles are the same, the negative rotation angle may be easier for you to visualize.

Command: VPOINT

Purpose: VPOINT sets a general view direction in 3D space.

Initiate with:

- On the command line enter VPOINT.
- From the View pull-down menu select 3D Views, and then select VPOINT.

Options:

VPOINT displays the current view direction coordinates on the command line and offers the following options:

- Rotate

This option is initiated by entering the letter *r* (you can also enter the entire word *rotate*) when you are prompted to choose an option after starting VPOINT from the command line. AutoCAD will prompt you to enter two angles:

```
Enter angle in XY plane from X axis <current>: Specify an angle.
Enter angle from XY plane <current>: Specify an angle.
```

The angles of the present viewpoint are offered as defaults. VPOINT has no maximum angle limit, with horizontal angles greater than 360 degrees and vertical angles greater than 90 degrees wrapping around. The command also accepts either positive or negative values for angles. Positive angles indicate counter-clockwise view angle rotation, and negative angles indicate clockwise rotations, unless you have set AutoCAD's **angdir** system variable to measure positive angles clockwise.

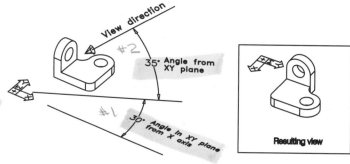

The figure on the right shows the viewpoint resulting from a 30-degree angle in the X-Y plane from the X axis, and a 35-degree angle from the X-Y plane. Notice that even though the vertex of each angle is at the WCS origin, the resulting view centers on the 3D model: VPOINT establishes a view direction rather than a specific viewing point in space.

- Vector

You initiate this option by entering the coordinates of a 3D point when you are prompted for an option after starting VPOINT from the command line. Although the command displays the coordinates of the current viewpoint (regardless of the option used to specify the viewpoint), you cannot press the Enter key to accept them—you must type in three new coordinate values, separated by commas, then press Enter. The resulting view direction will be the same as the direction of a line drawn from the specified point to the origin.

Thus, you could set a viewing direction by entering the vector coordinates 0.7094, 0.4096, 0.5736 when AutoCAD

Resulting view

12

prompts for a viewpoint option. You could also enter the coordinates 7.0941, 4.0958, 5.7358, or even the coordinates 70.9406, 40.9576, 57.3576, to obtain the same viewpoint since the coordinates establish a viewing direction rather than a viewing point.

- Tripod

  This option is initiated by selecting VPOINT (note VPOINT is in upper case in the menu) from the View/3D Views pull-down menu or by pressing Enter when you are prompted to select an option after starting VPOINT from the command line.

  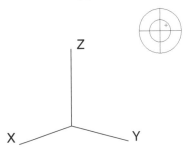

  Your model will disappear as AutoCAD switches to a special screen showing three mutually perpendicular lines labeled X, Y, and Z, which meet at a point to form a tripod-like object, and a bull's-eye-type target. Beginning with Release 14, AutoCAD also shows the UCS icon in its existing position on the screen. The UCS icon, however, is static, and plays no role in selecting a viewpoint.

  A small cross will be in, or near, the bull's-eye target, and as you move your pointing device, the small cross will move and the axes will rotate about their common point. The position of the small cross within the bull's-eye determines the view direction, while the tripod helps you see how the view direction relates to the coordinate system.

  The bull's-eye target consists of two concentric circles, a horizontal line, and a vertical line. The position of the small movable cross within the target is related to the viewpoint as follows:

- When the cross is in the exact center of the circles, the viewpoint will be perpendicular to the X-Y plane from the positive Z direction. In other words, it will result in a plan view.

- When the cross is in the inner circle, the viewpoint will look down from the positive Z direction toward the X-Y plane.

- When the cross is on the perimeter of the inner circle, the viewpoint will look at the edge of the X-Y plane.

- When the cross is in the outer circle, the viewpoint will look up from the negative Z direction toward the underside of the X-Y plane.

- When the cross is below the horizontal line, the viewpoint looks toward the positive Y direction. When the cross is above the horizontal line, the viewpoint looks toward the negative Z direction.

- When the cross is to the right of the vertical line, the viewpoint looks toward the negative X direction. When the cross is to the left of the vertical line, the viewpoint looks toward the positive X direction.

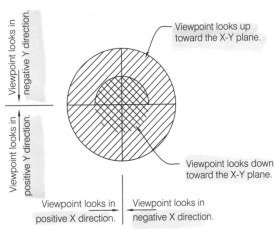

When you have a viewpoint to your satisfaction, press the Pick button on your pointing device. AutoCAD will restore the graphics screen, using the newly specified viewpoint.

Notes:

- It is very important that you recognize that VPOINT, despite its name, sets a viewing direction rather than a point in space from which you are viewing your model.

- Even though VPOINT bases viewpoints, whether they are specified as rotation angles or as vector coordinates, on the coordinate system origin, the model will always be centered in the resulting view, even if it is located a considerable distance from the origin. Also, the zoom level of the resulting view is always the equivalent of a Zoom-Extents.

- Unless the system variable **worldview** has been changed from its default value of 1 to 0, the view direction will be based upon the WCS even if a UCS is being used. AutoCAD will automatically switch from the current UCS to the WCS when VPOINT is started and will switch back to the UCS when the command is finished.

- When multiple viewports exist, VPOINT affects only the current viewport.

Related system variables:

- **angdir**

  This system variable controls the rotation direction, and the measurement direction, of positive angles. Its default setting is 0.

  0 Positive angles are measured counter clockwise.
  1 Positive angles are measured clockwise.

- **viewdir**

  This read-only system variable contains the coordinates of a 3D point. The view direction is equivalent to that of a line drawn from this 3D point to coordinate system origin (0,0,0).

- **worldview**

  This system variable controls whether viewpoints set by VPOINT and DVIEW are to be based upon the WCS or the UCS. It will have an integer value of 0 or 1.

  0 View directions will be based upon the UCS.
  1 View directions will be based upon the WCS. This is the default setting.

Setting Viewpoints through a Dialog Box

DDVPOINT is a dialog box version of VPOINT's Rotate option, in which you can use your pointing device in image tiles to set both the horizontal and vertical viewing angles. While this dialog box is neither faster nor easier to use than the command line version of VPOINT, you may like the protractor-like display of angles that the dialog box uses. Also, its up-front ability to switch the view direction angles from the WCS to the UCS will occasionally be useful, and it gives you another way to set plan views.

Command: DDVPOINT

Purpose: This command enables you to set viewpoint rotation angles graphically through a dialog box.

Initiate with:

- On the command line enter DDVPOINT.

- From the View pull-down menu pick 3D Views and then Viewpoint Presets.

Dialog box description:

- Set Viewing Angles

    This section of the dialog box contains two radio buttons. When the button labeled Absolute to WCS is set, the viewpoint will be relative to the WCS. When the button labeled Relative to UCS is set, the viewpoint will be relative to the UCS.

- Image Tiles

    The image tile on the left sets the horizontal view direction, in units of degrees, from the X axis, while the image tile on the right sets the vertical view direction angle from the X-Y plane. You can use your pointing device within these image tiles to set a view direction angle. A red arm indicates the current view direction angle, and a black (or white, depending on your screen color) arm indicates the new angle. If you pick a point in one of the outer bounded areas, the angle snaps to the labeled degree value. Picking a point within the inner areas sets a precise angle.

- From

    These two edit boxes, labeled X Axis and XY Plane, show the angles selected within the image tiles. They can also be used to directly type in view direction angles.

- Set to Plan View

    This button will set a viewpoint looking straight down on the X-Y plane. It is equivalent to setting the horizontal angle from the X axis to 270 degrees, and the vertical angle from the X-Y plane to 90 degrees.

Notes:

- This command and dialog box is based upon an AutoLISP program named DDVPOINT.LSP and a Dialog Control Language file named DDVPOINT.DCL.

- The two radio buttons in the cluster labeled Set Viewing Angle turn the system variable **worldview** on and off.

Setting Plan Views

Virtually all 2D drafting with AutoCAD is done using a viewpoint that looks straight down from the positive end of the Z axis toward the X-Y plane. Since it is such an often-used viewpoint, AutoCAD has a special command—PLAN—for setting it. Even though you will generally do your 3D work from a viewpoint that is askew to the principal axes, you will occasionally want to work in a plan view. And, the PLAN command is more convenient than VPOINT in establishing plan views. By default, PLAN sets the plan view according to the current User Coordinate System, but you can set it according to WCS, and even to a UCS orientation that has been named and saved by AutoCAD's UCS command. We will discuss the UCS in detail in the next chapter.

Command: PLAN

Purpose: This command sets a view direction that looks straight down on the X-Y plane from the positive Z direction.

Initiate with:

- On the command line enter PLAN.

- From the View pull-down menu, pick 3D Views, pick Plan View, then pick one of the three options.

Options:

The options for the PLAN command are presented in a command line menu.

- Current UCS

  This option sets the view direction perpendicular to the positive side of the X-Y plane of the current UCS. It is the default option.

Original viewpoint   Current UCS option of PLAN   World option of PLAN

- UCS

  This option sets the plan view relative to a UCS position and orientation that has been given a name and saved through an option in the UCS command. See the description of AutoCAD's UCS command for details on named UCSs. When you select this option of PLAN, AutoCAD will issue a command line prompt for you to specify a UCS name and will give you an opportunity to see a list of all named UCSs.

- World

  When you select this option, the plan view will be relative to the WCS, regardless of whether a UCS does or does not exist.

Notes:

- All options of the PLAN command display the model with a zoom level that is the equivalent of Zoom-Extents.

- When multiple viewports exist, PLAN affects only the current viewport.

16

- The World option of PLAN is equivalent to the VPOINT command's direction coordinates of 0,0,1 when the system variable **worldview** is set to 1.

- The Current UCS option of PLAN is equivalent to the VPOINT command's direction coordinates of 0,0,1 when the system variable **worldview** is set to 0.

Setting Orthographic Views

In AutoCAD 2000, options were added to the VIEW command for setting orthographic and isometric viewpoints. In the dialog box displayed by this command, select the tab labeled "Orthographic & Isometric Views." The names of the six principal orthographic views plus the four isometric views that look down on the X-Y plane will be shown in a list box. You can click on one of these names, and then click the Set Current button to set the viewpoint to that of the selected view. If the check box labeled "Restore orthographic UCS with View" is checked and an orthographic view is to be the current view, the UCS will rotate so that its X-Y plane is perpendicular to the view direction. This check box controls the **ucsortho** system variable. When the box is checked, **ucsortho** is set to a value of 1, and when it is cleared **ucsortho** will have a value of 0. Autodesk intended for this action to be a convenience, but you will probably prefer to set the UCS yourself and you will clear this check box so that the UCS does not change when you use the VIEW command to set a viewpoint.

The **ucsortho** system variable also controls the behavior of the UCS when the View/3D Views pull-down menu and the View toolbar are used to set orthographic viewpoints, because the VIEW command is used to initiate those viewpoints. Therefore, you will need to manually change the value of **ucsortho** from its default value of 1 to 0 if you do not want the UCS to change when you set an orthographic viewpoint. We will discuss the relationship between the UCS and orthographic viewpoints more in the next chapter.

Specifying Points in 3D Space

Pointing

All wireframe objects are drawn by specifying points in 3D space—lines begin and end at points, circles are based on a center point, and polylines are a based on a series of vertex points. Your pointing device is the most efficient method for specifying points; however, it is confined to the X-Y plane unless you use object snaps on existing objects.

To circumvent this problem, AutoCAD long ago (in 1985 with Version 2.1) introduced a command named ELEV that allows you to move the drawing plane to a position that is either above or below the X-Y plane. The command prompts you to enter a distance value, then moves the drawing plane to the specified elevation. The current elevation of the drawing plane is stored in AutoCAD's **elevation** system variable. The ELEV command also sets the extrusion thickness of certain wireframe objects. Extrusion thickness is an object property that is completely unrelated to drawing plane elevation. It is a surfacelike property that we will discuss extensively in Section Two of this book.

Although AutoCAD still supports the ELEV command, along with its associated system variable **elevation**, it is an obsolete command representing an early attempt by Autodesk to incorporate 3D features within AutoCAD. It is limited to simply moving the drawing plane up or down from the X-Y plane. It cannot tilt or rotate the drawing plane, or move its origin away from the Z axis. Moreover, it is a potentially confusing command since the only evidence that the drawing plane has been moved is that AutoCAD's grid will move along with the drawing plane (provided, of course, it is turned on), and beginning with Release 14 the cursor location coordinates on the status bar will show a Z coordinate other than 0.

The best way to reposition the drawing plane is to move the X-Y plane with the UCS. Since it is the key to successfully building 3D models, we will discuss the UCS command in detail in the next chapter.

Command: ELEV

Purpose: This command controls two unrelated parameters. It sets the elevation of the drawing plane, and it sets the extrusion thickness of wireframe objects.

Initiate with:

• On the command line enter ELEV.

Options:

ELEV issues two options in the form of prompts on the command line.

`Specify new default elevation <current elevation>:` *Specify a distance, or press Enter to accept the current elevation.*

The drawing plane—the plane on which you can freely use your pointing device to specify point locations—will be moved to the elevation specified. Positive values move the drawing plane above the X-Y plane, while negative values move it below the X-Y plane. The Z coordinate in the cursor location displayed on the editing screen status bar will reflect the new elevation. If AutoCAD's grid is displayed, it will move to match the current elevation. The UCS icon, however, will remain on the X-Y plane of the current UCS.

`Specify new default thickness <current extrusion thickness>:` *Specify a distance, or press Enter to accept the current thickness.*

This option gives wireframe objects (such as lines, 2D polylines, circles, and arcs) height in the Z direction. Thus, a line will be drawn as a wall, and a circle will be drawn as a cylinder. This property is called *extrusion thickness* because the objects appear to have been stretched, or extruded, in a direction that is perpendicular to the drawing plane. Positive values extrude objects in the positive Z direction, while negative values extrude objects in the negative Z direction.

Notes:

• The ELEV command is obsolete, even though it is still present in AutoCAD. You should use the UCS command, rather than ELEV, for positioning the drawing plane.

• Although the command can be used to set extrusion thickness, it is easier to set that property directly through the **thickness** system variable.

18

- The extrusion thickness of existing objects, even if they were drawn with no extrusion thickness, can be changed through the CHANGE, CHPROP commands. The CHANGE and DDCHANGE commands can also change the elevation of existing objects. In AutoCAD 2000, the PROPERTY command can change thickness, but not elevation.

Related system variables:

- **elevation**

  The current elevation of the drawing plane—its distance from the X-Y plane—is stored in this system variable.

- **thickness**

  This system variable stores the extrusion thickness that is currently in effect.

Entering 3D Coordinates

Entering point coordinates from the keyboard is relatively commonplace when working in 3D. Consequently, AutoCAD provides several methods for you to enter point coordinates.

X, Y, Z Coordinates

The most common method for specifying the location of a point with the keyboard is to enter the point's X, Y, and Z coordinates. You can also precede the coordinates with the @ symbol to signify that the coordinates represent a point relative to the previous point. When entering relative coordinates, you can skip the Z coordinate if you intend to remain in the elevation of the last specified point. Moreover, you can use relative polar coordinates to indicate a point's location in the last elevation specified. Absolute polar coordinates, however, will place the point on the current drawing plane.

For example, you could draw a series of lines at an elevation of 1.5000 with the following command line input:

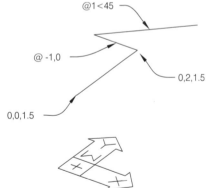

```
Command: LINE (Enter)
Specify first point: 0,0,1.5 (Enter)
  Absolute with three coordinates
Specify next point or [Undo]: 0,2,1.5 (Enter)
  Absolute with three coordinates
Specify next point or [Undo]: @-1,0 (Enter)
  Relative with two coordinates
Specify next point or [Close/Undo]: @1<45 (Enter)
  Relative with polar coordinates
```

XYZ Point Filters

While you will generally specify all three coordinates of a point at once by (1) picking a location with your pointing device, by (2) using an object snap, or by (3) typing in coordinates, AutoCAD has filters that permit you to enter each of the three coordinates independently. You can implement these filters anytime AutoCAD is looking for a point by entering a period followed by the coordinate you want to filter: .x for the X coordinate, .y for the Y coordinate, and .z for the Z coordinate. After you specify a coordinate to be filtered, AutoCAD will ask you to identity a point that can supply that coordinate. Often you will use an object snap to do this. AutoCAD will then prompt for the missing coordinates, and you can use filters for them also.

Suppose, for example, that you have a partially constructed 3D room that has two walls and a rectangular-topped table. In preparation for a rendering, you want to place a point light over the middle of the table, at a height equal to the top of the walls. (Rendering, and lights for rendering, will be discussed in Section Five. For now, all you need to know is that a point light is positioned at a point in space, and that it radiates light in all directions from that point.) You do not know the coordinates of any of these positions. When the LIGHT command prompts you to specify the location of the light, you could use the following input:

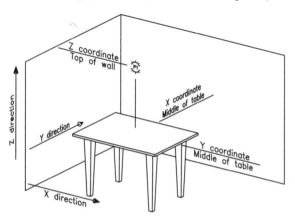

```
Enter light location <current>: .x
    (Enter)
of (use a midpoint snap on the long
    side of the table top)
(need YZ): .y (Enter)
of (use a midpoint snap on the short
    side of the table)
(need Z): (use an endpoint snap to pick
    the top of the wall)
```

Notice that AutoCAD uses the word *of* as it prompts you to specify the filtered coordinate. No filter was needed for the Z coordinate since that was the only one remaining. If in this same example you wanted the light to be placed over the center of the table as before, but 6 feet from the floor, rather than at the top of the wall, you could have entered 6' (or 72) for the Z coordinate.

Sometimes a single point can supply two coordinates. In those situations you can filter a pair of coordinates by typing in a period followed by the two coordinates you want to filter: .xy for the X and Y coordinates, .xz for the X and Z coordinates, and .yz for the Y and Z coordinates.

For an example of this type of filter, consider the same 3D room, but with a round-topped table instead of one with a rectangular top. You could position a light over the center of the table at a height equal to the wall with the following command line input:

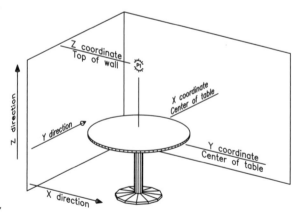

```
Enter light location <current>: .xy
    (Enter)
of (use a center object snap on the top
    of the table)
need Z: (use an endpoint snap to pick
    the top of the wall)
```

None of the pull-down menus and tool bars in Release 14 and AutoCAD 2000 refer to point filters because (evidently) a new technique for isolating point locations, called *tracking*, can do many things that point filters can do when you are working in 2D. Tracking, however, does not work in specifying 3D points because all selected points are projected onto the current drawing plane.

In Release 14 and AutoCAD 2000, you can initiate point filters by pressing the second button on your pointing device (usually the right-hand button on a two-button mouse) as you hold down the shift key. A menu will pop up on the computer screen. Select Point Filters from this menu, then select a specific filter from the resulting flyout menu. You can also, of course, specify point filters from the command line, as we did in the previous examples.

Cylindrical Coordinates

Even though the locations of 3D points are stored as XYZ coordinates, AutoCAD has two alternate methods for specifying them. One of these two input methods is to use cylindrical coordinates. The format for cylindrical coordinates is

distance<angle, height

where   *distance* represents the point's horizontal distance from the origin for absolute entry or from the last point specified for relative entry.

<angle represents the angle on the X-Y plane from the X axis to the point. The angle's direction depends upon the setting of AutoCAD's **angdir** system variable. By default, angle directions are counterclockwise.

height represents the point's elevation relative to the X-Y plane for absolute entry, or from the last point specified for relative entry.

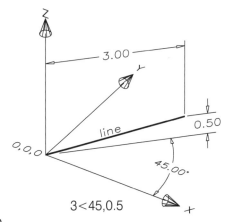

You probably noticed that this format is the same as that for 2D polar coordinates, with the addition of a height value. The following command line input will draw a line from the origin to a point 45 degrees from the X axis on the X-Y plane, 0.5 units above the X-Y plane, and 3.0 units from the origin on the X-Y plane.

```
Command: LINE (Enter)
Specify first point: 0,0,0 (Enter)
Specify next point or [Undo]: 3<45,.5 (Enter)
Specify next point or [Undo]: (Enter)
```

The actual length of this line will be longer than 3.0 units. Further examples of cylindrical coordinates are in Chapter Five, where we use them for drawing 3D helical curves.

Spherical Coordinates

The second alternate format for specifying a 3D point is spherical coordinates. Its format is

distance<hor_angle<ver_angle

where   *distance* represents the point's distance from the origin for absolute entry, or from the last point specified for relative entry.

<hor_angle> represents the angle on the X-Y plane from the X axis to the point.

<ver_angle> represents the angle from the X-Y plane.

Positive directions of the angles depend upon the setting of AutoCAD's **angdir** system variable. By default, this system variable is set to 0, which means that angles are measured counterclockwise. The following command line input with spherical coordinates will draw a line from the origin to a point 3.0 units away on the X-Y plane, 45 degrees from the X axis on the X-Y plane, and 30 degrees from the X-Y plane.

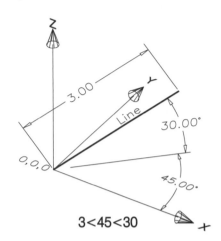

3<45<30

```
Command: LINE (Enter)
Specify first point: 0,0,0 (Enter)
Specify next point or [Undo]: 3<45<30
   (Enter)
Specify next point or [Undo]: (Enter)
```

The actual length of this line will be 3.0 units.

For an example application of spherical coordinates, suppose you wanted to install a spotlight in a rendering of the 3D room with a circular table that we used a few paragraphs ago in an example of coordinate filters. (We will discuss lights for renderings extensively in Section Five of this book. For now all you need to know about them is that spotlights have a location, and they are pointed toward a target. Both the light location and its target are 3D points.) You want the light pointing 45 degrees toward the center of the table top, to be rotated 20 degrees in the X-Y plane, and to be 5.0 units away. To achieve this, you could use the following command line input when AutoCAD prompts for light target and light location points:

```
Enter light target <current>: (Use a
   center object snap to pick the
   center of the round table top.)
Enter light location <current>:
   @5<20<45 (Enter)
```

Exercises

The following two exercises in making simple wireframe models will give you an opportunity to experiment with the principles and commands covered in this chapter. Start a new drawing with the default English settings. These will not be models that you will need to keep, so your AutoCAD setup of layers, text, and so forth is not important. To make point specification easier, though, you should activate AutoCAD's snap mode, with a snap spacing of 0.5. Also, you should turn on the grid and set it to 0.5, to help you visualize the X-Y plane. Use the following command line input to position the UCS icon in the lower-left corner of the AutoCAD graphics area:

```
Command: UCSICON (Enter)
Enter an option [ON/OFF/Noorigin/Origin] <ON>: N (Enter)
```

Exercise One

In this first exercise, we will use the ELEV command to help draw a wireframe model. Start by drawing a rectangle that is 3 units long in the X direction and 2 units long in the Y direction. Base the lower-left corner of the rectangle at the 0,0,0 point of the WCS. Your rectangle should look similar to the one shown on the right, except your drawing will not display the coordinates shown in the figure. So far, your wireframe is strictly a 2D drawing of a rectangle.

Next, move the drawing plane up 2 units in elevation using the following command line input:

```
Command: ELEV (Enter)
Specify new default elevation <0.0000>:
  2 (Enter)
Specify new default thickness <0.0000>:
  (Enter)
```

Since your viewpoint is one that looks straight down on the X-Y plane, nothing in the graphics area of your computer screen will be changed. Nevertheless, the drawing plane has been moved up 2 units, and the Z coordinate on the AutoCAD status bar will read 2.0000.

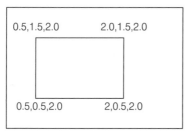

Use your pointing device to draw another rectangle—one that is 1.5 units in the X direction and 1.0 units in the Y direction— using the coordinates shown in the figure on the left. Drawing this rectangle is also exactly like drawing in 2D.

This rectangle is 2 units higher than the previous one, even though that is not apparent from your current viewpoint. To obtain a better look, use the following command line input to set up an isometric viewpoint:

```
Command: VPOINT (Enter)
Current view direction: VIEWDIR=0.0000,0.0000,1.0000
Specify a view point or [Rotate] display compass and tripod: 1,-1,1 (Enter)
```

You can obtain this same viewpoint by selecting an SE Isometric view from AutoCAD's View/3D Views pull-down menu, as well as from AutoCAD's Viewpoint toolbar. After stepping back with a zoom level of approximately 0.5X, your model should look similar to the first one shown on the next page. Even though the smaller rectangle may appear to be on the same plane as the larger rectangle, it is actually 2 units higher.

Finish the wireframe by drawing a line from each corner of one rectangle to the corresponding corner of the other rectangle. The easiest way to do this is to turn the snap-to-grid off and turn the object-endpoint-snap on. Then simply draw a line from each corner on one rectangle to the matching corner on the other. Your completed wireframe model should look similar to the one shown on the right.

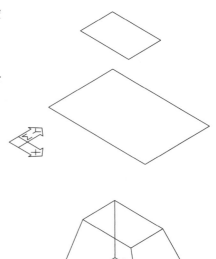

You should now return the drawing plane back to the X-Y plane. This time, move the drawing plane by changing the value of the **elevation** system variable rather than by using the ELEV command. The command line input to do this is

```
Command: elevation (Enter)
New value for ELEVATION <2.0000>: 0 (Enter)
```

The Z coordinate for the cursor location in the status bar will change to 0 and the grid will shift, indicating that the drawing plane has moved back to the X-Y plane. In the next chapter you will see how the UCS command does a much better job than ELEV in establishing a drawing plane. This finishes Exercise One. You do not need to save the drawing, although you may want to use its setup for Exercise Two.

Exercise Two

In this exercise, we will use the keyboard to input point locations while drawing a wireframe with two rectangles and one triangle that are slanted to the X-Y plane. Start the exercise by either beginning a new drawing having the grid and UCS icon options we listed earlier, or by erasing all of the objects used for the previous exercise.

If your viewpoint is an isometric type, switch to a plan view by using the following command line input:

```
Command: PLAN (Enter)
Enter an option [Current ucs/Ucs/World] Current: (Enter)
```

Since the current UCS is equivalent to the WCS, both the Current UCS and World options of PLAN result in the same viewpoint.

Now, use the point coordinates shown in the figure on the next page to draw five connected lines. You can conveniently use your pointing device, with snap set to 0.5 or 1.0, to draw these lines, since they are on the WCS's X-Y plane.

Next, use the following command line input to set up an isometric-type viewpoint:

```
Command: VPOINT (Enter)
Current view direction: VIEWDIR=0.0000,0.0000,1.0000
Specify a viewpoint or [Rotate/display compass and tripod]: r (Enter)
Enter angle in XY plane from X axis <270>: 305 (Enter)
Enter angle from XY plane <90>: 35 (Enter)
```

This will result in a viewpoint that looks toward the top-front-right side of the model. Since

our viewpoint is 305 degrees in the XY plane from the
X axis, rather than the 315 degrees that a true isometric
view would have, there is less likelihood that lines will
hide one another.

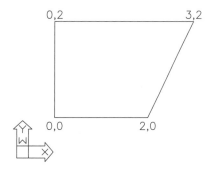

AutoCAD will do the equivalent of a Zoom/Extents
as it changes viewpoints, so use a method of your own
choosing to create some drawing space by zooming out.
When you are satisfied with your zoom level, use the
following command line input to draw a rectangle that
is above, and tilted to, the X-Y plane.

```
Command:  LINE (Enter)
Specify first point:  0,.5,1 (Enter)
Specify next point or [Undo]:  @1.5<0 (Enter)
Specify next point or [Undo]:  @1.5<90,.5 (Enter)
Specify next point or [Close/Undo]:  @1.5<180 (Enter)
Specify next point or [Close/Undo]:  c (Enter)
```

Notice that the end of the first line was established by 2D polar coordinates. If you do not
specify a Z coordinate when you use relative input (which is signified by the @ character), Auto-
CAD stays at the last elevation specified (which, in this case, is 1.0). The third line was also
drawn using polar coordinates.

The end of the second line was established by cylindrical coordinates. Their format is the
same as for 2D polar coordinates, with an elevation tacked onto the end. Our input signified
that the end of the line was to be 1.5 units in the Y direction (90 degrees) and 0.5 units in the Z
direction. The actual length of the line is longer than 1.5 units. If we had wanted it to be
exactly 1.5 units long, we would have used spherical coordinates, similar to the following:

@1.5<90<20

The first angle in this input means that the line will be 90 degrees counterclockwise from the X
axis, while the second angle tilts the line 20 degrees from the X-Y plane.

Your wireframe model should now look similar to the one shown below, except of course,
yours will not have the text.

Finish the model by connecting the line
endpoints as shown in the figure on the
next page. This is best accomplished by first
turning on a running endpoint object snap.
We will not show the command line input
to do this or to draw the lines, since you
are undoubtedly well acquainted with
those steps.

Before you abandon this wireframe model, you should use it in setting some viewpoints. The figure below shows the top, front, and side views of the model. You can set each of these viewpoints by typing in view direction coordinates on the command line with the VPOINT command, by selecting them from the View/3D Viewpoints pull-down menu, or by selecting them from the Viewpoint tool bar. You will not be able to see all three views at one time, as shown in the figure. We will discuss multiple viewports in Chapter Three. Until then we will work with just a single viewport.

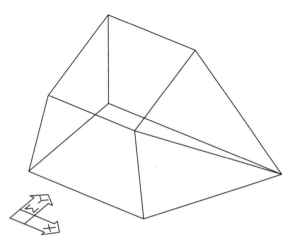

This finishes Exercise Two. We will not use this model in any future exercises, so you do not need to save or retain it.

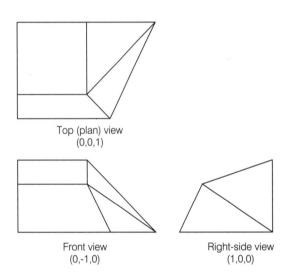

Top (plan) view
(0,0,1)

Front view
(0,-1,0)

Right-side view
(1,0,0)

Managing AutoCAD's User Coordinate System

A utoCAD's movable local coordinate system—the User Coordinate System—will be explored extensively in this chapter. The UCS is one of AutoCAD's most important 3D features because it allows you to use the same techniques in making 3D models that you have always used in making 2D drawings. It makes working in 3D practical. This chapter will

- describe the characteristics of the UCS and the commands for controlling the UCS;
- explain how to choose the best option for setting up a UCS;
- demonstrate how use the UCS while building two wireframe 3D models.

The key to working successfully in 3D space—whether you are making wireframe, surface, or solid models—is AutoCAD's User Coordinate System. It enables you to efficiently use your pointing device in 3D space, and it allows you to use the same techniques in making 3D models that you have long used in making 2D drawings. The snap and ortho modes, as well as the commands associated with 2D, such as ARRAY, MIRROR, BREAK, and ROTATE, work just as well on the X-Y plane of the UCS as they do on the X-Y plane of the World Coordinate System we discussed in Chapter One. The UCS X-Y plane, however, can be positioned anyplace in the WCS you want.

Conceptually, the UCS is easy to understand. It is a 3D coordinate system that is identical to the WCS, but it is a movable coordinate system whose origin can be placed in any location within the WCS, and its principal axes can be rotated into any orientation. It is a local coordinate system for working in a specific area.

In your everyday life, you often use local coordinate systems without even thinking about them. For example, if you were to measure the length, width, and height of a box that is located somewhere in a room, you would undoubtedly base those measurements on one corner of the box. Although the room could be considered to be a global coordinate system (similar to the WCS) and you could base all of the box measurements on one corner of the room, you are not likely to do so. Even if the position of the box within the room was important, you would probably specify its location relative to one key point on the box—not to every corner of it.

In AutoCAD revisions 10 through 14, only one UCS can exist at any given time, but in AutoCAD 2000 each viewport can simultaneously have its own UCS. We will discuss multiple viewports and multiple UCSs in the next chapter.

The UCS Command

AutoCAD's appropriately named UCS command manages the User Coordinate System. Since it is such an important command, you will want to become very familiar with it so that you will be able to quickly and precisely set UCSs.

Typically, you will work in one plane at a time as you build 3D models. You will set up a UCS, draw the portion of the model that is on the X-Y of the UCS, then set up another UCS so that you can work in another section of the model.

Pull-down menus for the UCS

You can initiate the UCS command and access its more than twenty options through any one of four different ways—from AutoCAD's command line, through the UCS and UCS II toolbars, through the UCS flyout on the Standard toolbar, and by choosing one of the UCS selections in AutoCAD's pull-down menu labeled Tools. The UCS toolbar is an especially convenient method of selecting UCS options, and you will probably want it somewhere on your screen so that you have ready access to the most useful UCS options.

28

Command: UCS

Purpose: The UCS command sets the location and orientation of the User Coordinate System and allows you to name, save, restore, and manage specific UCS orientations.

Initiate with:

- At the Command Line prompt, enter UCS.
- Choose the UCS flyout from the Standard toolbar or select an option from the UCS or UCS II toolbars.
- From the Tools pull-down menu, select one of the four UCS option groups.
  The options listed on the command line for UCS are

  `New/Move/orthoGraphic/Prev/Restore/Save/Del/Apply/?/World.`

- New

  When you select New from this list, the command line prompt will be

  `Specify origin of new UCS or [ZAxis/3point/Object/Face/View/X/Y/Z]<0,0,0>:`

  ○ Origin

    This is the default option in the New category. It moves the UCS to a new location in 3D space without changing the orientation of the X, Y, and Z axes. AutoCAD will prompt you for a point in 3D space at which to locate the origin.

    `Specify origin of new UCS <0,0,0>: Specify a point.`

You can use any of the standard methods in specifying this point. Typed-in coordinates are relative to the current UCS origin rather than to the WCS origin.

Original UCS location · Resulting UCS location

  ○ ZAxis

    Two point locations are required for this option. The first point specifies the new UCS's origin, while the positive direction of the Z axis is established by the second point specified. The X-Y plane will be located on the first point selected and will be perpendicular to a line from the first point to the second point.

    `Specify new origin point <0,0,0>: Specify a point.`
    `Specify point on positive portion of Z-axis <current direction>: Specify a point.`

AutoCAD will set the direction of the X axis to one that is parallel with the WCS X-Y plane. If you accept the current location of the origin and specify a new Z axis direction, Auto-CAD will tilt the X-Y plane. If you specify a new origin

New origin point · Point for Z axis direction

Original UCS location · Resulting UCS location

while accepting the current Z axis direction, the X-Y plane of the new UCS will remain parallel to that of the old UCS (similar to the Origin option).

◦ 3point

This option asks for three points. The first point sets the origin of the new UCS, the second point establishes the direction of the X axis relative to the new origin, and the third point determines how the X-Y plane is to be rotated in space. The third point does not have to be on the Y axis. It can be anywhere off of the line between the first two points.

```
Specify new origin point <0,0,0>: Specify a point.
Specify point on the positive portion of the X-axis <current direction>:
    Specify a point.
Specify point on the positive-Y portion of the UCS XY plane
    <current direction>: Specify a point.
```

If you accept the default point for the first point, the origin of the new UCS will be the same as that of the old UCS. If you accept the default for the second point, the X axis direction of the new UCS will be the same as the current X axis. And, if you accept the default for the third point, the X-Y plane of the new UCS will be parallel to the X-Y plane of the old UCS.

Original UCS location

Point on X-Y plane
Point on X axis
New origion

Resulting UCS location

◦ OBject

This option moves and orients the UCS according to an existing object. The Z axis direction of the new UCS will be the same as the object's extrusion direction. The location of the UCS origin depends on the type of object selected, and the directions of the X and Y axes are dependent on the location of the object selection point, as shown in Table 2-1. The option's follow-up prompt is

```
Select object to align UCS: Select an object.
```

You must select an object by picking a point on it—window and crossing selection methods are not allowed. Any object type can be selected, except for the following: 3D solid, 3D polyline, spline, polygon mesh, viewport, mline, region, ellipse, ray, xline, leader, and mtext.

Original UCS location

Object selection point

Resulting UCS location

TABLE 2-1 THE OBJECT OPTION'S CHOICE OF ORIGIN AND X AXIS DIRECTION		
Object Type	**Origin Location**	**Direction of X Axis**
Arc	Center of arc	The X axis passes through the arc endpoint closest to the object pick point.
Circle	Center of circle	The X axis passes through the object pick point.
Dimension	Midpoint of dimension text	The X axis will be parallel to the X axis of the UCS in effect when the dimension was placed.
Line	Endpoint nearest the object pick point	The X axis will be on the selected line.
Point	The location of the point	The direction of the X axis is controlled by AutoCAD's Arbitrary Axis Algorithm.
2D polyline	Start point of the polyline	The X axis will pass through the polyline's second vertex.
Solid	Start point of the solid	The X axis will pass through the solid's second point.
Trace	Start point of the trace	The X axis will pass through the second point of the trace, ignoring the trace's width.
3D face	Start point of the 3D face	The X axis will be on the edge between the first and second point of the 3D face. The positive direction of the Y axis will be from the first and fourth point of the 3D face, or from the first and third point if the 3D face has only three edges.
Text, blocks, and shapes	Insert point of the object	The X axis will be in the direction of the rotation angle of the object. Therefore, the selected object will have a rotation angle of 0 in the new UCS.

° Face

This option places the UCS on the flat face, or surface, of a 3D solid. The option's prompts are

```
Select face of solid object: Select an object.
Enter an option [Next/Xflip/Yflip] <accept>: Enter an option or press Enter.)
```

You select the face by picking a point on its surface or on one of its edges. The edges of the selected face will be highlighted, and the UCS X-Y plane will move to the face with its origin in a corner nearest the pick point. If you choose the Next option, the next suitable face will become the selected face. Its edges will be highlighted, and the UCS X-Y plane will move to it. The Xflip option rotates the UCS X-Y plane 180 degrees about the X axis, while the Yflip option rotates the X-Y plane 180 degrees about the Y axis.

° View

The View option reorients the UCS so that the X-Y plane is perpendicular to the current view direction. The X axis will be parallel to the bottom of the viewport, the Y axis will be pointed vertically, and the Z axis will be pointed out of the screen toward the viewer. The origin of the UCS is not changed. No follow-up prompts are issued.

Original UCS location   Resulting UCS location

° X/Y/Z

Each of these three options rotate the other two principal axes about the specified axis. The location of the origin is unchanged. AutoCAD will issue the follow-up prompt:

```
Specify rotation angle about N
    axis <90>: Specify an angle.
```

The letter *N* will be replaced by X, Y, or Z in the actual prompt. You can respond to the prompt by either typing in an angle or by picking two points representing an angle.

Original UCS location   Rotated 45 degrees
                               about the X axis

• Move

This option controls the UCS origin. It issues the following command line prompt:

Then rotated 90 degrees   Then rotated 33 degrees
   about the Y axis   about the Z axis

```
Specify new origin point or [Zdepth] <0,0,0>: Enter a z, or specify a point.
```

When you select a point, the UCS origin will move to that point. The Zdepth option moves the origin to a new location along the Z axis. This option prompts you to specify a distance. Positive values move the X-Y plane in the positive Z axis direction, while negative values move it in the minus Z axis direction. If you pick two points to specify a distance, the direction is always positive.

When an orthographic UCS is in effect, the Move option not only sets the origin of the current orthographic UCS, it sets the origin for subsequent calls to that particular orthographic UCS. Suppose, for example, the Front orthographic UCS is in effect and the Move option is used to relocate the origin. Then, suppose you restored the WCS, and next you selected the Front orthographic UCS option again. The origin of the UCS would be on the point established by the last Move option—not on the origin of the base UCS for orthographic UCSs.

- orthoGraphic

This option moves the UCS origin to the origin of a named UCS stored in the **ucsbase** system variable and rotates the Z axis so that it points in one of the six principal directions of that UCS. It issues the prompt:

```
Enter an option [Top/Bottom/Front/Back/Left/Right] <current>: Enter an option or
    press Enter.
```

The results of the options are shown in the following table:

Option	Z Direction Relative to Named UCS
Top	Positive Z direction
Bottom	Minus Z direction
Front	Minus Y direction
Back	Positive Y direction
Left	Minus X direction
Right	Positive X direction

- Prev

This option, which uses no additional prompts, returns the UCS to the previous location and orientation. Prev can be repeated to step back through the last ten UCS settings in model space and through the last ten settings in paper space.

- Restore

The Restore option brings back a UCS location and orientation that has been saved by the Save option of UCS. AutoCAD will issue the follow-up prompt:

```
Enter name of UCS to restore or [?]: Enter a name or ?.
```

The question mark option will bring up another prompt that you can use to obtain a list of the names of all UCSs that have been saved.

- Save

The current UCS location and orientation can be saved by this option. AutoCAD will ask for a name to be assigned to the UCS:

```
Enter name to save current UCS or [?]: Enter a name or ?.
```

The question mark option will bring up a prompt that can be used to obtain a list of existing UCS names. Names can be up to 255 characters long and can contain letters, digits, dollar signs ($), hyphens (-), underscores (_), and even spaces.

- Del

  This option allows you to delete one or more named UCSs.

  `Enter UCS name(s) to delete <none>:` *Enter a name list.*

  You may delete more than one UCS by using the question mark (?) and asterisk (*) wild card characters, or by entering several UCS names, separated by commas.

- Apply

  When multiple viewports exist, you can use this option to set the UCS of a selected viewport to be the same as that of the current viewport. It issues the command line prompt:

  `Pick viewport to apply current UCS or [All] <current>:` *Specify a viewport, enter A, or press Enter.*

  You specify a viewport by moving the screen cursor to within it and pressing the pick button of your pointing device. If you select the All option, the UCS of the current viewport will be applied to all viewports. No changes will occur if you press the Enter key.

- ?

  The question mark option allows you to see information about all named UCSs. AutoCAD will prompt for a name list.

  `Enter UCS name(s) to list <*>:` *Enter a name list.*

  A list of all saved UCSs, including their names, their origin locations, and the directions of their X, Y, and Z axes relative to the current UCS, will be displayed. Also, the name of the current UCS will be displayed. If the WCS is currently being used, it will be listed as *WORLD*. If the current UCS is not a named UCS and is not the WCS, it will be listed as *NO NAME*. You can also use wild card characters to obtain a filtered list of named UCSs.

- World

  This, the default option, restores the WCS.

Notes:

- Beginning with AutoCAD 2000, the UCS can vary between viewports. When multiple viewports exist, the UCS command affects only the current viewport (except for the Apply option, which applies the UCS of the current viewport to another viewport).

- You can initiate the suboptions of New from the main UCS prompt, even though they are not listed in the main prompt. To start the Face option, though, you must enter its entire name or its first two letters—entering just the letter *F* does not work.

- Unless the system variable **ucsfollow** has been set to a value of 1, changing a UCS location or orientation will not change the viewpoint, or the zoom level. This is true even when named UCSs are restored.

- Although the UCS command has no provisions for renaming a saved UCS, you can use the RENAME or the UCSMAN commands to do so.

System variables:

- **angdir**

  The direction of positive rotation is controlled by this toggle-type system variable. When **angdir** is set to 0, which is the default setting, rotation direction follows the right-hand rule. Thus, positive rotation is counterclockwise when viewed from the positive direction of the rotation axis.

- **ucsaxisang**

  This system variable stores the default angle of revolution offered in the X, Y, and Z axes options of UCS. Its initial value is 90 degrees.

- **ucsbase**

  The name of the UCS used for the origin and axes orientation of the Orthographic options of UCS is stored in this system variable.

- **ucsfollow**

  This is a toggle-type system variable having a value of either 0 (off) or 1 (on). When it is set to 1, AutoCAD automatically switches to a plan view whenever you change from one UCS to another. As in the PLAN command, AutoCAD will perform the equivalent of a Zoom/Extents when setting up the plan view.

- **ucsname**

  The name of the current UCS is stored in this read-only system variable. If the current UCS is unnamed or is the WCS, **ucsname** will contain just a pair of quotation marks.

- **ucsorg**

  This read-only system variable holds the origin of the current UCS as a 3D point relative to the WCS.

- **ucsxdir**

  The direction of the current UCS X axis as a point offset from the WCS origin is stored in this read-only system variable.

- **ucsydir**

  This read-only system variable contains the direction of the current UCS Y axis. It is stored as a 3D point representing a direction from the WCS origin.

- **worlducs**

  If this system variable contains a value of 1, the current UCS is the same as the WCS. If the UCS is different from the WCS in origin, axes orientation, or both, then **worlducs** will have the value of 0. It is a read-only system variable.

Choosing the Right UCS Option

Over twenty options are available with the UCS command. This abundance of options does not mean that the command is complicated to use; it means that you have a variety of tools and methods for setting up a UCS.

In AutoCAD 2000, the command line options are

```
New/Move/orthoGraphic/Prev/Restore/Save/Del/Apply/?/World
```

When you select the New option a secondary prompt containing the following options will appear:

`Origin/ZAxis/3point/OBject/Face/View/X/Y/Z`

As with all AutoCAD command line menus, you can select an option by typing in the entire option name or just the uppercase letters in the option name. You can use this method to start the Origin, ZAxis, 3point, OBject, View, X, Y, and Z options, even through those options are not listed in the main prompt. You can also start the Face option from the main prompt by entering its first two letters or its entire name.

Your choice of an option will be governed by the desired position and orientation of the new UCS X-Y plane and on the availability of objects that can be used for point selections. Quite often two or more steps will be needed before the UCS is positioned as you want it, and there will often be more than one way, and more than one choice of options, for setting the UCS in the position and orientation you need.

The options of the UCS command can be conveniently divided into five categories.

- Options that move the UCS origin while leaving the orientation of the principal axis as it is. The Move and Origin options are in this category.

- Options that move the UCS origin and, at the same time, position the principal axes in a specific orientation. The options that can do this are ZAxis, 3point, Face, and OBject.

- Options that change the orientation of the UCS axes without moving the UCS origin. Four options are within this category: View, X, Y, and Z.

- Options that return the UCS to a previously established origin location and axes orientation. The Prev, World, and Restore options do this directly, while the Save, Del, and question mark (?) options manage previous UCS configurations.

- Options that point the Z axis perpendicular to the principal planes of a base coordinate system. These are the orthographic options.

An option that does not fit in any of these categories is Apply. When multiple viewports exist, you can use this option to set the UCS of a selected viewport to be the same as that of the current viewport. In the next few pages, we will look at the options within the five categories to see how they work and how you can put them to use.

Options That Move the UCS Origin without Changing the Axes Orientation

The Move and Origin options fall within this category. The Move option is for relocating the origin of the orthographic views, while the Origin option is for general use in positioning the UCS origin. Often you will use these options to move the UCS to a plane that is higher, or to one that is lower, than the current X-Y plane without changing the orientation of the principal axes. You might, for example, after drawing the base of a wireframe, use the Origin option to raise the drawing plane in preparation for drawing the top of the wireframe.

Draw the
wireframe's base.

Then move the UCS
up to draw the
wireframe's top.

Also, you will sometimes use the Origin option as the first of two or more steps in positioning the UCS. For instance, you might first move the origin to a specific point, then use another UCS option to rotate the axes into a new orientation.

Options That Move the UCS Origin and Also Change the Axes Orientation

Original UCS location   Move the UCS origin   Then rotate the UCS

Four UCS options can move the UCS origin and, at the same time, rotate the principal axes. They are ZAxis, 3point, OBject, and Face. The first two are especially flexible, allowing you to move the origin or leave it in its current location, as well as to selectively rotate certain axes. OBject, on the other hand, moves the origin and points the axes according to rules that are dependent upon the type of object selected. The Face option can be used only on 3D solid objects, which will be discussed in Section Three.

The ZAxis option is more versatile than it first appears to be. You can use it to relocate the UCS origin and also tilt the X-Y plane, or you can use it to simply tilt the X-Y plane. The option issues a follow-up prompt for two points. The first point establishes the origin, while the second point establishes the positive direction of the Z axis. The X-Y plane will be perpendicular to a line drawn between the two points, and the X axis will be parallel with the X-Y plane of the WCS.

For example: if, from the WCS, you keep the UCS origin at 0,0,0 and point in the minus Y direction for the new Z axis direction, AutoCAD will simply tilt the X-Y plane. The result is the same as rotating the UCS 90 degrees about the X axis.

On the other hand, if from the WCS you keep the UCS origin at 0,0,0 and point in the positive X direction for the new Z axis direction, AutoCAD will both tilt and rotate the X-Y plane. The result is the same as rotating the UCS 90 degrees about the Z axis, then rotating it 90 degrees about the X axis.

When you become used to it, the ZAxis option can be handy in quickly setting the UCS with minimum input. With one step you can attain the

Using the ZAxis option to move and tilt the UCS X-Y plane

Pick here for Z axis direction.

Pick here for origin.

Pick here for origin,

and here for Z axis direction.

Result

Pick here for origin,

and here for Z axis direction.

Result

same results as several steps used to rotate the X-Y plane about an axis.

Using the 3point option of UCS

Point 3   Point 2   Point 1

Resulting UCS

X-Y plane of the UCS

The 3point option is very useful for precisely setting a UCS that matches existing objects. Typically, you will use object snaps in specifying the three points. The first point sets the origin location, and the second point sets the direction of the X axis. The third point establishes the orientation of the X-Y plane—not the direction of the Y axis. Consequently, the third point can be anywhere off of the line between the first two points. It does not have to be 90 degrees from the line establishing the X axis.

The OBject option of UCS moves and orients the coordinate system according to an existing object. In AutoCAD Releases 10 through 12, this option was named Entity," and even in later releases, AutoCAD will accept that name, or just a typed-in letter E. This option requires that you select the object by picking a point on it because the UCS origin, as well as the directions of the X and Y axes, are sometimes dependent upon the selection point. See Table 2-1 for details.

Often the OBject option is used to change the UCS for editing an existing object. Prior to Release 13, when the orientation of the UCS was critical for operations such as fillets, trims, and breaks, this option was needed more than it is now. But it is still useful in preparing to change an object, for locating text relative to an existing object, and for making sure the UCS is located on a particular object.

The Face option places the UCS X-Y plane on the flat face, or surface, of a 3D solid object. (See Section Three of this book for information about 3D solids.) You will be prompted to select a face. You can do this by picking a point on an edge or on the surface of the face (even in wireframe viewing modes, when the surface is transparent). Usually, though, you will have better control if you pick a point on an edge. AutoCAD will highlight the edges of the selected face, move the UCS origin to the corner on the face nearest the pick point, and issue the prompt:

```
Enter an option [Next/Xflip/Yflip] <accept>:
```

Select the Next option to switch to the other possible face. That face will become highlighted, the UCS origin will move to it, and the prompt will be repeated. The Xflip option rotates the X-Y plane of the UCS 180 degrees about the X axis, while the Yflip option rotates it 180 degrees about the Y axis. When the UCS is on the face you want, and oriented as you want, press the Enter key.

Selected 3D solid face

Selection Point

Highlighted edges

Resulting UCS

38

Options That Rotate the Principal Axes without Moving the Origin

Four options of the UCS command leave the UCS origin location unchanged as they rotate the UCS principal axes about the origin. Of these, the View option is the most straightforward. No additional input is needed—the axes are simply rotated so that the X axis is parallel to the horizontal sides of the current viewport, while the Y axis is parallel to the vertical sides. The Z axis points straight out of the computer screen. The result is similar to the PLAN command, but the operations themselves are opposite. PLAN rotates the viewpoint so that the line of sight is directly down on the X-Y plane, while the View option of UCS rotates the X-Y plane so that it is perpendicular to the line of sight.

The View option is useful for ensuring that text placed in 3D space for an illustration or presentation is seen head-on. In fact, much of the text in the figures of this book was added after using the View option of UCS. The View option is also good, when used with paper space viewports, for properly orienting the UCS for adding dimensions to a 3D model. We will discuss that use of the View option when we explain how to make dimensioned 2D drawings from 3D models in Section Four of this book.

Original UCS orientation

Orientation after a 90-degree rotation about the Y axis

Each of the three options designated by the letters X, Y, and Z rotate the other two principal axes about the specified axis. The Y option, for instance, rotates the X and Z axes about the Y axis. AutoCAD will prompt for a rotation angle when you choose one of these options, and you can respond by typing in an angle or by picking two points to show the angle to AutoCAD. The default angle of revolution is stored in the **ucsaxisang** system variable.

The positive rotation direction is counter-clockwise when you look down the rotation axis toward the origin. An easy way to visualize rotation direction is to mentally grasp the rotation axis with your right hand, so that your thumb is pointed away from the origin. Positive rotation will be in the direction of your curled fingers.

You may prefer to use negative rotation angles in specifying clockwise rotation, even though you do not have to use them. For example, if you want to revolve the UCS clockwise around the Z axis, it may be easier for you to think in terms of -45-degree rotation rather than 315-degree rotation, even though they are equivalent.

One final note about rotation direction: if you have AutoCAD's **angdir** system variable set to 1, positive rotation will be in the opposite direction from what we have just described.

Options for Restoring a Previous UCS

The fourth category of UCS options restores a previous UCS. One of the choices, the Prev option, allows you to step back through as many as ten UCS configurations. (You can also step back through up to ten UCS configurations in paper space. We will discuss paper space in Section Four.) This option uses no additional prompts. The process is similar to stepping back through Zooms, although the Prev option affects only the UCS, not zooms or views.

You will often go from one UCS to another as you build 3D models, but occasionally you will find it beneficial to return to the WCS before you move on. Also, it is not a bad idea to develop the habit of restoring the WCS when you complete a 3D model. World, the default option of the UCS command, restores the WCS. You could also describe the result by saying the UCS is configured exactly like the WCS, because in some subtle ways, AutoCAD considers a UCS to exist at all times, even though it is sometimes equivalent to the WCS.

Named User Coordinate Systems

The remaining four options of this category are for saving, recalling, and managing named UCSs. You will use named UCSs when making complicated 3D models that have planes to which you will return, especially when you have a critical UCS that may be difficult to set up and you want to ensure that you can return to it with minimal effort.

Save will be the first of these options that you will use. AutoCAD will ask you for a name and will save the current UCS origin and axes orientation in the drawing file's database. The Restore option will change the current UCS to one that has been saved. If you forget the name of a saved UCS, you can use the question mark option (?) to bring up a list of UCSs, along with their origins and axes directions relative to the current UCS. Whenever you want to get rid of a saved UCS, you can delete it with the Del option.

If you have more than one named UCS, you will probably prefer to use AutoCAD's UCSMAN command for managing and restoring them, rather than the UCS command, because UCSMAN displays a dialog box showing all of the names.

The Orthographic Options

The six options in this category place the UCS origin on the origin of a base coordinate system and point its Z axis perpendicular to one of the principal planes of the base coordinate system. The name of the base coordinate system is stored in the **ucsbase** system variable. By default it is the WCS, but it can be any named UCS. The Move option also affects the location of the UCS origin. The names of the orthographic options and the direction their Z axis points relative to the base coordinate system are shown in the following table.

Option	Direction of Z Axis Relative to the Base Coordinate System
Top	Positive Z direction
Bottom	Negative Z direction
Front	Negative Y direction
Back	Positive Y direction
Left	Negative X direction
Right	Positive X direction

While you are not likely to often use the orthographic options of the UCS command, they can be useful when you are starting a 3D model, and also when you have a complex model, on which you have established some named UCSs that are suitable for the base coordinate systems for orthographic views. You may also find them useful in creating orthographic views for a multiview 2D drawing of a 3D model. (Multiview 2D drawings will be discussed in Section Four of this book.)

The DDUCS and the DDUCSP commands do not exist in AutoCAD 2000, and all references to them have been deleted. The following is text for the command that replaces them.

Command: **UCSMAN**

Purpose: This command restores and manages named and preset UCS configurations, controls the UCS icon setting, and controls the relationship of the UCS with viewports and view directions.

Initiate with:

- On the command line, enter UCSMAN.
- From the Tools pull-down menu, select Named UCS.
- From the UCS and UCSII Toolbars, select Display UCS Dialog.
- A dialog box having three tabs will be displayed. Each tab opens one of the following secondary dialog boxes.

Named UCSs:

The names of all of the UCS configurations currently in the drawing will be displayed in a list box, with the current UCS shown above the list box. The names of all saved UCSs will be listed, and if more than one UCS has been used during the current AutoCAD editing session, a UCS named Previous will be included. When the current UCS does not have a name, it will be shown as Unnamed. You can highlight any of these UCSs by clicking its name.

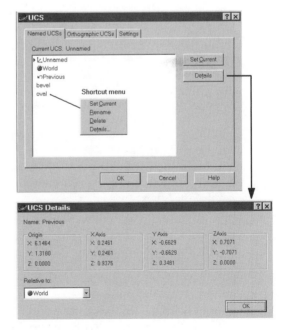

A shortcut menu (displayed by pressing the return button of your pointing device) allows you to make the highlighted UCS the current one, to rename it, and to delete it. This shortcut menu is a convenient way to name the current UCS if it is unnamed. You cannot rename or delete the World and Previous UCSs. The Details option in this shortcut menu brings up a secondary dialog box that shows the origin and the directions of the principal axes of the highlighted UCS. The information is in the form of 3D points relative to any of the other UCSs, except Prevous. The Set Current and Details dialog box buttons duplicate the results of the same options in the shorcut menus.

- Orthographic UCSs:

The dialog box opened by this tab is similar to the one for the Named UCSs tab. The listed UCSs, though, are six that are preset by AutoCAD. The Z axis of each preset UCS points in one of six principal directions relative to the UCS shown in the dropdown list box in the lower-left corner of the dialog box. The name of the reference UCS for the orthographic UCSs is stored in the **ucsbase** system variable.

By default, the origin of the preset UCS is the same as the origin of the reference UCS. When you override the default by specifying a depth, the origin will be moved in the Z axis direction by the specified depth. Thus, if you specified a depth of 2.0 for a Right UCS, the Z axis of the UCS would point in the WCS X axis direction and its origin would be on the WCS point having the coordinates of 2,0,0. This example assumes that the WCS is the reference coordinate system for orthographic UCSs. You can set the Depth through a shortcut menu, or by double-clicking the Depth value in the list box.

ucsbase system variable

The Details and Set Current options produce the same results as those in the Named UCSs dialog box. The Reset option restores the original origin of the orthographic UCS.

- Settings:

The dialog box for this tab has three check boxes for setting the same UCS icon parameters controlled by the UCSICON command. The check box labeled On controls whether or not the UCS icon will be displayed, and the check box labeled Display at UCS origin point controls whether the UCS icon will be located on the UCS origin (provided the origin is within the viewport) or will always be located in the lower-left corner of the viewport. When the check box labeled Apply to all active viewports is checked, the settings for the other two check boxes will effect all viewports; otherwise, they will apply only to the current viewport.

The check box labeled Save UCS with viewport controls the relationship of the UCS of the current viewport to other viewports. When it is checked, the UCS of the viewport will be independent of the UCS in other viewports. When it is cleared, the UCS of the

42

viewport will change as needed to match the UCS of the current viewport. This check box controls the value of the **ucsvp** system variable for the current viewport. When it is checked, **ucsvp** is set to 1, and when it is cleared, **ucsvp** is set to 0.

Exercises

Practice and use are the best ways to become skillful in manipulating the UCS. The following two exercises will lead you through the steps of moving and orienting the UCS in building two wireframe models. The first is a simple warm-up exercise, while the second is more involved.

Exercise One

In this exercise you will remake the wireframe you made during Exercise Two in Chapter One. In that exercise, you had to type in the coordinates to draw the lines that were off the WCS X-Y plane. In this exercise, you will move and orient the UCS so that you can use your pointing device to draw all of the wireframe's lines.

You will not want to keep this wireframe, so your drawing setup is not important. However, since the lengths of the lines will be in increments of 0.5 units, you may find it convenient to turn on AutoCAD's snap mode with a snap spacing of 0.5.

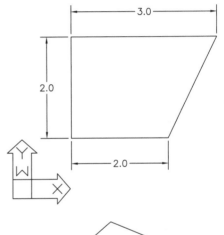

Draw the figure shown on the right, using four lines and the given dimensions, on the WCS X-Y plane. Its actual location on the X-Y plane is not important.

Next, switch to an isometric-type view by using VPOINT with rotation angles of 305 degrees in the X-Y plane from the X axis, and 35 degrees from the X-Y plane. Zoom back and pan as necessary to give yourself room to work.

In preparation for drawing the left side of the wireframe, use the ZAxis option of the UCS command to place the UCS origin on the left end of the 2.0-unit-long horizontal line and rotate the UCS X-Y plane so that it is perpendicular to this line. The command line input to do this is

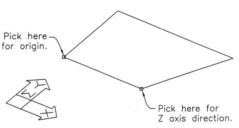

```
Command:  UCS (Enter)
Current UCS name: *WORLD*
Enter an option
   [New/Move/orthoGraphic/Prev/Restore/Save/Del/Apply/?/World]<World>: ZA (Enter)
Specify new origin point <0,0,0>: (Use an endpoint object snap to pick the point
   shown in the previous figure.)
Specify point on positive portion of Z-axis <0.0000,0.0000,1.0000>: (Use an endpoint
   object snap to pick the point shown in the previous figure.)
```

Notice that you can start the ZAxis option from the main UCS menu, even though it does not appear in the menu. Now draw the left side of the wireframe model, using the dimensions shown in the figure at the top of the next page.

Use the 3point option of the UCS command to set the UCS X-Y plane in a position that will enable you to draw the slanted rectangular face on the front of the model.

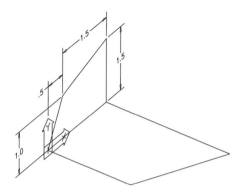

```
Command:  UCS (Enter)
Current UCS name: *NO NAME*
Enter an option [New/Move/orthoGraphic/Prev/Restore/Save/Del/Apply/?/World]<World>:
   3 (Enter)
Specify new origin point <0,0,0>: (Press the Enter
   key to accept the present location.)
Specify point on positive portion of X-axis
   <1.0000,0.0000,0.0000>: (Use an endpoint object
   snap to pick the point shown in the figure on
   the right.)
Specify point on positive-Y portion of the UCS XY
   plane <0.0000,1.0000,0.0000>: (Use an endpoint
   object snap to pick the point shown in the fig-
   ure on the right.
```

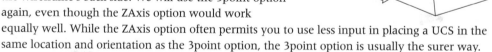

Pick here for point
on positive Y portion
of X–Y plane.

Pick here for
point on X axis.

1.5

Start line with
endpoint object
snap here.

Once the UCS is in position, draw the 1.5-unit line representing the top of the face and the slanted line that ties into the line previously drawn on the WCS X-Y plane, as shown in the figure on the right. You will have to start the 1.5-unit line with an endpoint object snap and draw the line using AutoCAD's ortho mode, since its location does not match our snap setting.

Next we will set the UCS in a position for completing the wireframe's back side. We will use the 3point option again, even though the ZAxis option would work equally well. While the ZAxis option often permits you to use less input in placing a UCS in the same location and orientation as the 3point option, the 3point option is usually the surer way.

```
Command:  UCS (Enter)
Current UCS name: *NO NAME*
Enter an option [New/Move/orthoGraphic/Prev/Restore/Save/Del/Apply/?/ World]<World>:
   3 (Enter)
Specify new origin point <0,0,0>: (Use an endpoint
   object snap to pick the point shown in the figure
   on the right.)
Specify point on positive portion of X-axis
   <1.0000,0.8944,-1.7889>: (Use an endpoint object
   snap to pick the point shown in the figure on the
   right.)
```

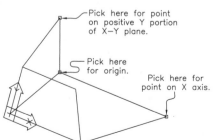

Pick here for point
on positive Y portion
of X–Y plane.

Pick here
for origin.

Pick here for
point on X axis.

44

Specify Point on positive-Y portion of the UCS XY
    plane <0.0000,1.8944,-7.7889>: *(Use an endpoint
    object snap to pick the point shown in the
    figure on the previous page.*

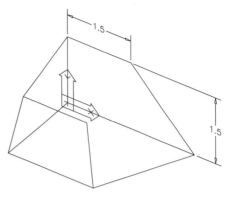

Draw the remaining two lines of the wireframe's back using the dimensions shown in the figure on the right.

All of the vertex points have now been established on the wireframe, so you can use object endpoint snaps to draw the remaining three lines. Your completed wireframe model should be similar to the one shown in the figure on the right.

This finishes the exercise. On the CD-ROM that comes with this book, you will find the finished wireframe model in file mfe02108.dwg.

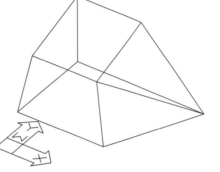

Exercise Two

In this exercise, you will construct a wireframe model of a sheet-metal part. Such a 3D model can be used by sheet-metal unfolding programs to make a flat pattern of the part. Some of these programs are AutoCAD add-on products, while others are stand-alone programs (but able to import DXF files). Their flat patterns account for metal deformation through bends so that the part can be cut to shape and the holes punched on a flat piece of sheet metal and still meet the 3D dimensions when the metal is folded.

Building this wireframe will reinforce your knowledge of AutoCAD's UCS and will also introduce some techniques that are useful in building 3D models of any type.

Start the part by drawing the three lines and two circles shown in the figure on the right on the WCS X-Y plane. The dimensions in this figure are for your use and should not be added to your model. Be certain that you draw the two lines that are parallel to the Y axis exactly 0.56 units long. The lines represent outside edges on the sheet-metal part, while the two circles represent holes in its surface. Then use the ZAxis option of the UCS command with the points shown in the figure on the top left of the next page to move and reposition the X-Y plane of the UCS. We will not show the command line input to do this since you used this option of the UCS command in Exercise One.

Now draw five lines using the dimensions shown in the figure on the top right. In this figure, the previously drawn lines and circles are shown in dashed line types.

When you have drawn the five lines, use the ZAxis option of the UCS command to move the UCS once more. Use endpoint object snaps to pick points for the new origin and Z axis direction, as shown in the figure below on the left.

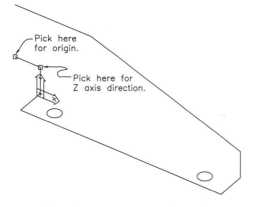

When the UCS is positioned, draw three lines and two circles in accordance with the dimensions given in the figure above on the right.

This finishes all of the edges and holes on the outside surface (which is the side that has the outside, or larger, bend radius) of the sheet-metal part. We will use copies of them to make the inside surface. Since our sheet-metal part is to be made of 16-gauge (0.060 inches thick) carbon steel, the copy displacement distance will be 0.06 units.

Before making the copies, use the World option of AutoCAD's UCS command to return the UCS to the WCS position and orientation. Then copy the three lines and two circles that are on the X-Y plane 0.06 units in the Z direction. Probably the easiest way to do this is to use command line input to specify the displacement distance of the copies.

```
Command: COPY (Enter)
Select objects: Select the three lines and
    two circles.
Specify base point or displacement, or
    [Multiple]: 0,0,.06 (Enter)
Specify second point of displacement or
    <use first point as displacement>:
    (Enter)
```

Then copy the five lines that are in a plane parallel to the WCS Z-X plane 0.06 units in the minus Y direction.

```
Command: COPY (Enter)
Select objects: Select the five lines.
Specify base point or displacement, or
    [Multiple]: 0,-.06 (Enter)
Specify second point of displacement or
    <use first point as displacement>:
    (Enter)
```

Finally, copy the three lines and two circles that are in a plane parallel to the WCS Y-Z plane 0.06 units in the X direction.

```
Command: COPY (Enter)
Select objects: Select the three lines and
    two circles.
Specify base point or displacement, or
    [Multiple]: .06,0 (Enter)
Specify second point of displacement or
    <use first point as displacement>:
    (Enter)
```

Fillet the lines representing the inside surface of the sheet-metal part 0.06 units, as shown in the figure on the right. Provided you are using a version of AutoCAD more recent than R12, you can make these fillets regardless of how the UCS is oriented.

Next, fillet the lines on the outside corners of the bends 0.12 units, as shown in the figure on the bottom of this page.

Your wireframe model should now look similar to the one shown in the figure on the top left of the next page.

To finish the wireframe, use object endpoint snaps to draw lines across the sharp corners between the front and back surfaces of the sheet-metal part as in the figure below right.

Although many would consider the wireframe model finished, other people would draw lines across the wireframe connecting the points of tangency between the fillets and the straight edges as shown in the figure below left. This is easily done by using object endpoint snaps to draw the lines.

In Section Four of this book we will show you how to make 2D multiview drawings from 3D models such as this. Such a drawing of this wireframe, without the tangency lines, would be similar to the one in the figure above right.

The completed wireframe model is in file mfe02213.dwg on the CD-ROM that comes with this book.

Using Multiple Viewports

T his chapter will show you how AutoCAD's screen graphics area can be divided into multiple sections, called viewports, that allow you to simultaneously view and work with your 3D model from different viewpoints and under different conditions. The chapter will

- *describe the properties and characteristics of model space viewports;*
- *show you how to create multiple viewports;*
- *offer suggestions for fully utilizing multiple viewports;*
- *describe the relationships between multiple viewports, the UCS, and views.*

The flat, 2D computer screen you work with will always be a major problem as you build 3D models because it gives you no depth perception. Everything you draw will appear to be in the same plane. To help alleviate this problem, AutoCAD can divide its screen graphics area into multiple sections, called *viewports,* which allow you to simultaneously see your model from different view directions. You can then compare the different views of your model to gain a better idea of its shape and of the relationships of its components and points.

The figure on the right shows an AutoCAD graphics area divided into three viewports. Although you can see three circles in the upper-left viewport, you cannot tell whether the circles represent holes or cylinders from that viewport alone. By looking in the other viewports, though, you can see that the two smaller circles are really holes, and moreover, one of them does not go completely through the model.

Also, while the view direction of the upper-left viewport is that of a plan view of the UCS, you have no idea where the UCS X-Y plane is actually located. It could be on the top surface of the model, on its lower surface, or even in some location that is not even close to the model. By looking in the right-hand viewport, however, you can see exactly where the UCS X-Y plane is located relative to the model.

AutoCAD refers to these viewports as *tiled viewports* because, like ceramic tiles on a floor or wall, they always abut one another—there can be no space between adjacent viewports. Unlike operating system windows, these tiled viewports have no title bars, and they cannot overlap, be dragged to other locations, or be stretched to another size. AutoCAD does have more Windows-like viewports, called *floating viewports*. However, they are for making 2D drawings from models and are restricted to AutoCAD's paper space mode. We will discuss paper space and floating viewports in Section Four of this book.

Characteristics of Tiled Viewports

In addition to fitting tightly next to one another, tiled viewports are always rectangular in shape, and they always completely fill the AutoCAD graphics area. Each viewport can have its own view direction and zoom level, as well as its own snap and grid settings. Each viewport can also have a different setting for the UCS icon, and its own UCS origin location and axes orientation.

Although multiple viewports may exist, you are confined to working in just one of them in any instance in time. This viewport, called the *current viewport*, will have a slightly thicker border than the others, and it will be the viewport that contains the cursor crosshairs. All additions and changes made in the current viewport, however, are instantly shown in the other viewports (provided the changes are in a location covered by the viewport). Also, only the contents of the current viewport can be printed. In the figure below, the upper-left viewport is the current viewport.

Screen redraws (with AutoCAD's REDRAW command) and regenerations (with REGEN) normally affect only the current viewport. You can, though, issue the REDRAWALL command to redraw all viewports, and you can use the REGENALL command to regenerate all viewports.

Internally, AutoCAD assigns an identification number to the viewports and stores their lower-left and upper-right corner locations as decimal fractions of the sides of the full graphics area. The lower-left corner of the graphics area is represented as 0,0, and the upper-right corner of the graphics area is represented as 1,1. In the command line versions of VPORTS you can use the question mark option to see this information for the current set of viewports.

50

For example, the viewport configuration shown in the figure below would be listed as

id# 3
    corners: 0.0000,0.0000 0.5000,1.0000
id# 2
    corners: 0.5000,0.5000 1.0000,1.0000
id# 4
    corners: 0.5000,0.0000 1.0000,0.5000

The current viewport the one containing the crosshair cursor, is always listed first. Furthermore, since AutoCAD reserves identification number 1 for the main paper space viewport, the lowest identification number that a model space viewport can have is 2. AutoCAD sometimes changes viewport identification numbers when a new drawing editing session is begun. Thus, if you exited and then re-opened the drawing used for the previous figure, the large viewport might be number 2, rather than number 3.

Most of the time, you will have no need to know the viewport identification numbers and the coordinates of the viewports, but they are useful (as we will demonstrate later in this chapter) in application programs related to viewports.

Creating Tiled Viewports

(-VPORTS) = INFORMATION)

By default AutoCAD starts with a single viewport that fills the entire graphics area. Additional tiled viewports are created and managed by AutoCAD's VPORTS command, which also goes by the name VIEWPORTS. Both a dialog box and a command line version of VPORTS exists. Most of the time you will use the dialog box version. However, the command line version, which is started by preceding the command's name with a hyphen (-VPORTS), has an option for joining viewports and another for obtaining information about viewports that are not available in the dialog box version.

(4 VPORTS TOTAL)

Both versions of the command allow you to make up to four viewports at a time, but since you can divide the current viewport, more than four viewports can be created by repeating the command. The total number of viewports allowed, as well as the minimum viewport size, depends upon your computer's video system. Not having enough viewports, however, is not likely to ever be a problem. Generally, three or four viewports are enough.

By joining and subdividing viewports, you can create viewport arrangements that go beyond the standard options of the VPORTS command. For instance: suppose you want to have one large viewport covering the bottom two-thirds of the graphics area, and have three side by side viewports in the remaining one-third of the graphics area. You could make such an arrangement by first creating three horizontal viewports, then joining the two lower viewports, and lastly dividing the top viewport into three vertical viewports.

Create three horizontal viewports.   Join the two lower viewports.   Create three vertical viewports in the top viewport.

The dialog box version of VPORTS, which is the default version of the command, is an especially convenient way to create viewports. Select its New Viewports tab, and then select the name of a viewport arrangement from the list on the left side of the dialog box. The selected arrangement will be displayed in the image tile on the right. The Apply to drop-down list box allows you to specify whether the current viewport or the entire graphic area is to be divided. When 2D is selected from the Setup drop-down list box, the viewpoint in all of the new viewports will be that of the current viewport: when 3D is selected, the viewpoints will be as shown in the figure on the left.

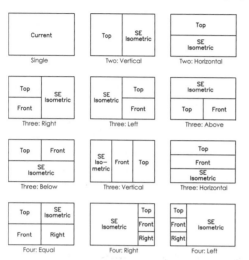

You can, though, change the viewpoint of selected viewports by selecting an orthographic or isometric view from the drop down list box labeled Change view to. Suppose for example you wanted to create two horizontal viewports, with the upper viewport showing the top of your model and the lower viewport showing its front, rather than the default SE isometric view. You would select Two Horizontal for the viewport arrangement, and 3D as the Setup; click in the lower viewport shown in the image tile to make it the current one, and select Front as the view type.

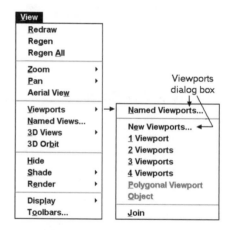

Command: VPORTS or VIEWPORTS

Purpose: This command enables you to divide AutoCAD's graphics area into multiple tiled viewports.

Initiate with:

- At the Command Line prompt enter VPORTS or VIEWPORTS.

- From the View pull-down menu, pick Viewports, then select an option from the resulting flyout menu.

New Viewport options:

- New name
  Enter a name in this edit box to save the current viewport configuration. The rules for the length of the name and the characters that are allowed to be in it are the same as for other AutoCAD named objects—such as layers, views, and UCSs. Entering a name is optional.

- Standard viewports

  The names of the twelve standard viewport arrangements, plus the current viewport arrangement, are shown in this list box. Click a name to select it.

- Preview

  The viewport arrangement of the selected viewport name will be displayed in this image tile. The type of viewpoint in each viewport is listed.

- Apply to

  The two choices in this drop-down list box—Display and Current Viewport—control whether the selected viewport arrangement is to apply to the entire graphics area or to just the current viewport. This option has no effect when Single has been selected as the viewport arrangement.

- Setup

  When 2D is selected from this drop-down list box, the view directions in the viewports will be the same as that of the current viewport. When 3D is selected, each viewport will initially have an orthographic or isometric viewpoint, as indicated in the Preview image tile.

Current viewport

Three viewports

After Single

- Change view to

  This drop-down list box, which is enabled only when 3D has been selected as the Setup type, enables you to change the viewpoint in selected viewports. First, select a viewport from the Preview image tile, and then select a view direction for that viewport from this list box.

Named Viewports Options:

- Named Viewports

  The names of all saved viewport configurations will be displayed in

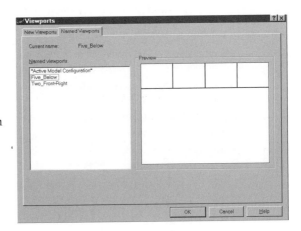

this list box. To choose a configuration, click on its name. You can rename or delete a saved configuration through a right-click menu.

- Preview

The viewport arrangement of the selected named viewport will be displayed in this image tile.

Command line options:

When you precede VPORTS with a hyphen, the following command line options will be displayed:

`Save/Restore/Delete/Join/Single/?/2/3/4/`

The Save, Restore, Delete, Single, 2, 3, and 4 options all correspond to options that are available in the New Viewports and Named Viewports dialog boxes. The Join and question mark (?) options, however, are available only from the command line.

- Join

This option combines two viewports. The viewports must share a common edge, and the resulting viewport must be rectangular. A follow-up prompt asks you to select the dominant viewport, offering the current viewport as a default. The properties and viewpoint of the resulting viewport will be those of the dominant

Dominant viewport

Viewport to join

Viewports before Join

Viewports after Join

viewport. Next, AutoCAD will ask for the viewport that is to be joined to the dominant viewport. Viewports are selected by picking a point inside their borders.

- ?

The question mark option displays each viewport's identification number along with its lower-left and upper-right corners, expressed as a decimal fraction of the sides of the graphics area. The current viewport is listed first. This list is followed by the names of saved viewport configurations and the lower-left and upper-right corners of their viewports.

Notes:

- The smallest allowable viewport size depends upon your computer's video system. If you continue to make viewports within a viewport, AutoCAD will eventually issue the message "The current viewport is too small to divide" and will not allow further division of that viewport.
- Viewports created when the 2D option of the New Viewports dialog box is in effect will have the UCS of the current viewport. When the 3D option is selected, the behavior of the UCS in each viewport with an orthographic view is affected by the **ucsortho** system variable. When **ucsortho** is set to 0, the UCS will not change; when **ucsortho** is set to 1, the UCS will be oriented so that its Z axis points out of the computer screen.
- Beginning with AutoCAD 2000, VPORTS works in paper space to make floating viewports, as well as in model space to make tiled viewports. The paper space version of VPORTS, however, is very similar to the MVIEW command that will be discussed in Section Four.

Related system variables:

- **vport**

  The identification number of the current viewport is stored within this system variable. Since the main paper space viewport is always viewport number 1, no model space viewport will have an ID number less than 2.

- **tilemode**

  When **tilemode** equals 1, tiled viewports are made. When **tilemode** equals 0, floating viewports are created.

- **ucsvp**   (POSITION UCS SYMB.)

  This system variable is set on a viewport-by-viewport basis. When **ucsvp** equals 0, the UCS of the viewport will change to match the UCS of the current viewport. When **ucsvp** equals 1, the UCS of the viewport will not change.

- **ucsortho**

  When the 3D setup of VPORTS is in effect, the UCS of viewports having orthographic views is controlled by this system variable. When **ucsortho** equals 1, the UCS of viewports having orthographic views will have their Z axis pointed directly out of the viewport. When **ucsortho** equals 0, the UCS of viewports for orthographic views will not change.

Using Multiple Viewports

Although you can work in only one viewport at a time, you can freely move from one viewport to another, even in the middle of most commands. You can, for instance, start a line in one viewport and finish it in another. You can also start picking objects for a selection set in one viewport, continue building the selection set in other viewports, and switch to still other viewports to specify such things as displacement locations.

The current viewport—the one that you can work in—is indicated by a viewport border that is slightly thicker than those of the other viewports. It will also be the only viewport that has the crosshair cursor. When you move your pointing device to another viewport, the crosshair cursor will remain in the current viewport while movement of your pointing device is indicated by a small arrow.

The most common method for selecting a new current viewport is to move your pointing device to the desired viewport and press the pick button on your pointing device. AutoCAD identifies the first pick in a new viewport as a viewport selection pick, even if it is looking for point input. Once a new current viewport has been established, you can continue picking points or selecting objects.

Beginning with AutoCAD Release 14, you can also change viewports by simultaneously pressing your computer's Ctrl and R keys until you get to the viewport you want. Yet another way to change viewports is by setting the system variable **cvport** to the value of the identification number of the viewport that you want to become the current viewport. Although this is not a practical method while manually using the VPORTS command, it is a useful method for setting the current viewport in AutoLISP programs.

You will most likely have a different view direction and zoom level in each viewport. While there are no rules, or even standard conventions, for setting view directions, many people find it helpful to establish viewports that show the principal views of the model plus one with an isometric-type viewpoint.

Viewports and the UCS

Beginning with AutoCAD 2000, each viewport can have its own UCS. This very useful property can save you steps as you work with 3D models because you do not need to move and reorient the UCS as often as you did when only one UCS at a time could be used. It is also a potentially confusing property, because you cannot determine the UCS location in a viewport by observing its location in other viewports. Consider, for example, the UCS and the viewports shown in the figure on the right. By merely looking at the computer screen, you cannot be certain where the UCS is located in the upper-left viewport. It could be in the same location as the UCS in the lower-left viewport, or in the same location as the UCS in the right-hand viewport, or anywhere along the axis of the round hole.

You must know exactly where the UCS is placed in every viewport. Therefore, you may prefer to not use the 3D setup of VPORTS New Viewports dialog box, so that you can set both the UCS and the viewpoint as you wish in each viewport.

AutoCAD has two tools for ensuring that the UCS in one viewport is the same at that of another viewport. One of these tools is the Apply option of the UCS command. In effect, the Apply option places the copy of a UCS from one viewport into another viewport. To use this option, make the viewport that has the UCS you wish to copy to be the current viewport. Then invoke UCS and choose its Apply option. Make the viewport you want to receive the copy be the current viewport, and press the Enter key. This option also allows you to apply the UCS of a viewport to all viewports.

The other tool for ensuring that the UCS in one viewport is the same as that of another viewport it the **ucsvp** system variable. This system variable, which accepts a value of either 0 or 1, is viewport specific; **ucsvp** can be set to 0 in some viewports and to 1 in other viewports. When **ucsvp** is set to 0, the viewport's UCS will always match that of the current viewport. In the three figures on the right, **ucsvp** has been set to 0 in the right-hand viewport. Notice in the second and third figures that the UCS of this viewport is automatically moved and oriented to match that of the current viewport. You will usually leave **ucsvp** at its default value of 1, but occasionally you will want to set it to 0 in a viewport so that you can, in effect, place a copy of a UCS from another viewport into it.

Utilizing Saved Viewport Configurations

The Save option of the VPORTS command (or New name in the New Viewports dialog box) does more than simply save the current number and arrangement of viewports—it also saves

- the grid and snap settings in each viewport;
- the UCS and the UCS icon setting in each viewport;
- the view direction and zoom level in each viewport.

A convenient way to keep a particular arrangement of viewports, along with the settings within them that you often work with, is to save it as a named viewport configuration in a prototype, or template, drawing. You can have AutoCAD start with the viewport configuration, or you can start with a conventional single viewport and restore your named set of viewports whenever it is convenient.

Saved viewport configurations can also be useful in setting up paper space floating viewports. The command that creates paper space floating viewports, MVIEW, has an option to translate saved model space viewport configurations into floating viewports. We will discuss this option in detail in Section Four of this book.

Using AutoLISP to Create Viewports

A minor disadvantage to using named and saved viewport configurations in prototype and template drawings is that the zoom level in the viewports may not be appropriate for the size of the model you are constructing. Say, for example, you are building a 3D model house, but the zoom level in the saved viewport configuration is more suitable for working with small mechanical objects. You will have to go into each viewport and zoom out so that you can see the entire house.

Even though this is only a slight inconvenience, you can use AutoLISP to create viewports having zoom levels that fit the model you are currently working on. The AutoLISP program 4_LgR.LSP is an example. It divides the AutoCAD graphics area into four viewports—one large one on the right side of the area and three small ones arranged vertically on the left side. The large viewport on the right shows an isometric-type view, the topmost small viewport on the left shows a plan view, the middle one shows a front view, and the lower small viewport shows the right side of the model.

The resulting viewport configuration is comparable to that of the Four Left configuration of VPORTS New Viewports dialog box when 3D has been selected as the setup style. This AutoLISP program has some advantages over the VPORTS configuration, though: It does not set the UCS in any of the viewports, it zooms back a little in each viewport to give you some working room, and it sets a slightly off-center isometric-type view direction in the large viewport (which is better to work with than a true isometric viewpoint).

The program, which is on the CD-ROM that accompanies this book, is heavily commented to help you understand how it works. If you look through the program, you will notice that it starts by making sure that **tilemode** is set to 1, then it creates and joins viewports until a large viewport, taking up three-fourths of the graphics area, is on the right. The left-hand one-fourth of the graphics area is then divided vertically into three viewports.

After creating the four viewports, the program steps through each one of them, setting the viewing direction and the zoom level to the equivalent of 0.9 Zoom/All. The three small viewports show the top, front, and right-side views of the model, while the large viewport shows an isometric-type view of it.

Direction coordinates are used with the VPOINT command within the program to set viewing directions. The coordinates used for setting the isometric-type view (0.8112, -1.1585, 1.0) are equivalent to the VPOINT rotation angles of 305 degrees in the X-Y plane from the X axis, and 35 degrees from the X-Y plane.

The program uses AutoCAD's **cvport** system variable when it needs to go to a viewport. It also makes use of AutoLISPís **vports** function. This function, which takes no arguments, returns a list for the current viewport configuration showing the identification number of each viewport and its corner coordinates. The corner coordinates are shown as decimal fractions of the sides of the graphics area, just as they are by the question mark option of the VPORTS command.

For example, the **vports** function might return the following for the viewport configuration 4_LgR.LSP creates:

```
( (4 (0.0 0.666667) (0.25 1.0))
  (3 (0.25 0.0) (1.0 1.0))
    (2 (0.0 0.0) (0.25 0.333333))
    (5 (0.0 0.333333) (0.25 0.666667) )
```

The corner coordinates for this viewport arrangement will always be as shown here, but the viewport identification numbers and the order they are in may vary from one AutoCAD session to another, and the order also depends on which viewport is the current one.

Views and UCSs

Beginning with AutoCAD 2000, the VIEW command has options for restoring one of ten preestablished views. Six of these views, which are shown in the figure on the right, are orthographic, while the other four are isometric. To restore one of the views, open the Orthographic & Isometric Views tab of the VIEW command's View dialog box, and select the view you want from the list box. You can use any of three methods to make the selected view become the current view.

- Click the Set Current button.

- Double-click the highlighted view name.

- Right-click the highlighted view name, and
  select Set Current from the menu.

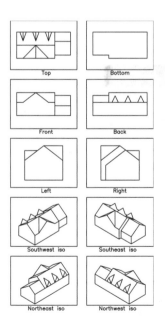

Once you have selected a view, click the OK button of the dialog box to restore it. You can also set one of these ten views by selecting a view button in the Views toolbar, or by selecting an orthographic or isometric option in the View/3D Views pull-down menu. Prior to AutoCAD 2000, both the View toolbar and the 3D Views menu used the VPOINT command to set orthographic and isometric views.

If the check box labeled Restore Orthographic UCS with View is checked, the X-Y plane of the UCS will revolve so that the Z axis points directly out of the computer screen when an orthographic view is restored. If the check box is cleared, the UCS will not change as the orthographic view is created. This check box controls the value of the **ucsortho** system variable. When **ucsortho** is set to a value of 0, the UCS is not changed when an orthographic view is created. When **ucsortho** is set to 1, the UCS rotates so that its X-Y plane is perpendicular to the view's line of sight. This system variable only affects orthographic views established by the VIEW command, and by the 3D option of the VPORTS command. It has no affect when isometric views are restored, or when another command (such as VPOINT) is used to set an orthographic viewpoint.

The origin and orientation of the UCS is relative to the coordinate system stored in the **ucsbase** system variable. By default this base coordinate system is the WCS. You can, however, store the name of any UCS that has been named and saved by the UCS or UCSMAN commands. The drop-down list box labeled Relative to in the Orthographic & Isometric Views tab is a convenient way to store a named UCS in the **ucsbase** system variable.

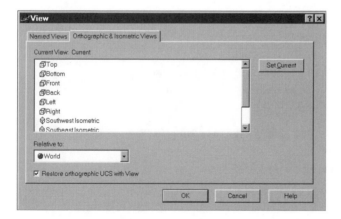

2D Wireframe Objects in 3D Space

W*e will explore the relationship of 2D wireframe objects to 3D space in this chapter. The topics that will be covered are*

- *the properties of 2D wireframe objects in 3D space;*
- *how 2D editing commands can be used in 3D space;*
- *how to build the wireframe skeleton of a 3D house;*
- *four special AutoCAD commands for editing and manipulating objects in 3D space—ROTATE3D, MIRROR3D, 3DARRAY, and ALIGN;*
- *how to build the wireframe model of an automobile oil pan.*

Most objects in 3D wireframe models are 2D objects—they can be defined completely by using just X and Y coordinates. Even a line is a 2D object, since the entire length of any one line lies in a single plane, despite the fact that all three coordinates are often used to define its endpoints. The only truly 3D AutoCAD wireframe objects are splines (those made by the SPLINE command, rather than 2D polylines converted to spline curves) and 3D polylines. While you will not often need those two object types, they are able to create geometries that no 2D object can create. Because of their uniqueness we will discuss 3D polylines and splines by themselves in the next chapter.

In this chapter we will discuss the properties of 2D wireframe objects in 3D space. We'll see how drawing and editing them in 3D space is different from when they are used to make 2D drawings. We'll also look at some special AutoCAD commands for editing and modifying objects in 3D space.

Relationships of 2D Wireframe Objects to 3D Space

While wireframe objects share the common characteristic of having no width or thickness, their relationship to 3D space varies among object types. Therefore, we will describe how each 2D AutoCAD wireframe database object type relates to three dimensions. Most of these objects can also be given a thickness, and some can be given a width as well, but they cease to be wireframe objects when they have either of those properties. They become surface objects, which will be discussed in Section Two of this book.

Arc

An arc always lies in a plane that is either on the current X-Y plane or is parallel to it. The first point specified for the arc sets its elevation. If you use object snaps to locate the other two points of the arc, AutoCAD will project (in a direction that is parallel with the Z axis) the object snap locations to the elevation of the first point. If you specify the subsequent coordinates from the keyboard, AutoCAD will reject points entered with a Z coordinate—you can enter only the X and Y coordinates.

Circle

A circle always lies on a plane that is on the current X-Y plane or is parallel to it. The first point specified sets the circle's elevation. If this point represents the center of the circle, the second point selected will be the circle's radius or diameter (depending upon the option selected), and if an object snap is used to specify the radius (or diameter), AutoCAD will give the circle a radius (or diameter) that is equal to the 3D distance from the circle's center point to the object snap point. In other words, AutoCAD does not project the object snap point onto the plane of the center point. The figure below shows an example.

   If, on the other hand, the 2P or 3P options for defining a circle are selected, the first point specified sets the elevation of the circle, and subsequent points selected by object snaps are projected to that elevation. If the Tangent-Tangent-Radius option is selected, both of the arcs or circles used for specifying a tangent must be on a plane that is parallel to the current X-Y plane. The subsequent circle is drawn on the X-Y plane, even if the circles or arcs are in other planes.

Dimension

AutoCAD always draws dimensions on the current X-Y plane, even if the object or the points selected are in other planes. With linear dimensions, horizontal dimensions are those that are parallel to the X axis, while vertical dimensions are parallel to the Y axis. If a linear feature that is not parallel to the X-Y plane is being dimensioned, the resulting dimension will not

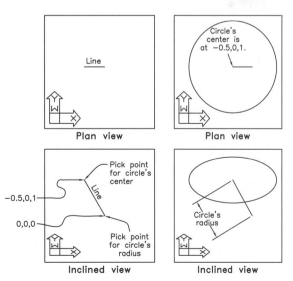

equal the feature's true length. AutoCAD is, however, able to properly determine the true radius and diameter of arcs and circles, even if they are not parallel to the current X-Y plane.

Ellipse

Ellipses, whether they are made as splines or as polylines, are always drawn on a plane parallel to the current X-Y plane. The ellipse is drawn on a plane having the same elevation as the first point selected for the ellipse. If object snaps are used to specify subsequent points, they are projected onto the ellipse's plane.

Circles, arcs, and ellipses must be drawn on the X—Y plane or on a plane parallel to it.

Leader

Leaders are always drawn on a plane parallel to the current X-Y plane. The first point specified for the leader determines the elevation of the leader's plane.

Line

A line may be drawn from any point in 3D space to any other point in 3D space. As a matter of historical interest, this hasn't always been true. Prior to Release 10, the LINE command was restricted to drawing lines on, or parallel to, the X-Y plane.

Mline

Multilines are always drawn on a plane parallel to the current X-Y plane, at the elevation of the first point specified. If object snaps are used to specify subsequent points, the points are projected to the multiline's elevation, even if the specified points have other elevations.

Mtext

AutoCAD always places multitext on a plane parallel to the current X-Y plane. The elevation of the first corner of the text box is used as the elevation for the multitext.

Point

You may place a point in any location in 3D space. If a point has a supplementary object (such as a cross or bull's-eye, as determined by the **pdmode** system variable) attached to it, the supplementary object is drawn on a plane parallel to the current X-Y plane.

2D Polyline

Polylines, along with polyline-based objects such as polygons and donuts, are always drawn on a plane that is parallel to the current X-Y plane, at an elevation equal to the first point specified. If object snaps in other elevations are used to specify points, they are projected to the elevation of the polyline.

Ray

Rays, which are generally used for construction lines, are linelike objects that extend an infinite distance from their starting points. The starting point can be located anywhere in 3D space, and the ray can extend in any direction from that starting point.

Shape

Shapes are objects that are defined by an external file having a file extension of .SHX, similar to ordinary AutoCAD text. Often they are used as symbols in electronic diagrams. They may be positioned in any elevation in 3D space, and they are always drawn in a plane parallel to the current X-Y plane.

Text

Text is always placed in a plane parallel to the current X-Y plane at an elevation equal to the insert point of the text.

Xline

Xlines, which are commonly used for construction lines, extend an infinite distance in both directions from a point. AutoCAD imposes no 3D restrictions in specifying the base point or the direction of an xline.

Editing Wireframe Objects in 3D Space

Editing is an important phase in creating both 2D drawings and 3D models, and you will use a variety of AutoCAD's editing commands as you work in 3D space. You will, for example, modify the shape of 3D models by changing the length of their objects (with the STRETCH, LENGTHEN, TRIM, and EXTEND commands), you will add to models by making copies of existing objects (with the COPY, ARRAY, and MIRROR commands), and you will use the interaction between two objects to create new objects (with the FILLET and CHAMFER commands).

For the most part, AutoCAD's editing commands work just the same in 3D space as they do on 2D drawings, but there are some subtle differences, and some of the commands have 3D extensions that you have no reason to use while making 2D drawings. Therefore, we will review AutoCAD's editing functions and commands, taking a special look at their 3D capabilities.

Object Snaps

AutoCAD recognizes most object snaps in 3D space. It has no problem, for instance, recognizing the endpoints and the midpoints of lines regardless of how they are oriented in 3D space. AutoCAD also has no problem performing perpendicular snaps or finding centerpoints of circles and arcs, even if the objects are not parallel to the current X-Y plane. However, quadrant and tangent snaps can be used only on circles, arcs, and ellipses that are parallel to the current X-Y plane.

Intersection object snaps also have no 3D restrictions, but the two objects must either actually intersect or, beginning with Release 13, intersect if they were to be extended. Also beginning with Release 13, AutoCAD is able to snap to apparent intersections of objects that are actually in different planes. Apparent intersection snaps can be initiated from the command line by entering APPINT or APP, from the Object Snap toolbar, or from the cursor menu (which is activated by holding down the Shift key as you press the Return button on your pointing device), whenever AutoCAD is expecting a point. If there is no intersection (real or apparent) at the point you select, AutoCAD will begin an apparent extended intersection object snap and will expect you to select a second object. Then, AutoCAD will snap to a point at which the two objects would appear to meet if they were extended.

Since this object snap is view-related, the apparent intersection will vary as the viewpoint varies. An example is shown in the figure on the right of two lines that are in different planes—the lines do not actually intersect. From the plan view, however, the two lines appear as an X, and AutoCAD will report that the coordinates of the apparent intersection point are 1,1,1. From another viewpoint, however, the apparent intersection point could be 1.201,1.201,1.201, and from yet another viewpoint their extended apparent intersection point could be -0.436,2.436,3.218.

As an example of how you can use apparent intersections, suppose you are drawing a wireframe model of a house that is to have a dormer on its roof. Three corners of the dormer, labeled A, B, and C in the figure below, will be on the roof surface.

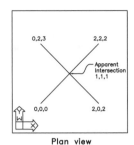

Two lines in different planes
isometric-type view

Plan view

Second isometric-type view

Third isometric-type view

Locating these points is not straightforward since the roof is empty space; nothing is there for you to attach anything to. You do know, however, the elevation of points A and B as well as their relative spacing and their location along the roof. Also, once those two points are established, you can draw the front edge of the dormer roof to set the elevation of point C.

To establish point A, you could move the UCS origin to a location on the plane of the house's front corresponding to point A's WCS X and Z distances from the house's front-left corner, then rotate the UCS so that the X axis points into the house. Then, you could draw a horizontal construction line into the roof of the house. Point A will be somewhere on this line. You would probably use the VPORTS command to divide AutoCAD's graphics area into two viewports; one viewport would have an isometric-type viewpoint, and the other would have a plan view of the current UCS.

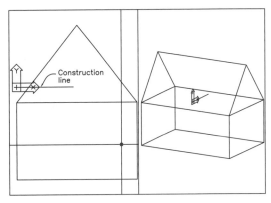

Next, using the viewport that has the plan view, you would invoke AutoCAD's BREAK command, select the construction line as the object to break, use an apparent intersection to pick the first break point, and pick the second point beyond an endpoint of the construction line to delete the line beyond the first pick point. It doesn't make any difference which end of the construction line you keep.

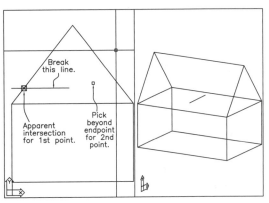

The end of the broken line will be point A. You would move the UCS origin to that point and rotate the UCS about the Y axis so that you could draw the front face of the dormer. After drawing the front of the dormer, you could draw a line from its apex in the minus Z direction through the roof. You could then break that line at its apparent intersection with the roof in the side view of the house to find point C on the dormer.

Finally, you can use object endpoint snaps to draw lines along the edge of the dormer's roof from point A to C and from C to B, as shown in the figure at the beginning of this example.

2D Editing Commands in 3D Space
COPY and MOVE

Although these two commands have different objectives, they both are implemented in the same way. After building a selection of objects to be moved or copied, you specify a base point and then a displacement point. These points are fully 3D, and you may use any of the methods we discussed in Chapter One to specify them.

OFFSET

The OFFSET command gives you one more way to make copies of existing objects. For lines and straight segments of polylines, the copy is placed parallel to the original object by a specified distance. For arcs, circles, and arc segments of polylines, the radius of the copy is also increased or decreased, depending upon whether the offset is outside or inside the original arc or circle. The copy is always offset in a direction that is parallel to the current X-Y plane. The objects, however, even if they are 2D polylines, do not have to be parallel to the current X-Y plane.

FILLET and CHAMFER

Since Release 13, AutoCAD's FILLET command works on any two wireframe objects that are in the same plane, regardless of how their plane is oriented relative to the UCS. In earlier AutoCAD releases, the plane of the wireframe objects had to be parallel to the UCS X-Y axis. You can also fillet two lines that are parallel—a 180-degree arc will be drawn between the two selected lines.

In the figure on the right, you can fillet the following pairs of objects:

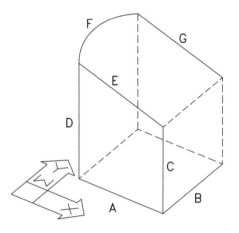

A and B	A and C	A and D	A and E	B and C
C and D	C and E	D and E	E and F	E and G
F and G				

You cannot fillet the following pairs of objects:

A and F	A and G	B and D	B and E	B and F
B and G	C and F	C and G	D and F	D and G

The CHAMFER command makes a beveled corner, rather than rounded corner, between two line objects. It does not work with arcs or with parallel lines, but the command is not affected by the current orientation of the UCS X-Y plane.

BREAK

The BREAK command is fully 3D beginning with AutoCAD Release 13. It will break a wireframe object, such as a line, arc, or circle, at the point (or points) specified, regardless of how the object is oriented within the UCS. In releases previous to Release 13, however, Auto-CAD reflects the specified points off of the current X-Y plane back onto the object. As a result, the breakpoints will not match the specified points unless the current X-Y plane is parallel to the plane of the object.

TRIM/EXTEND

Since the operation of AutoCAD's TRIM and EXTEND commands are similar (TRIM trims an object back to a boundary object, while EXTEND lengthens an object to a boundary object), we will discuss the 3D characteristics of just the TRIM command. For a description of how EXTEND works in 3D space, simply replace the word TRIM with EXTEND in the following discussion.

On the command line, the TRIM command issues the following messages and prompts:

```
Command: TRIM
Current Settings: Projection=UCS Edge=None
```

66

```
Select cutting edges ...
Select objects: Select one or more objects to serve as cutting edges.
Select object to trim or [Project/Edge/Undo]: Select an object or choose an option.
```

Notice that when the command starts, AutoCAD issues a message on the current settings of two modes **Projection** and **Edge**. The contents of this message vary to reflect the current status of these two modes. **Projection** determines how the cutting edge object is projected toward the object to be trimmed. It has three possible settings, which we will discuss shortly.

Edge controls whether the ends of the cutting edges can, or cannot, be extended. It has two possible settings: Extend or No extend. When **Edge** is set to No Extend, the boundary object and the object to be trimmed must intersect for the trim to occur. When **Edge** is set to Extend, the two objects do not have to intersect. When they do not intersect, the cutting boundary is extended to the point where it would intersect the object that is to be trimmed, and the length of the trim object is adjusted to that point.

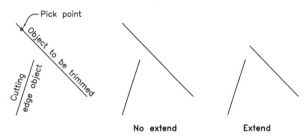

Both **Edge** and **Projection** can be set through options in the TRIM command's main menu. The Edge option in the main menu brings up a submenu for you to use in setting **Edge** to Extend or No Extend, while the Project option leads to a submenu for setting the **Projection** mode. This submenu is

```
None/Ucs/View <current mode>: Select an option.
```

When **Projection** is set to None, the cutting edge object and the object to be trimmed must be in the same plane. Thus, neither of the two circles shown in the figure on the left will trim the other circle.

When **Projection** is set to Ucs, the cutting edge object and the object to be trimmed do not have to be in the same plane. Therefore, either one of the circles shown in the figure on the left can be used as a cutting edge to trim the other circle when **Projection** is set to Ucs. This trim mode projects the cutting plane object perpendicularly (relative to the X-Y plane of the UCS) to the object that is to be trimmed. As a result, the two objects do not even have to intersect. The figure on the right shows the same two circles, but the inclined circle that is to be trimmed has been moved above the WCS X-Y plane and does not even touch the circle used as a cutting edge object. Nevertheless, it is still trimmed.

To visualize the trim points on an object, you can look at it from a plan view

of the current UCS. The point, or points, at which the object to be trimmed appear to intersect with the cutting edge will be the points at which it will be trimmed. The figure on the right shows a plan view of the same circles shown in the previous figure.

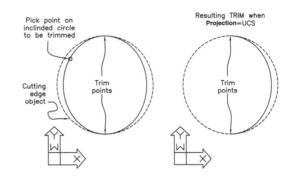

The third setting of **Projection** is View. When this mode is in effect, the cutting object is projected in the view direction and trims the object at the point, or points, where they visually intersect.

It is even possible, when **Projection** is set to View and **Edge** is set to Extend, to trim an object that does not intersect the cutting plane in the current viewpoint, but would if the cutting plane were extended.

The default setting for **Projection** when either the TRIM or EXTEND command is started is controlled by AutoCAD's **projmode** system variable. This system variable can have three possible values. These values and their results are

Projmode Setting	Result
0	No projection
1	UCS projection
2	View projection

Changing the value of the **projmode** system variable will cause the TRIM and EXTEND commands to offer different default **Projection** settings, but since it is so convenient to choose a projection mode from within the TRIM and EXTEND command, there is little reason to access the **projmode** system variable directly.

You can also change the **Edge** mode default for extending or not extending the cutting edge through a system variable. When AutoCAD's **edgemode** system variable is set to a value of 0, "no extend" will be offered as a default. When it is set to a value of 1, the default offered will be "extend."

ROTATE

AutoCAD's ROTATE command rotates objects about an axis that is perpendicular to the current X-Y plane. The rotation base point you select establishes the location of the rotation axis on the X-Y plane. Objects selected to be rotated are then revolved about this axis regardless of their orientation to the current X-Y plane.

MIRROR

MIRROR makes copies of objects by reflecting them on the opposite side of a plane that is perpendicular to the current X-Y plane. The two points you specify for the mirror line determine the angle of the mirroring plane relative to the X-Z and Y-Z planes. The distance between these two points is not important, since objects selected to be mirrored are reflected across the plane regardless of their spatial position.

ARRAY

AutoCAD's ARRAY command makes multiple copies of objects. The copies are arranged either in rows and columns—a rectangular array—or in a circle—a polar array. Rows are in the current Y axis direction while columns are in the current X axis direction. Therefore you can make rectangular and polar arrays in any orientation to the WCS by first orienting the UCS X-Y plane.

STRETCH

AutoCAD's STRETCH command works well on 3D wireframe objects. Although the *crossing selection window* appears to be a simple rectangle, it is actually a 3D fence extending in the view direction, having a depth that takes in all objects, regardless of the plane they are in. Since crossing windows are always drawn as rectangles with their sides parallel to the viewport sides, you will often use a *polygon crossing window* when you are using the STRETCH command in isometric-type views. You can even stretch objects in the Z direction, although you will have to type in coordinates for the displacement.

Exercise One

We will make the 3D skeleton of a house as an exercise in creating and manipulating wire-frame objects. This exercise will give you experience in using 2D editing commands in building 3D models. You will want to keep this model, because in Section Two of this book we will add surfaces to it, and in Section Five we will make a rendering of the house.

You should set up the drawing to use architectural units (feet and inches). Make a new layer, with a name such as OBJ01 or WF01, to be used for drawing the house wireframe. This

layer should have a continuous linetype and a color appropriate for your computer's display. Most lengths on this model will be in increments of 6 inches, so you may want to activate AutoCAD's snap mode with a snap spacing of 6 inches.

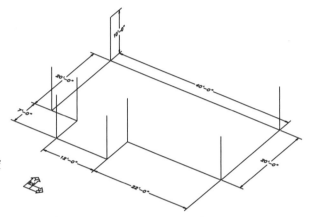

Begin the house by drawing an outline of its floor plan on the WCS X-Y plane, using the dimensions shown in the figure on the right. Its location on the X-Y plane is not important, but be certain that the long side of the house is parallel to the X axis.

When you have drawn the eight lines mak-ing up the floor outline, switch to an isometric-type view and draw a line in the Z direction that is 10 feet long from any of the floor's corners. You can either type in relative coordinates to specify the end of this line, or move and rotate the UCS to draw it by pointing. Then make seven copies of this vertical line so that there is one at each corner of the house.

Now, zoom in on the left side of the house so that you can draw one-half of one end of the house's roof as shown in the figure on the right. Notice that the roof extends 1 foot beyond all sides of the floor plan. The easiest way to set up the UCS for drawing the five lines of the overhang part of the roof is to use the ZAxis option of the UCS com-mand, and pick a point 1 foot to the left of the floor outline as the UCS origin and a point in the WCS X axis direction for the Z axis orientation.

Once the UCS is set, use the dimensions shown in the sketch on the next page to draw the end of the roof. In this sketch, the objects you have already drawn are shown as dashed lines. After drawing the five lines, copy two of them 1 foot in the WCS X direction, as shown in the sketch, to delineate where the roof meets the house wall.

Then use the MIRROR command, using a mir-ror plane through the midpoint of the left end of

70

the floor plan, to make the other half of this end of the roof. This end of your house should now look similar to the figure on the top left . You can then fillet the two pairs of lines, using a fillet radius of 0, that overlap to square them up.

Next, you should draw the gable on the front of the house. Use the dimensions shown in the figure on the top right to draw one-half of the gable. Notice that it too overhangs the floor plan by 1 foot and that its dimensions are the same as those of the main roof's end, except for the pitch of the roof.

After drawing one half of the gable, use AutoCAD's MIRROR command to make the other half, and fillet the two pairs of lines (with a 0 fillet radius) that overlap. You should then zoom back so that you can see the entire house, and mirror the roof end on the left side of the house to the right side. All of these uses of the MIRROR command can be done from the WCS by using midpoint object snaps on the house floor plan. Your house should now look like the one shown in the figure on the right.

The ends of the roof are complete, so you can now draw the eaves of the roof. Zoom in to the upper-left front corner of the house and position the UCS on the end of the roof as shown in the figure below. Since this UCS X-Y plane is parallel with the WCS X-Y plane, the easiest way to position the UCS is to make certain that the WCS is in effect, then

use the Origin option of the UCS command with an object endpoint snap on the bottom of one of the vertical lines of the roof end. When you have positioned the UCS, draw four lines from the endpoints of existing lines, as shown in the figure on the left. In this figure, previously drawn objects are shown in dashed lines.

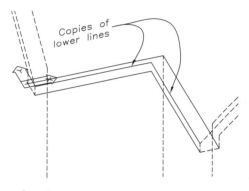

Copies of lower lines

Next, make a copy of the lower two lines. The location of these copies will be 6 inches above the original lines, as shown in the figure on the left.

Move the UCS to the other side of the front gable and use the same techniques to draw the eaves for the remaining front of the roof. Your house should now look like the one in the figure below (although previously drawn objects are shown in dashed lines in this figure).

Drawing the peak of the gable roof is best done by using two viewports. One viewport will have an isometric-type viewpoint, and the other will have a viewpoint looking straight toward the end of the house (such as that from the VPOINT coordinates of 1,0,0). See the figure below. Draw a line from the peak of the gable roof in the WCS Y direction. You will not know exactly where to stop this line. After drawing this line, go to the viewport showing the end of the house and use the TRIM command (or EXTEND, if your line doesn't reach the main roofline) with **Projection** set to View to clip the line at the point where the gable peak intersects the main roof.

Draw a line from the roof peak in WCS Y direction.

Trim the line to the main roof with **Projection=View** in an elevation view of the house.

Finish the house wireframe by drawing lines from the end of the gable peak to its eaves, the back eaves, and the main roof peak. You can use object endpoint snaps to draw all of these lines. Your 3D wireframe house should look like the one shown in the figure on the right. On the CD-ROM that comes with this book, the model is in file mfe04110.dwg. In the next section of this book we will add surfaces to this wireframe.

3D Editing Commands

AutoCAD has four commands intended specifically for 3D work. Three of these commands—ROTATE3D, MIRROR3D, and 3DARRAY—are enhanced versions of 2D commands, while the fourth—ALIGN—has no 2D counterpart. It performs a move-and-rotate type of operation, and it can be useful in 2D drawings as well as in 3D models. Although all of these commands are based on external programs, they are automatically loaded, are ready for use at any time, and operate just like built-in AutoCAD commands. They are listed under the Modify/3D Operation pull-down menu.

You should read the following descriptions of these commands and remember their purposes and characteristics so that you can use them when the need arises. While you can use standard AutoCAD commands to duplicate their results, these 3D commands are often much more convenient to use. They can perform some tasks in only one step that would take several steps with standard commands.

Command: 3DARRAY

Purpose: This is an enhanced version of AutoCAD's ARRAY command. It is able to make rectangular arrays that have copies in the Z direction as well as in the X and Y directions. Also, polar arrays are not restricted to axes that are pointed in just the Z direction.

Initiate with:

- At the command line prompt enter 3DARRAY.

- From the Modify pull-down menu, pick 3D Operation, then select 3D Array.

Options:

After selecting the objects to be copied, the command will offer you the choice of arranging the copies in a rectangular or polar array.

- Rectangular

This option makes copies arranged in rows (the Y direction), columns (the X direction), and levels (the Z direction). You are first prompted to specify the number of copies to be made in each direction:

```
Enter number of rows (--) <1>: Enter a positive integer.
Enter number of columns (|||) <1>: Enter a positive integer.
Enter umber of levels (...) <1>: Enter a positive integer.
```

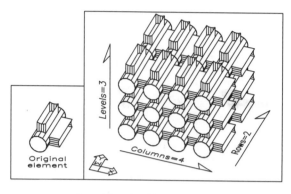

If you specify a quantity of 1 for any direction, no copies are made in that direction. If you specify a quantity of 1 for all three directions, no copies will be made, so the command reissues the three prompts. Specifying a quantity of 1 for each level is equivalent to a 2D rectangular array.

After you specify the number of rows, columns, and levels, the command prompts for a distance in each direction in which more than one copy was specified:

```
Specify the distance between rows (--): Specify a distance.
Specify the distance between columns (|||): Specify a distance.
Specify the distance between levels (...): Specify a distance.
```

Positive distance values generate the copies in the positive axis direction, while negative values generate the copies in the negative axis direction. The figure above shows a rectangular array having four columns, two rows, and three levels.

- Polar

While this option makes copies arranged in a circle similar to the polar option of the 2D ARRAY command, you can specify an axis that is oriented in any direction in space, rather than in just the Z direction. Its first three prompts are

```
Enter the number of items in the
    array: Enter a positive integer.
Specify the angle to fill (+=ccw, -
    =cw) <360>: Enter an angle or
    press Enter.
Rotate arrayed objects? [Yes/No]
    <Y>: Enter Y, N, or press Enter.
```

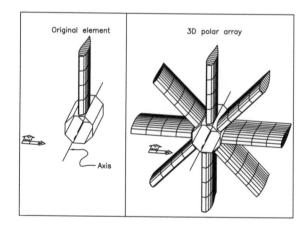

You can enter a negative angle to reverse the normal rotation direction of the copies. Usually you will want the copies to be rotated as they are copied. Finally, the command will ask you to define the rotational axis by specifying two points:

```
Specify center point of array:
    Specify a point.
Specify second point on axis of
    rotation: Specify a point.
```

Object to be arrayed and its axis

Polar array, 3 copies, 180 degrees, objects rotated

Polar array, 3 copies, 180 degrees, objects not rotated

The order in which you pick these points is important, since the positive direction of the axis is from the first point to the second point. You can visualize the rotation direction by mentally grasping the axis with your right hand so that your thumb is pointed in the positive direction of the axis. The copies will be placed in the direction in which your curled fingers are pointing.

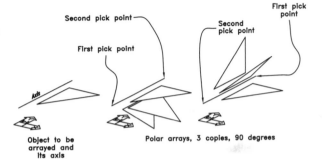

First pick point

Second pick point

First pick point

Second pick point

Axis

Object to be arrayed and its axis

Polar arrays, 3 copies, 90 degrees

Notes:

- This command is based on an AutoLISP program named 3DARRAY.LSP.

Command: MIRROR3D

Purpose: This command creates a mirror-image copy of selected objects on the opposite side of a user-specified plane. Options for the command provide a wide variety of methods for specifying the mirror plane.

Initiate with:

- At the Command Line prompt enter MIRROR3D.
- From the Modify pull-down menu, pick 3D Operation, then select Mirror 3D.

Options:

After selecting the objects to be copied, MIRROR3D offers eight options for defining a mirror plane. After a mirror plane is defined, you will be given the option of retaining or deleting the original objects that were selected to be copied.

- 3points

This option, which is the default option and can be started by selecting a point in response to the main MIRROR3D menu, allows you to define the mirror plane by specifying three points. You will be prompted to specify three points on the mirror plane. They can be specified in either a clockwise or counterclockwise order.

Pt 1

Pt 2

Pt 3

Before MIRROR3D
3Points option

After MIRROR3D

- Object

This option uses an existing object to define the mirror plane. It issues the follow-up prompt:

```
Select a circle, arc, or 2D-polyline
   segment: Select an object.
```

Notice that you cannot use a line to define a mirror plane, although you can use the straight segment of a 2D polyline, even if the entire polyline consists of only a single straight line segment.

The actual location of the mirror object is not important, since its plane is extended for an infinite distance. In the second figure on the right, for instance, the circle used to define the mirror plane is away from the objects that are to be mirrored.

Before MIRROR3D
Object option

After MIRROR3D

- Last

  The Last option uses the previous mirror plane as the current mirror plane. If there is no previous mirror plane, the main MIRROR3D options menu is repeated.

MIRROR3D, Object option

Before   Result

Isometric-type view

- Zaxis

  With this option, you define a mirror plane by picking a point on the plane and a point away from the plane. The mirror plane will be oriented perpendicular to a line drawn between the two points. The option's prompts are

```
Specify point on mirror plane: Specify
  a point.
Specify point on Z-axis (normal) of
  mirror plane: Specify a point.
```

In geometry, the word *normal* is often used to represent a direction that is perpendicular to a plane. The wording used in this option is as if the mirror plane is the X-Y plane of a coordinate system, and the normal of the mirror plane is its Z axis direction.

Before   Result

Front view

Before MIRROR3D
Zaxis option

After MIRROR3D

- View

  This option orients the mirror plane perpendicular to the current view direction. A follow-up prompt asks for the location of the plane:

```
Specify point on view plane
  <0,0,0>: Specify a point.
```

View option of MIRROR3D

Current viewport
Viewpoint=1,-1,1

Secondary viewport
Viewpoint=-1,-1,0

76

In the current viewport, you will not be able to see the results of the operation, since the new objects will be aligned exactly with the old objects. In a viewport that has a different viewpoint, however, the mirrored objects will be visible.

- XY/YZ/ZX

Each of these three options orients the mirror plane so that it is parallel to one of the principal planes. A follow-up prompt asks you to specify a point that the mirror plane is to pass through.

`Specify point on MN plane <0,0,0>:` *Specify a point.*

In the actual prompt, the letters MN will be XY, YZ, or ZX, depending upon which option was selected. The YZ and ZX options are equivalent to AutoCAD's MIRROR command when the two points selected for the mirror plane are parallel with the X or Y axes.

- Delete old objects

After a mirror plane has been defined using any of the options we have described, the MIRROR3D command will issue the following prompt:

Original objects are shown in dashed lines.

`Delete source objects? [Yes/No] <N>:` *Enter Y, N, or press Enter.*

If you respond by entering N or by pressing the Enter key, the original objects selected to be mirrored will be retained. If you enter Y, they will be deleted.

Notes:

- This command is based on an external Autodesk program named GEOM3D.ARX.

Command: ROTATE3D

Purpose: This command rotates objects about a user-specified axis.

Initiate with:

- At the Command Line prompt enter ROTATE3D.

- From the Modify pull-down menu, pick 3D Operation, then select Rotate 3D.

Options:

After selecting the objects to be rotated, this command gives you seven different options for defining the rotational axis. Each axis has a direction that determines the positive direction of rotation. You can visualize the positive rotation direction by mentally grasping the axis with your right hand so that your thumb is pointed in the positive direction of the axis. The positive direction of rotation will then be in the direction of your fingers when they are curled about the axis.

After defining the axis, you will be given the choice of specifying the rotation angle by entering its value directly or by supplying an old angle and a new angle.

- 2points

  This option, which can be started by picking a point or by entering a 2 in response to the main ROTATE3D prompt, uses two points to define the rotation axis. The positive direction of the axis is from the first point to the second.

- Axis by Object

  This option, which can be selected by typing in either an A or an O after selecting an object to be rotated, uses an existing object to define the rotation axis. It issues the follow-up prompt:

  ```
  Select a line, circle, arc,
    or 2D polyline segment:
    Select an object.
  ```

  The axis location and direction are shown in the table. In the figure after the table, an arc was selected to define the rotation axis, and the objects were rotated 135 degrees.

Object Type	Axis Location and Direction
Line	Along the line
Arc	Through the center of the arc and perpendicular to the plane of the arc
Circle	Through the center of the circle and perpendicular to the plane of the circle
Polyline line segment	Along the line segment
Polyline arc segment	Through the center of the arc segment and perpendicular to the plane of the arc

- Last

  This option uses the last defined rotation axis as the current rotation axis.

- View

  This option aligns the rotation axis to be parallel to the current view direction. The positive direction of the axis is out of the

screen, toward the viewer. A follow-up prompt will ask you to specify a point that the axis is to pass through. In the top figure on the next page, the triangle-shaped object is rotated 90 degrees counterclockwise in the right-hand viewport.

- Xaxis/Yaxis/Zaxis

  Each of these three options uses a rotation axis that is parallel to one of the principal axes. A follow-up prompt will ask you to specify a point that the axis is to pass through. The

Zaxis option is equivalent to AutoCAD's standard ROTATE command.

- Rotation Angle/Reference

After you specify a rotation axis, the ROTATE3D command displays the prompt:

```
Specify Rotation angle or
    [Reference]: Enter an angle or
    enter R.
```

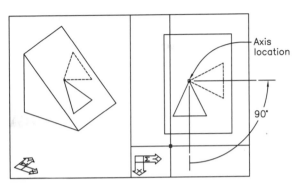

When an angle is specified, the objects in the selection set will be rotated around the axis by that angle. You can enter negative values to reverse the normal rotation direction.

The Reference option uses two pairs of points to establish a rotation angle by pointing. The first pair of points represents a base point and a point away from it for the current (or reference) angle, while the second pair represents a base point and a point away from it for the new angle. Its prompts are

Xaxis   Yaxis   Zaxis

```
Specify the reference angle <0>: Specify
    a point.
Specify second point: Specify a point.
Specify the new angle: Specify a point.
Specify second point: Specify a point.
```

You can also type in a reference angle and a new angle. When you do, the prompts for a second point are skipped. Unfortunately, specifying reference rotation angles by pointing works properly only when the current X-Y plane is perpendicular to the rotation axis. The points for specifying the angles are projected onto the X-Y plane, and the resulting rotation angles may not match the 3D angles.

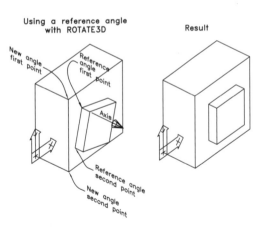

Using a reference angle with ROTATE3D   Result

Notes:

- This command is based on an external Autodesk program named GEOM3D.ARX.

Command: **ALIGN**

Purpose: This command moves and rotates objects in 3D space. It is especially useful for aligning one object, or a set of objects, with another.

Initiate with:

- At the Command Line prompt enter ALIGN.

- From the Modify pull-down menu, pick 3D Operation, then select Align.

Options:

The ALIGN command first asks you to select the object (or objects) to be moved and aligned. Then it will ask you to specify up to three pairs of source and destination points. The first pair of source and destination points moves the selected object, the second pair rotates the object in one 3D direction, and the third pair rotates the object in another 3D direction. AutoCAD will draw a temporary line between each source and destination point. You may stop the command anytime after the first pair of points has been entered by pressing the Enter key when prompted for a source point.

- Specifying One Pair of Points

When just one pair of points is used, the object (or objects) is simply moved by the distance and direction from the source point to the destination point. It is equivalent to AutoCAD's MOVE command.

```
Select objects:  Select the smaller box.
Specify first source point: Pick the
   indicated point on the smaller box.
Specify first destination point: Pick
   the indicated point on the larger box.
Specify second source point: Press Enter.
```

ALIGN with one pair of source and destination points

Result

1st destination point   1st source point

- Specifying Two Pairs of Points

By specifying two pairs of source and destination points you are able to move the object (or objects), then tilt it in one direction.

```
Select objects:  Select the ring
   shaped object.
Specify first source point: Pick the
   indicated center point.
Specify first destination point: Pick
   the indicated center point.
Specify second source point: Pick the
   indicated center point.
Specify second destination point: Pick
   the indicated center point.
Specify third source point: Press
   Enter.
Scale objects based on alignment points?
   [Yes/No] <No>: Press Enter.
```

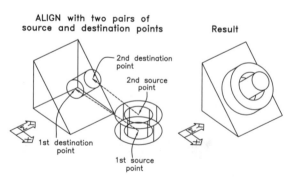

ALIGN with two pairs of source and destination points

Result

2nd destination point

2nd source point

1st destination point

1st source point

The option to scale the objects as they are moved and rotated was introduced with Release 14. It can be useful when the size of the object (or objects) to be moved and rotated does not match the stationary object. The option is presented whenever you stop ALIGN after specifying two sets of source and destination points. If you respond to it with a yes, the aligned objects are scaled by a ratio

ALIGN using object scale

2nd destination point

2nd source point

1st destination point

1st source point

Result

The aligned objects are scaled by a ratio based on the distance between the source points and the distance between the destination points.

based on the distances between the two source points and between the two destination points.

- Specifying Three Pairs of Points

When three pairs of source and destination points are used, the first pair represents the move displacement, the second represents a rotation in one direction, and the third represents a rotation in a second direction.

```
Select objects: Select the L-shaped object.
Specify first source point: Pick the indicated point.
Specify first destination point: Pick the indicated point.
Specify second source point: Pick the indicated point.
Specify second destination point: Pick the indicated point.
Specify third source point: Pick the indicated point.
Specify third destination point: Pick the indicated point.
```

Notice that the second and third destination points represent directions from the first destination point rather than distances from it.

Notes:

- This command is based on an external Autodesk program named GEOM3D.ARX.

ALIGN with three pairs of source and destination points

2nd destination point

1st destination point

2nd source point

1st source point

3rd destination point

3rd source point

Result

Exercise Two

Our second exercise in this chapter will be to build a wireframe for a surface model of an oil pan (similar to one that an automobile might have). This surface model will have just one surface—it will not try to simulate the thickness of the metal. Such a surface model could be used to make a mold or die for manufacturing the oil pan. You will want to keep this wireframe. We will add to it in the next chapter, and we will add surfaces to it in Section Two.

Set the drawing up to use inches, and make a new layer that has a name such as WF01 to be used for drawing the wireframe objects. Much of the wireframe's dimensions will be in increments of 0.25 inches, so you may want to use AutoCAD's snap mode much of the time, with the snap spacing set to 0.25.

Start the wireframe by drawing the top flange of the oil pan, using the dimensions given in the figure on the right. Draw these wireframe objects on the WCS X-Y plane, with one edge of the flange on the X axis, and another edge on the Y axis. Do not draw the lines shown in dashed linetypes. We will add those lines in the next chapter.

Since these lines and arcs are going to be used as surface boundaries, they require a slightly different treatment than if they were part of a 2D drawing. That is why the flange is divided into rectangles. Also, the four outside corners should be drawn as 2D polylines, having a line segment 1.75 inches long, a 1.0-inch-radius arc, and another 1.75-inch-long line segment.

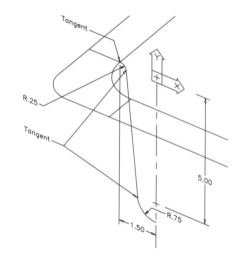

When you have finished drawing the flange, move the UCS to the center of the lower-left inside arc and rotate the UCS 90 degrees about the X axis. Then use the dimensions shown in the second figure to draw two arcs and one line that represent the tapered vertical side of the oil pan. You should also draw the vertical centerline along the current Y direction. Use a layer that has a CENTERLINE linetype for this line. Its length is not critical.

Next, use a polar array to make a copy of the two arcs and the line that is tangent to them. The copy will be rotated 90 degrees from the original objects. This is a convenient occasion to use the 3DARRAY command, since you can use the just-drawn center-line as a rotation axis. Then, copy the copy eight units in the X axis direction. This copy will be on the opposite end of the flange segment (next to the missing section on the flange).

Now, move the UCS to the center of the lower-right corner flange inside arc and point the UCS Y axis in the WCS Z direction. Draw two arcs and a line representing the tapered vertical side of the oil pan on this end. Use

the dimensions shown in the figure on the top of the page. You will notice these are the same dimensions that were used for the other end,

except the center of the 0.75 radius arc is 3.50 inches from the flange top, rather than 5.00 inches. You should also draw a vertical centerline in the center of the flange arc.

Make a 90-degree polar array copy of the two arcs and one line, then copy the copy 4.75 inches in the minus X direction. These operations will be similar to those used at the other end of the oil pan.

Restore the WCS and use AutoCAD's MIRROR command to make mirror-image copies of the six sets of lines and arcs on the opposite side of the oil pan. You do not need to make copies of the centerlines. Your wireframe model should look similar to the one shown in the third figure. (The viewing directions for this figure are 305 degrees from the X axis and 35 degrees from the X-Y plane. Your viewpoint, of course, may be different.)

Finish this stage of the wireframe model by connecting the lower end of the large arcs with lines to form two rectangles that are parallel with the WCS X-Y plane. A running endpoint snap is convenient when drawing these eight lines. Your model should be similar to the one shown in the last figure. On the CD-ROM that accompanies this book, the wireframe model is in file mfe04207.dwg. We will connect the two sections as an exercise in the next chapter.

3D Curves

C urves that can twist and turn through 3D space are discussed in this chapter. These curves enable you to create geometric shapes that cannot be made by any of the 2D objects discussed in the previous chapter. Specifically, this chapter will

- describe the characteristics and uses of 3D polylines;
- explain how to use the 3DPOLY command;
- show you how to make 3D helix and spiral curves;
- describe how to use PEDIT in modifying 3D polylines;
- describe the properties of NURBSs;
- show you how to use the SPLINE command;
- explain how to modify splines with SPLINEDIT;
- finish building a wireframe model of an automobile oil pan;
- lead you through an exercise that creates a wireframe for the surface model of an airplane propeller.

3D curves

Most of the curves on your wireframe models will lie on a plane, even though that plane may be skewed to the principal planes of the WCS. Once you locate and align the plane for such a curve, the curve itself can be defined by using only X and Y coordinates. Occasionally, though, your models will need a curve, or some wireframe geometry, that does not fit on a plane. These are 3D curves, and all three coordinates—X, Y, and Z—are needed to define their shape. Examples of such curves are the edges of screw threads, the wire centerline of coil springs, the edge of a propeller blade, and even the edge of automobile trunk lids.

AutoCAD has two commands that can make 3D wireframe geometry—3DPOLY and SPLINE. We will explore both of these commands in this chapter, seeing what they can do, what they are good for, how to implement them, and how to modify them.

3D Polylines

While 3D polylines, which are made by the 3DPOLY command, are the same AutoCAD database object type as 2D polylines (which are made with the PLINE command), 3D polylines are not confined to a single plane. They also cannot have arc segments, width, or thickness. Furthermore, 3D polylines can be drawn only in the continuous linetype. You can assign a noncontinuous linetype, such as HIDDEN, to them, but AutoCAD will still draw them with solid, continuous lines.

Characteristics and Uses of 3D Polylines

Although we sometimes refer to 3D polylines as 3D curves, they are actually composed of line segments. On your computer screen a 3D polyline may look exactly like a set of ordinary lines that are connected end to end. It is, however, a single object that can be moved, copied, erased, and rotated the same as any other single object. 3DPOLY, the command for making 3D polylines, also works in the same way as AutoCAD's LINE command, offering the same options after the first point has been specified. These options are (1) to specify an endpoint, (2) to close the polyline back to the first point, and (3) to return to the previous point. Unlike the LINE command, though, these options are offered in a command line menu rather than being implied.

Command: 3DPOLY

Purpose: This command makes polylines composed of straight-line segments of width 0. Unlike 2D polylines, the vertices in 3D polylines can have different Z coordinates.

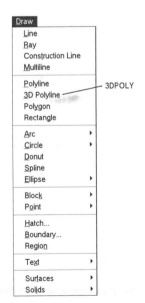

Initiate with:

- On the command line, enter 3DPOLY.

- From the Draw pull-down menu, select 3D Polyline.

Options:

The 3DPOLY command prompts you to draw two segments of the 3D polyline, and then displays the following command line prompt:

`Specify endpoint of line or [Close/Undo]:`

- Endpoint of Line

You can respond to this option by specifying a point or by pressing the Enter key. When a point is specified, AutoCAD draws a line to it from the previous point, then repeats the command line prompt.

- Close

  This option draws a line segment from the last specified point to the starting point of the 3D polyline and ends the command.

- Undo

  The last segment is removed when this option is selected, and the command line prompt is redisplayed. You can step back to the first point.

Notes:

- This command operates very much like AutoCAD's ordinary LINE command, and the resulting 3D polyline looks exactly like ordinary lines. The lines making a 3D polyline, however, are connected to make a single object.

- AutoCAD considers to be *open* polylines that were finished by specifying a vertex on the same point as the polyline's first point and then ending the 3DPOLY command. It considers to be *closed* those that were ended by using the Close option.

You will use 3D polylines in a wireframe model anytime you want a set of lines to behave as a single object. In surface models you will sometimes use 3D polylines as surface boundaries. We will discuss this use in Section Two of this book. 3D polylines can also serve as an extrusion path while making a solid model. We will discuss solid models in Section Three.

Even though 3D polylines are made of straight linelike segments, you can create curves that appear to be reasonably smooth by keeping the segments relatively short. You can also use an option in the PEDIT command to transform the 3D polyline into a B-spline curve. The resulting curve, however, will still be made of linelike segments—it will not be a true B-spline curve. You have to look very closely before the individual lines are discernable, but they are there nevertheless. Also, splines made from polylines require a relatively large amount of data, which tends to increase both file size and computation time. Moreover, since the edges of AutoCAD surfaces are always made of straight lines (as can be seen in the previous figure), there is generally no advantage in using spline-curved 3D polylines for surface boundaries. A final drawback is that AutoCAD's solid modeler does not allow spline curves to be used as extrusion paths.

Using 3D polylines for surface boundaries

Two 3D polylines for the surface boundaries

The surface has been added.

Magnified view showing the straight line segments

Spline-curved 3D polyline

If you need a B-spline curve, you will in most cases be better off using the SPLINE command to make them. We will discuss this command later in this chapter. Incidentally, 3D polyline spline curves can be transformed into true splines through the SPLINE command.

Drawing Helixes and 3D Spirals

You will not have any trouble using the 3DPOLY command since it works so much like the LINE command that you have long used. Nevertheless, some forethought and planning is required to fully utilize the command's ability to make 3D objects, as well as the use of input methods that you would not use in making lines.

One example is in drawing helixes and 3D spirals. A helix is a curve form you can obtain by wrapping a string around a cylinder; a spiral is a curve that can be obtained by wrapping a string around a cone. Generally, the word *pitch* is used to signify the distance between adjacent coils along the cylinder or cone. Screw threads, coil springs, barber poles, spiral staircases, and some parking and freeway ramps are examples of objects based on helixes and spirals.

Helix   3D spiral

AutoCAD's cylindrical coordinates, which we discussed in Chapter One, are especially useful for drawing helixes and 3D spirals. You will recall that cylindrical coordinates for specifying a point location have the form:

distance<angle, height

In this case *distance* is the point's distance from the origin for absolute input, or from the last point for relative input; *angle* is the horizontal angle to the point from the X axis; and *height* is the point's distance in the Z direction from the X-Y plane for absolute input or from the last point for relative input.

The process for making a wireframe helix involves moving around and along a cylinder, using cylindrical coordinates to set 3D polyline endpoints. Distance will remain the same, angle will be used to step around the cylinder, and the height component will be used to move up the cylinder. Notice that this method does restrict you to drawing helixes and spirals around a centerline pointed in the Z direction. Also, the method works best if the helix centerline passes through the UCS origin. Otherwise, you have to use relative input, which can be cumbersome.

A 3D spiral can be made in the same way, but distance will change as the spiral follows a cone shape. Pitch usually stays constant, but there is no reason (other than the complexity it will cause) it too cannot change as the helix or spiral grows.

Before you start drawing your helix or spiral, you need to do some planning and arithmetic. First, you need to decide how many steps around the cylinder you want to take with each revolution. This will determine the relative coarseness of the resulting curve. More steps make a smoother curve, but they also require more work. Then you will divide the number of degrees for each revolution (360 degrees) by the number of steps per revolution. The angle in each cylindrical coordinate input will increase by this angle for each step around the cylinder.

Suppose, for example, you decide to make a helix that will have eight steps per revolution. Since the quotient of 8 into 360 is 45, the cylindrical coordinate angle will increase 45 degrees with each step around the cylinder. The angle for the first point will be 0, for the second step it will be 45, for the third it will be 90, and so forth, until the first revolution is completed. Then the angle will drop back to 0.

Next, you need to decide what pitch your helix is to have. Divide that pitch by the number of steps per revolution to determine the height increment for the cylindrical coordinates. If, to continue our example, you chose a pitch of 2.0, then the increment for each height will be 0.25 (2.0 divided by 8). The helix will start with an elevation of 0, the next point will have an elevation of 0.25, the elevation of the third point will be 0.50, for the fourth point it will be 0.75, and so forth. Unlike angle, height will continue to increase through each revolution.

The command line input to draw one revolution of our example helix, with a radius of 2.0 units, would be

```
Command: 3DPOLY (Enter)
Specify start point of polyline: 2,0,0
  (Enter)
Specify endpoint of line or [Undo]: 2<45,.25 (Enter)
Specify endpoint of line or [Undo]: 2<90,.50 (Enter)
Specify endpoint of line or [Close/Undo]: 2<135,.75 (Enter)
Specify endpoint of line or [Close/Undo]: 2<180,1.00 (Enter)
Specify endpoint of line or [Close/Undo]: 2<225,1.25 (Enter)
Specify endpoint of line or [Close/Undo]: 2<270,1.50 (Enter)
Specify endpoint of line or [Close/Undo]: 2<315,1.75 (Enter)
Specify endpoint of line or [Close/Undo]: 2<360,2.00 (Enter)
Specify endpoint of line or [Close/Undo]: (Enter)
```

"SPIRAL- HELIX"

The resulting helix is shown on the left in the figure below. It is admittedly not very impressive. You can use the PEDIT command to transform it into a spline curve, though. This, as shown on the right in the figure below, improves its looks greatly. Actually, a smooth helix can be obtained by using only four points per revolution if it is transformed into a B-spline with PEDIT.

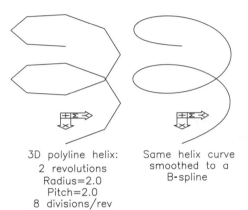

3D polyline helix:
2 revolutions
Radius=2.0
Pitch=2.0
8 divisions/rev

Same helix curve
smoothed to a
B-spline

Nevertheless, since AutoCAD approximates the edges of curved surfaces with short straight segments, there is no point in smoothing 3D polylines that are to be used for surface boundaries. Moreover, AutoCAD does not allow splines to be used as extrusion paths for 3D solids.

A major disadvantage in using such command line input to draw a 3D helix is that it is tedious and error prone. Script files are a good alternative to command line input. You will recall that script files are external text files that can initiate a command and provide all of its command line input, just as if you were typing it in. A script file to draw our example helix would consist of eleven lines. The first line would simply be the word 3DPOLY, the next nine lines would be the point inputs, and the eleventh line would be just a line break (made by pressing the Enter key). In other words, the file contains the human side of the command line interface.

You can make script files with any word processor or text editor that can save files in text format (which is sometimes referred to as ASCII format). NOTEPAD, the editor that comes with the Windows operating systems, is such a text editor. The extension name used for the script file must be .SCR.

A script file for drawing the previous example is included on the CD-ROM that comes with this book. It is named HELIX_01.SCR. To use this script file, invoke AutoCAD's SCRIPT command. A dialog box titled Select Script File will appear. This dialog box has the ability to search through various directories and drives to find files with an extension of .SCR. When you find the HELIX_01.SCR script file, click on it to highlight it, and click the Open button. The helix will be automatically drawn in the positive Z direction at the UCS origin.

The CD-ROM contains another script file, which has the name HELIX_02.SCR, for a more complex example. As shown in the figure on the right, this script file draws a combination helix-spiral curve. It increases in diameter through two revolutions, maintains a constant diameter through the third revolution, and reduces in diameter through the final two revolutions. It makes sixteen steps per revolution. The script file has more than eighty lines of cylindrical coordinate input. Making the script file, however, was not especially difficult, since a spreadsheet

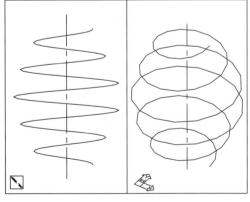

program was used to do the arithmetic. Three spreadsheet columns were used—the first was for the cylindrical coordinate's distance, the second was for the rotation angle, and the third was for height. Each spreadsheet row represented a cylindrical coordinate point. The spreadsheet was saved in a text format, and the word *3DPOLY,* along with the characters needed for AutoCAD's cylindrical coordinate input, were added with a text editor.

While script files can be useful for drawing helixes and 3D spirals that have unusual, and perhaps varying, shapes, an AutoLISP program is more convenient for drawing the majority of the helix and 3D spiral forms you will encounter. The data in script files is absolute, and any change—such as in diameter, pitch, or the number of revolutions—requires a new script file. With AutoLISP, on the other hand, many parameters can be in the form of variables that are assigned a value when the program is executed.

Although it is not difficult to write an AutoLISP program for drawing helixes and 3D spirals, Autodesk already has such a program. It is named SPIRAL.LSP. Originally it was written to draw 2D spirals, but it was modified for release 12 to draw 3D spirals as well. Although this program is not included with subsequent AutoCAD Releases, it works well in them. This AutoLISP program is included on the CD-ROM that accompanies this book. You are free to use, copy, modify, and distribute the program, as long you retain the program's Autodesk copyright notice.

Once you have loaded this program, you can draw either a helix or a 3D spiral by entering 3DSPIRAL on the command line. The program will ask you for the following input:

Prompt	User Input
Center point	Specify a center point. It does not have to be on the X-Y plane.
Number of rotations	Enter a number. It cannot be 0, negative, or null (that is, you cannot just press the Enter key).
Starting radius	Specify a number. It cannot be 0, negative, or null. You can, however, specify it by pointing.
Horizontal growth per rotation	Enter a number. It can be 0 or negative. You cannot, however, give a null response. A 0 value will create a straight helix coil.
Vertical growth per rotation	Enter a number. A negative number will cause the coil to grow in the minus Z direction. You cannot enter 0 or give a null response.
Points per rotation <30>	Enter a number or press Enter to accept the default of 30 points per rotation.

Modifying 3D Polylines

Once a 3D polyline has been created, it can be modified by any of AutoCAD's standard editing commands. It can be moved, stretched, rotated, lengthened, trimmed, extended, and broken into two 3D polylines. This hasn't always been true. The BREAK and TRIM commands do not work on 3D polylines in versions of AutoCAD earlier than Release 13.

For more specialized editing, you will use the PEDIT command. Even though this is the same command that is used for editing 2D polylines, AutoCAD recognizes a 3D polyline when it is picked to be edited, and it issues a command line menu of editing functions that are appropriate for 3D polylines. Missing in this menu are the Join, Width, Fit, and Ltype gen options found in the menu for 2D polylines.

One of the main reasons you will use PEDIT with a 3D polyline will be to edit its vertices. You can add or remove vertices from 3D polylines through the Edit vertex option of PEDIT. You can also move vertices with PEDIT, but you will probably find grips or the STRETCH command to be just as convenient for this task.

Prior to Release 13, the Spline curve option was another good reason for using the PEDIT command. However, since spline curves made with the SPLINE command (which was introduced in Release 13) are true B-splines, and are just as easy to make as splines from polylines, you seldom now have any reason to smooth 3D polylines to B-splines.

You can also edit 3D polylines through the PROPERTIES command that was indroduced in AutoCAD 2000. This command displays a dialog box for you to use in changing the same properties of a selected 3D polyline that the PEDIT command changes, plus its general properties, such as color and layer. Unlike the PEDIT command, PROPERTIES allows you to select on the fly whether the spline's equation is to be quadratic or cubic.

Occasionally you will want to join two 3D polylines. For example, you may want to increase the number of coils in a helix-shaped 3D polyline or you may want to add a hook, or some other curve, to its endpoints. However, AutoCAD has no provision for joining 3D polylines as it does for 2D polylines. Nevertheless, it can be done by the AutoLISP program named JOIN3DPL.LSP that is on the CD-ROM that accompanies this book.

Once you have loaded the program, simply enter JOIN3DPL on the command line and select the two 3D polylines you want combined. The 3D polylines must be open, and the endpoint of one must touch an endpoint of the other. Also, they cannot have been spline-fit.

—LOAD/
STARTUP/
CONTENTS
(ADD)

Command: PEDIT

Purpose: This command performs editing operations on 3D polylines. It allows you to open a closed 3D polyline or to close one that is open, to smooth the polyline's segments into a relatively smooth curve, and to edit individual vertices. You cannot, however, use it to join 3D polylines.

Initiate with:

- From the Command Line enter PEDIT.

- From the Modify pull-down menu, select Polyline.

Options:

When you pick a 3D polyline in response to the PEDIT command's prompt to select an object, AutoCAD offers the following command line menu of options appropriate for 3D polylines:

```
Close/Edit vertex/Spline curve/Decurve/Undo.
```

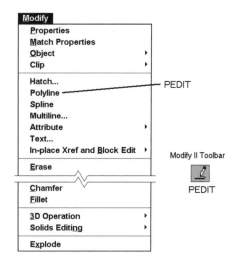

- Close

  This option will be offered only if the 3D
  polyline is open. AutoCAD will draw a
  line segment from the 3D polyline's last
  point to its first point and will change the
  status of the polyline from Open to
  Closed. If the 3D polyline was finished by
  drawing a segment back to the start point,

  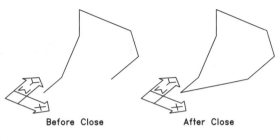

  Before Close   After Close

  no segment will be added, but the status of the polyline will change from Open to Closed.
  When this option is completed, AutoCAD will redisplay the main option menu.

- Open

  This option will be offered only if the 3D
  polyline is closed. The segment of the
  polyline that was drawn by the Close
  option of the 3DPOLY or PEDIT commands will be removed, and the status of
  the polyline will change to open. Auto-
  CAD will return to the main PEDIT
  option menu when this option is finished.

  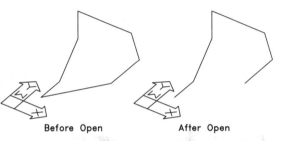

  Before Open   After Open

- Edit vertex

  You can edit a 3D polyline on a vertex-by-vertex basis with this option. It allows you to
  break a 3D polyline into two 3D polylines, replace several segments with a single segment,
  insert new vertices, and remove existing vertices. The option will display the following secondary command line menu:

  ```
  Next/Previous/Break/Insert/Move/Regen/Straighten/eXit <N>:
  ```

  An X marker will be positioned on the first visible polyline vertex that is closest to the initial point.

  - Next

    This option, the original default option, moves the X marker to the next vertex away
    from the beginning point of the polyline. If you continue to specify this option, the
    marker will stall on the last vertex of the polyline, even if the polyline is closed. It
    will also stall if the next vertex is not visible.

  - Previous

    This option moves the X marker to the previous vertex—the one closer to the beginning
    of the polyline—and changes the default option of the Edit vertex menu to Previous. If
    the previous vertex is currently not visible, the X marker will not move.

  - Break

    This option allows you to break a 3D polyline into two separate 3D polylines at one or
    more vertices. The current location of the X marker is used as one break point, and the
    following submenu is displayed for you to use in specifying the other break vertices:

    ```
    Next/Previous/Go/eXit <N>:
    ```

92

Next and Previous move the X marker to another vertex. The Go option performs the break and returns to the Edit vertex menu. If Go is selected without having moved the X marker, the polyline is broken without the removal of a segment. If one of the selected vertices is an end vertex, then the polyline will be shortened. At least one of the selected vertices must be an interior vertex. The eXit option is an escape that allows you to return to the Edit vertex menu without performing a break.

Second X—marker location

Original X—marker location

Before Break   After Break

o Insert

This option inserts a new vertex after the vertex that has the X marker. AutoCAD will prompt for the point location of the new vertex.

New vertex location

Vertex X—marker

Before Insert   After Insert

o Move

The position of the vertex with the X marker can be moved with this option. AutoCAD will ask for the new location of the vertex.

New location

Vertex X—marker

Before Move   After Move

o Regen

This option regenerates the 3D polyline.

o Straighten

This option removes the vertices and line segments between two vertices and replaces them with a single line segment. The current location of the X marker establishes the first vertex. AutoCAD will display the following submenu for you to use in specifying the other vertex:

Second X—marker location

Original X—marker location

Before Straighten   After Straighten

`Next/Previous/Go/eXit <N>:`

The Next and Previous options in this menu move the X marker to a vertex marking the other end of the section to be straightened. The Go option performs the straightening operation and returns to the main Edit vertex menu. The eXit option can be used to return to the main Edit vertex menu without straightening the 3D polyline.

   ○ eXit

   Exit returns to the main PEDIT menu.

- Spline curve

  This option in the main PEDIT menu smooths the 3D polyline to a shape that approximates a B-spline curve. The curve will still be made of line segments, but the lines will generally be so short that the curve appears to be smooth. The relative length of the line segments is controlled by AutoCAD's **splinesegs** system variable. Its default value is 8. Individual segments of spline-curved 2D polylines are made of arcs, rather than straight lines. When **splinesegs** is given a negative number, however, the negative sign is ignored when 3D polylines are smoothed.

  The degree of the equation used to make the spline curve is controlled by AutoCAD's **splinetype** system variable. When **splinetype** is set to 5, a quadratic equation is used, and a cubic equation is used when the **splinetype** is set to 6 (its default setting). The vertex points of the polyline are used as control points for the spline. Consequently, except for the endpoints, the spline will not pass through the polyline's original vertex points. Quadratic splines usually come closer to the original vertex points than cubic splines.

- Decurve

  This option restores the original shape and condition of a spline-curved 3D polyline. Spline-curved polylines that have been edited with AutoCAD's BREAK or TRIM commands cannot be decurved. Those edited by the LENGTHEN, EXTEND, and STRETCH commands, however, can be decurved.

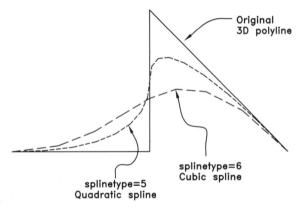

Original 3D polyline

splinetype=6 Cubic spline

splinetype=5 Quadratic spline

Notes:

- Spline-curved 3D polylines can be converted to true spline objects through the SPLINE command's Object option.
- You will seldom need to use PEDIT's Spline curve option, since you can make reasonably smooth-looking 3D polyline curves by using closely spaced vertex points.
- PEDIT does not have any provisions for joining 3D polylines as it does with 2D polylines.

Related system variables:

- **splframe**

  This system variable can have a value of either 0 or 1. When it is set to 1, the original shape of a spline-curved polyline will be displayed along with its spline-curved form. A screen regen is required for this to take effect. The default setting of **splframe** is 0.

- **splinesegs**

  This system variable controls the relative size of the line segments used to draw spline-curved polylines. Its default setting is 8, and you will seldom have any reason to change it.

- **splinetype**

  The degree of the equation used for making polyline spline curves is controlled by this system variable. When **splinetype** is set to a value of 5, the shape of spline curve will be based on a quadratic (second degree) equation. When **splinetype** is set to a value of 6, spline-curved polylines will be based on a cubic (third degree) equation. The default setting of **splinetype** is 6.

Splines

Splines are natural curves. Your garden hose is a good example of a spline (as long as it is not kinked), as it twists through your lawn and garden. Its curves gradually blend into each other so that it is impossible to determine exactly where one curve ends and another curve starts. Also, changing the curvature, location, or direction of any section of the hose affects the neighboring sections as well. Those sections closest to the change are affected the most, with the effects gradually diminishing so that sections some distance away are not affected at all. The new curves still smoothly blend together.

Curves in splines blend smoothly into each other. When a section is moved, the spline's curves adjust to maintain the smooth curve transitions.

Thin, flexible strips of metal, wood, and plastic also form spline curves. In fact, such strips have long been used by drafters to draw profiles for ships and airplanes. Weights, which are often called *ducks*, are attached to the strips to hold them in position. In some cases the shape of the spline is fine-tuned by using some weights that are heavier than the others. These strips are called *drafting splines*, which is where the name for the computer-based curves comes from.

Drafting spline and weights

NURBS

The shape of AutoCAD B-splines is controlled by equations rather than metal strips. For computational purposes, a spline is divided into segments. The spline's shape for one segment is computed, then the shape for the next segment is computed, and so forth, through the total length of the spline. The ends of these segments are generally referred to as *knots*. Although some computer graphic programs show the knots along B-splines, AutoCAD does not. Some spline algorithms use segments of equal length, while others, including the one AutoCAD uses, use segments of unequal length. Therefore, you will occasionally see references to *uniform B-splines* and to *non-uniform B-splines*.

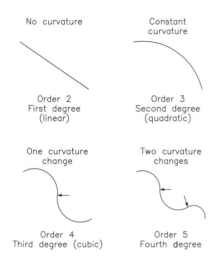

No curvature

Order 2
First degree
(linear)

Constant
curvature

Order 3
Second degree
(quadratic)

One curvature
change

Order 4
Third degree (cubic)

Two curvature
changes

Order 5
Fourth degree

The equation used to calculate the shape of a spline segment has a property called *degree*, which represents the value of the largest exponent in the equation. For example, an equation whose greatest component is squared is a second-degree (quadratic) equation, and one whose greatest component is raised to the third power (cubed) is a third-degree equation. We have already encountered these terms during our discussion of the spline fit options for 3D polylines within PEDIT.

Sometimes the word *order* is used rather than degree. The order of an equation is its degree plus 1. Thus, a third-degree equation is an order 4 equation. From a graphical standpoint the degree (and order) of an equation determines how many curvature changes may occur within one segment of a spline. The number of curvature changes is equal to the degree of the equation minus 2. Therefore, a third-degree equation can have one curvature change, and a fourth-degree equation can have two curvature changes.

The computer version of spline weights, or ducks, are *control points*. These points, which are invariably off of the curve (except for the spline endpoints), pull the spline into position. The number of control points used for shaping a spline is determined by the degree of the spline's equations. Most of the time all of the control points for a spline have an equal effect, but you can give some control points more weight, and consequently a greater effect in shaping the curve, than others. B-splines with unequally weighted control points are called *rational B-splines*.

A B-spline curve that has non-uniform segment lengths and unequally weighted control points is called a *Non-Uniform Rational B-Spline*. This name is almost always shortened to the acronym of *NURBS*. (The acronym sounds as if it is a plural word, but it isn't.) Splines made by smoothing 2D and 3D polylines are not NURBS, but AutoCAD can create true NURBS curves through the SPLINE command, which was introduced in Release 13.

Spline control points

While a spline made with the SPLINE command does not have unequally weighted control points when it is created, and is therefore not a rational spline (and therefore not actually a NURBS), through editing, some control points can be given a weight that is different from the others, which will make it a rational B-spline (and, thus, a true NURBS). Usually though, unequally weighted control points are needed only in special situations to fine-tune the shape of a curve.

Command: SPLINE

Purpose: This command creates true 3D wireframe B-spline curves. The spline can be based on user-specified points or on an existing 2D or 3D polyline that has been spline-fit.

Initiate with:

- On the command line enter SPLINE.

- From the Draw pull-down menu, select Spline.

- Select the Spline button from the draw toolbar.

Options:

AutoCAD begins the SPLINE command with a command line menu containing two options:

```
Specify first point or [Object]:
```

- Object

This option will bring up a prompt for you to select one or more objects to be converted into a spline. The objects selected must be 2D or 3D polylines that have already been fit to a spline through the PEDIT command. The shape of the spline is not changed during the conversion. If the system variable **delobj** is set to 1, the old spline is automatically deleted as the new one is created.

- Enter first point

The default option of the SPLINE command is to enter the starting point of the spline. As soon as the starting point is selected, AutoCAD will prompt for a second point. When you have entered two points, the following secondary menu is displayed:

```
Specify next point or [Close/Fit tolerance]<start tangent>:
```

○ Next point

Specify another point location to continue drawing the spline. A rubber-band line, anchored on the previous point, will be displayed, along with the extension to the spline itself. Moreover, the spline will dynamically change shape as you move the screen cursor. AutoCAD refers to each of these user-specified points as a *fit point*. The secondary menu is repeated after each point is specified.

○ Undo

This option exists, even though it is not listed in the secondary menu. Entering the letter *U*, or the entire word *undo*, will remove the last point. You can undo back to the first point.

○ Start tangent

When you press Enter in response to the secondary menu, AutoCAD will stop drawing the spline and will issue prompts for its start and end tangents. If you respond to these prompts by pressing the Enter key, AutoCAD will allow the spline to swivel about the start point or end point as it assumes its shape. If you respond by specifying a point, AutoCAD will aim the spline end toward the specified point.

Start and end tangents not specified

Start and end tangents specified as shown

- Close

  When you select this option, AutoCAD will draw a segment back to the start point of the spline and prompt for a tangent direction. Both the start and end segments of the spline use this single tangent, and the spline will adjust its shape to accommodate the tangent direction.

Close tangent not specified

Close tangent specified as shown

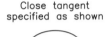

Close tangent specified as shown

- Fit Tolerance

By default, splines pass through each fit point. When you apply a fit tolerance, however, the spline will bypass the interior fit points. (It will always pass through the first and last fit points.) When this option is selected, which can be done by entering either *F* or *T*, AutoCAD will issue the command line prompt:

`Enter Fit Tolerance <Default>:`

The initial default fit tolerance value is 0. The value entered controls the relative distance by which the spline deviates from the fit points. While you can change the fit tolerance at any point as you draw a spline, the entire spline will assume the last value specified. Consequently, you cannot have one tolerance apply to some fit points and another apply to other fit points. AutoCAD retains the last tolerance specified and will use it as a default even when a new spline is started. If you exit the drawing, however, AutoCAD resets the default tolerance value to 0 when you re-open the drawing.

Fit tolerance=0   Fit tolerance=0.25

Notes:

- Since spline objects require much less computer computation and space in the drawing file's database, you should convert 2D and 3D polylines that have been fit to a spline curve to true splines whenever it is convenient.

- Splines made from 2D and 3D polylines do not have any fit points. Moreover, other splines will lose their fit points when certain editing operations are performed on them.

- You also can set, as well as modify, the start and end tangents of an existing spline through the SPLINEDIT command. This command can also change the fit tolerance of a spline.

- In Release 13, spline-fit tolerance works in a different manner than in subsequent releases. In Release 13, gradually increasing the tolerance value of a spline does not cause the spline to gradually pull away from the fit points. Instead, there are threshold values at which the spline will change shape and pull away from the fit points. That shape is maintained until some specific higher tolerance value is reached, at which it will pull further from the fit points. These threshold values vary by spline size, shape, and end tangents.

Related system variables:

- **delobj**

  When this system variable is set to 1, its default setting, 2D and 3D spline-fit polylines will be deleted when they are converted to true splines. When **delobj** is set to 0, the original polyline will be retained.

- **splframe**

  This system variable can have a value of 0 or 1, with 0 being its default value. When it is set to 1, AutoCAD will display a set of lines (a frame) between the control points of a spline.

- **useacis**

  Splines having a nonzero fit tolerance that were created in AutoCAD Release 13 may have a different shape in Release 14. You can retain the shape of the spline by using this system variable, which first appeared in AutoCAD Release 14.01. Set **useacis** to 1, open the file having a nonzero fit tolerance spline from Release 13, and use the SPLINEDIT command to purge the spline's fit data. The default value of **useacis** is 0.

Creating Spline Curves

Although AutoCAD splines appear to be simple, smoothly curved objects, they have properties and characteristics that are significantly different from other AutoCAD object types. Probably the easiest way to explore these properties and characteristics is by drawing a simple 2D spline. Therefore, you should draw a spline using the command line sequence of prompts and input shown below. While you can grasp how the SPLINE command works by merely reading through this sequence, you will find it more helpful to actually duplicate the input within Auto-CAD, since you will be able to see the spline's process and behavior as it is drawn. You will also find AutoCAD's LIST data for this spline interesting, and you can see how modifying its properties affects its shape. It will take you just a few seconds to draw this spline, and it does not require any special drawing setup. We'll use integer coordinate values so that you can specify points readily from the keyboard, or by setting snap to 1, and using your pointing device.

```
Command:  SPLINE (Enter)
Specify first point or [Object]: 0,0 (Enter)
Specify next point: 1,0 (Enter)
Specify next point or [Close/Fit tolerance] <start tangent>: 1,1 (Enter)
Specify next point or [Close/Fit tolerance] <start tangent>: 2,0 (Enter)
Specify next point or [Close/Fit tolerance] <start tangent>: (Enter)
Specify start tangent: a1<180 (Enter)
Specify end tangent: a1<270
```

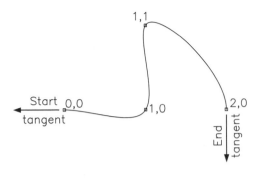

Your spline should look like the one shown in the figure on the left. Two things were especially noticeable as you drew this simple 2D spline. First, unlike the splines made from 2D and 3D polylines with the PEDIT command, the curve goes through each point you specified. As you will recall from the section on 3D polylines in this chapter, splines made from 3D polylines through PEDIT use the original polyline vertices as control points. Consequently, except for their first and last points, those splines are not likely to go through any of the original vertices. (We did not discuss 2D polylines, but splines made from them have basically the same properties as those made from 3D polylines.) Generally, you will like this SPLINE command characteristic of drawing the curve through the selected points because it makes it easier to control the shape and location of the curve.

You can, though, use the Fit Tolerance option (which is offered after the second spline point has been specified) to have the curve bypass the fit points. This option will show you the current fit tolerance value (it will initially have a value of 0) and allow you to enter a new one. Then, the perpendicular distance from each fit point to the curve will be proportional to the value assigned to fit tolerance. The net effect is that as you increase fit tolerance, the spline becomes straighter and less curvy. The endpoints of the spline will always be exactly on their fit points.

Any one spline can have only one fit tolerance in effect, even though the option for setting it is offered each time a point is to be specified. If, for example, you set the fit

Fit tolerance=0   Fit tolerance=0.05   Fit tolerance=0.15

tolerance to 0.15 just before specifying the fourth point on our demonstration spline, the spline will move away from the previous two fit points.

Most likely, you will seldom use the Fit Tolerance option as you create a spline. You can also set a fit tolerance value with the SPLINEDIT command (which we will discuss shortly), and you may occasionally assign a fit tolerance in an attempt to improve the shape of a spline.

The second thing you probably noticed as you drew the spline was the effect that the start and end tangent directions have on the shape of the spline. As soon as you pressed the Enter key to signal an end to spline-fit point input, AutoCAD anchored a rubber-band line on the spline's start point and prompted for the spline's start tangent direction. Although this input establishes a direction, you must specify a point—you cannot type in just an angle, such as 180. If you used your pointing device in specifying the start tangent, you could see the spline dynamically change shape as you moved your pointing device around, changing the tangent direction. The spline segment between the first and second fit points was affected the most, the change in the middle segment was not as pronounced, and there were very slight changes in the last segment. After you specified the start tangent to be in the minus X direction (180 degrees), AutoCAD prompted for the end tangent direction, and the spline changed shape

100

again as you moved your pointing device about. We selected a tangent in the minus Y direction (270 degrees).

These tangents force the ends of the spline to point in the specified direction, and the spline assumes a shape to accommodate those directions while maintaining perfectly smooth curves. If you press the Enter key when prompted for a tangent rather than specify a point, AutoCAD allows the spline to swivel about the endpoint as it assumes its shape.

When you are trying to picture the shape of a spline, it helps to imagine the spline as a flexible steel rod and the fit points as round pins fixed in space. The flexible rod has a hole at each fit point location, through which one of the round pins is inserted. Thus, these points are fixed in space, but the flexible rod is free to swivel about the pins as it is bent. When you specify an end tangent, that end of the flexible rod is as if it were clamped and forced to point in the specified direction. If you do not specify an end tangent, the flexible rod is free to swivel about the endpoint.

Picturing a spline as a flexible steel rod

Fixed round pins are inserted through holes in the rod. The rod is free to swivel about the pins.

Clamp

Start tangent

Flexible steel rod

Clamp

End tangent

End tangents specified

Fixed round pins are inserted through holes in the rod. The rod is free to swivel about the pins.

Flexible steel rod

End tangents not specified

Most of the time you will want to specify the tangent of both ends, especially when the spline is to act as the continuation of, or be in line with, another object. As you would expect, you can use object snaps in specifying a tangent. You can even use the *Tangent* and *Perpendicular* object snaps. When the *Tangent* object snap is used in conjunction with an existing arc or circle, AutoCAD will base the tangent at a point on the arc or circle that is perpendicular to a line drawn from the end of the spline to the arc or circle. Consequently, your pick point on the arc or circle is not critical.

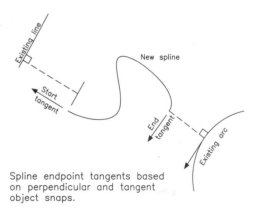

Existing line

New spline

Start tangent

End tangent

Existing arc

Spline endpoint tangents based on perpendicular and tangent object snaps.

Spline Data

When you use the LIST command on the simple 2D spline we have drawn as a demonstration, you will receive a surprisingly large amount of information, as shown in Table 5-1. In addition to listing the object type, its layer, and so forth, AutoCAD will tell you the spline's length along the curve and that it is a fourth-order spline. Therefore, a third-degree (cubic) equation was used in drawing each segment of the spline. AutoCAD always makes fourth-order splines, although you can increase a spline's order (with SPLINEDIT) after it has been drawn.

```
          TABLE 5-1  LIST Command's Report for a Typical Spline.

                SPLINE      Layer: OBJ01
                            Space: Model space
                  Handle = 10A
                         Length: 3.6058
                         Order: 4
                  Properties: Planar, Non-Rational, Non-Periodic
                  Parametric Range: Start    0.0000
                                      End    3.4142
        Number of control points: 6
        Control Points: X = 0.0000    , Y = 0.0000    , Z = 0.0000
                        X = 0.3333    , Y = 0.0000    , Z = 0.0000
                        X = 1.3860    , Y = -0.4233   , Z = 0.0000
                        X = 0.5472    , Y = 1.7444    , Z = 0.0000
                        X = 2.0000    , Y = 0.4714    , Z = 0.0000
                        X = 2.0000    , Y = 0.0000    , Z = 0.0000


        Number of fit points: 4


            User Data: Fit Points
                        X = 0.0000    , Y = 0.0000    , Z = 0.0000
                        X = 1.0000    , Y = 0.0000    , Z = 0.0000
                        X = 1.0000    , Y = 1.0000    , Z = 0.0000
                        X = 2.0000    , Y = 0.0000    , Z = 0.0000


        Fit point tolerance: 1.0000E-10


                        Start Tangent
                        X = 1.0000    , Y = 0.0000    , Z = 0.0000
                        End Tangent
                        X = 0.0000    , Y = -1.0000   , Z = 0.0000
```

Next, the LIST report shows the status of three properties of the spline. First it tells us that this spline is *planar*, which means that all of its fit points lie on a plane. In Exercises One and Two of this chapter, we will draw splines that are not confined to a plane; AutoCAD will list those splines as being *non-planar*. The property list also shows that the spline in *non-rational*, which means that its control points all have equal weight. AutoCAD always assigns a weight of 1.0 to control points when a spline is drawn, but as you will see when we discuss SPLINEDIT later in this chapter, you can change the weight of individual control points, thus transforming the curve into a *rational* spline.

The last of the three spline properties shown by LIST tells us that the spline is *non-periodic*, which means it is an open spline. If the spline had been closed with the Close option of the

SPLINE command, it would have been listed as a *periodic* spline. The terms *periodic* and *non-periodic* come from the Spatial Technology Inc. ACIS geometric modeler that AutoCAD uses in making splines. Spatial Technology refers to splines that have their start points and endpoints in the same location as being *closed*. If, in addition to being closed, the spline's start points and endpoints have the same tangent, they say the spline is *periodic*. Since AutoCAD uses a single tangent for the endpoints of splines that have been completed with the Close option of the SPLINE command, those splines are always periodic. AutoCAD does not make the distinction between open and closed splines that Spatial Technology does.

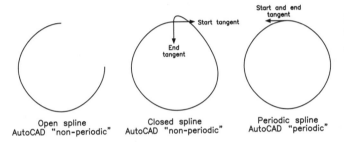

Open spline
AutoCAD "non-periodic"

Closed spline
AutoCAD "non-periodic"

Periodic spline
AutoCAD "periodic"

Following the list of curve properties, AutoCAD shows the spline's *parametric range*. Splines are often classed as parametric curves, with the word *parametric* referring to variables (parameters) within equations, rather than to the interrelationship of dimensions and features as it does in a parametric modeler, such as Designer. The LIST report for splines starts the parametric range at 0, and ends it with the cumulative straight line distance through the fit points. In the LIST report for the spline we've been looking at, the length of the spline is longer than its parametric range, even though they both represent distances through the fit points. This is to be expected since a straight line is the shortest distance between two points.

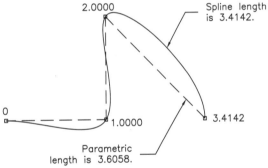

Next, the LIST report will show the coordinates of each control point. There are six control points for our spline, including those on the start points and endpoints. Although AutoCAD does not normally display the control points, you can see them by setting the **splframe** system variable to 1. After a regen ✳ AutoCAD will display the control points as the vertices of a framework of lines around the spline.

The coordinates of the fit points, which are the points selected while drawing the spline, are listed next. Not all splines have fit point data. Those made from spline-fit polylines have only control points. Also, splines that originally do have fit points can lose them when they undergo certain modifications (which we will discuss later in chapter). There are no surprises in the fit point data we have been examining.

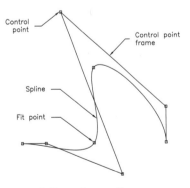

Spline when **splframe** is set to 1 and grips are activated

✳ SHOW POINT OR SPLINE SET TO # 1

Then, the LIST report shows the fit point tolerance used for the spline. Notice that, rather than the 0 that AutoCAD showed as the current tolerance while you were drawing the spline, the LIST report shows it as a very small number.

The last set of data shown are the coordinates of unit vectors (A unit vector is a 1-unit-long line used to indicate direction), for the start tangent and the end tangent, and there may be a surprise for you here. LIST shows the start tangent unit vector pointing in the positive X direction, even though we specified a minus X direction. This apparent discrepancy is because every spline has a specific direction, and AutoCAD points the tangent unit vectors in that direction. This spline was drawn from right to left (toward the positive X direction), so that is the direction of the tangent unit vector.

Modifying Splines

Although many of the general-purpose AutoCAD editing commands can be used to modify the shape of splines, the operations can also alter the spline's basic properties. You can BREAK and TRIM splines, for instance, but both of these operations cause the spline to lose its fit points. You cannot EXTEND, LENGTHEN, or EXPLODE splines.

The STRETCH command usually works well with splines. Normally, you must include a fit point in the crossing window used by STRETCH. You can also activate the spline's grips, which will be on the fit points of the spline, and use them in modifying its shape. If you set the value of the system variable **splframe** to 1 (which causes the control points to be shown as the vertices of connected lines), you can also stretch the spline by its control points. The spline's fit points, however, will be lost when you do this.

When a spline loses its fit point data, it also loses its tangent and fit tolerance data. You can identify a spline that no longer has fit data with the LIST

Grips when a spline has fit points

Grips when a spline does not have fit points

command. Also, the spline's grips will be on the control points rather than on the curve itself.

While the PROPERTIES command will show you the spline's properties, such as start and end tangents and order (although it uses equation degree rather than order), it does not allow you to change some of them. You must use the SPLINEDIT command when you want to fine-tune a spline's shape or modify its basic structure. Notice that there is only one E in the command's name. SPLINEDIT uses command line menus that have several levels of options in which it is easy to get lost. Probably your best strategy with this command is to remember what it can do and to review the explanation for making a particular change when you actually need to modify a spline.

Specifically, the SPLINEDIT command allows you to do the following:

Operations on fit points:

Open a closed spline, or close an open one, from fit point data.

Add a fit point.

Delete a fit point.

Move a fit point.

Remove (purge) all fit point data.

Modify the end tangents.

Modify the spline's fit tolerance.

Operations on control points:

Open a closed spline, or close an open one, from control point data.

Move a control point.

Add a control point.

Operations on spline properties:

Elevate the spline's order.

Modify the weight of a spline.

Reverse the direction of a spline.

Command: SPLINEDIT

Purpose: This command edits objects made by the SPLINE command. The following are some of the things it can do: add fit points and control points, open and close splines, change fit tolerance, change the spline's order, change control point weights, and change endpoint tangents.

Initiate with:

- From the command line, enter SPLINEDIT.

- From the Modify pull-down menu, select Spline.

- From the Modify II toolbar, pick the Edit Spline button.

Options:

The SPLINEDIT command will prompt you to select a spline. When you have done so, the spline's control points will be shown as grips, and the following command line menu will be displayed:

`Fit data/Close/Move vertex/Refine/`
`   rEverse/Undo:`

If the spline is closed (periodic), the Close option will be replaced by an Open option. If the spline has no fit points, the Fit Data option will not be offered.

- Fit Data

  This option, which can be started by entering either an F or a D, is for modifying a spline's fit points. The spline's control points will no longer be shown, with the fit points shown instead. AutoCAD will display the following secondary menu on the command line:

  `Add/Close/Delete/Move/Purge/Tangents/toLerance/eXit <eXit>:`

  ○ Add

    Fit points can be added to a spline with this option. They may be placed within the spline or beyond the spline's endpoints. When points are added beyond the endpoints, the original tangents are applied to the new endpoints. This option first asks you to pick an existing fit point on the spline. The prompts that will follow will depend upon the relative position of the selected point.

    First Fit Point

    If you select the first fit point of an open spline, the prompt displayed will be

    `Specify new point or [After/Before] <exit>:`
    `    Enter an option, specify a point, or press Enter.`

    If you press Enter, the option will end without adding a new point, and the Fit Data menu will be redisplayed. If you specify a point, it will become the first point in the spline. AutoCAD will continue to prompt for points to serve as a new first point until you press Enter in response to the prompt. You may undo a point by entering the letter *U*.

Adding a fit point before the first one

    The Before option produces the same results. If you want the new fit point to be between the first and second points of the spline, select the After option. AutoCAD will prompt for a point location and will continue to prompt for points between the first and second fit points until you press Enter. Enter the letter *U* to undo a point.

Adding a fit point after the first one

    Last Fit Point

    If you select the last fit point of an open spline, AutoCAD will highlight it and prompt for locations of new points until you press the Enter key. Entering the letter *U* will undo a point. You can add points only to the end of the spline. There is no option to add points

Adding a fit point after the last fit point

106

between the last fit point and the
next-to-last fit point.

Interior Fit Points

If you choose an interior fit point
in response to the option's
original prompt to select a point,
AutoCAD will highlight the
selected point and the next point

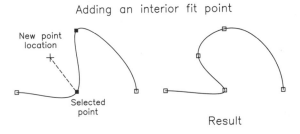

Adding an interior fit point

New point
location

Selected
point

Result

and will prompt for the location of a new point. You can add as many new fit points
between the two high-lighted points as you like. Press Enter when prompted for a new
point to return to the main Fit Data menu. To undo a point, enter the *U* key.

○ Close

This option will be available only if
the spline is open (non-periodic). If
the start point and the endpoint of
the spline are not in the same
location, AutoCAD will connect
them with a new segment and set
the end tangent equal to the start
tangent. If the start point and the
endpoint are in the same location,
AutoCAD will set the end tangent
equal to the start tangent and
reshape the last segment of the
spline. No additional prompts are
used by this option.

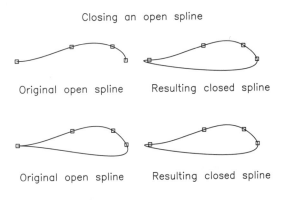

Closing an open spline

Original open spline   Resulting closed spline

Original open spline   Resulting closed spline

○ Open

This option will be offered
only if the spline is closed.
The last segment of the
spline is always removed,
even if the spline's start
points and endpoints were
originally in the same
location. No additional
prompts are used by this
option.

Opening a closed spline

Original open spline   Closed by SPLINEDIT   Reopened by SPLINEDIT

Original open spline   Closed by SPLINEDIT   Reopened by SPLINEDIT

Original closed spline   Opened by SPLINEDIT

○ Delete

Fit points are removed by
this option. You will be prompted to select a point. It will be deleted and the spline will
adjust its shape to maintain smoothness through the remaining fit points. If you delete a
start or end fit point, the tangent directions are moved to the new start or end fit points.

You can delete points until you press the Enter key or until only two points remain.

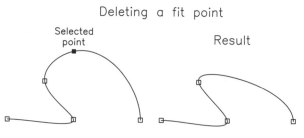

Deleting a fit point

○ Move

You can move fit points with this option. The first fit point in the spline will be highlighted and the following menu will be displayed:

`Specify new location or [Next/Previous/Select point/eXit]:` *Specify a point, select an option, or press Enter.*

This menu is repeated until you select the eXit option to return to the main Fit Data menu. Use the Next, Previous, or Select Point options to highlight the fit point you want moved, then specify a new location for the fit point. The Next option highlights the next fit point away from the spline's start point, and the

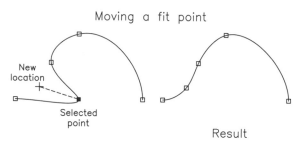

Moving a fit point

Previous option highlights the next fit point toward the spline's start point. The Select Point option permits you to go directly to the fit point you wish to move.

○ Purge

This option removes all fit point data from the spline. Once this data has been purged it cannot be restored. This option has no prompts: it returns you to the main SPLINEDIT menu without the Fit Data option.

○ Tangents

You can change the end tangents with this option. If the spline is open, it starts with the following prompt:

`Enter a S or D, press Enter, or specify a point.`

As soon as editing for the start tangent is finished, the following prompt will be displayed:

`Specify end tangent or [System default]:`*Enter an S or D, press Enter, or specify a point.*

If you use the system default, the end of the spline will swivel about the endpoint as necessary to obtain a continually smooth curve through the fit points. If you press the Enter key, the tangent will remain as it is. If you specify a point, AutoCAD will set the tangent equal to the direction from the spline endpoint to the selected point. The end of the spline will then be fixed to point in that direction, and the spline will adjust its shape to be continually smooth with that tangent and its fit points.

If the spline is closed (periodic), the option will issue the prompt:

`Specify tangent or [System Default]:` *Enter an S or D, press Enter, or specify a point.*

The direction (tangent) of the spline at its closing point will equal the direction from the closing point to the specified point. If the system default is accepted, the spline treats the closing point the same as the interior fit points when it assumes its continually smooth shape.

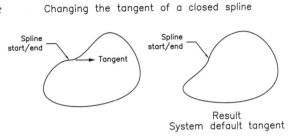

Changing the tangent of a closed spline

Spline start/end — Tangent

Spline start/end

Result
System default tangent

○ toLerance

Notice that you select this option by entering the letter *L*. When tolerance is 0 (AutoCAD will sometimes report it as 1.0000E-10), the spline will pass exactly through the fit points. When tolerance is given a value, the spline will pull away from the fit points in proportion to the specified tolerance value, thereby becoming straighter. The first and last fit points are always on the spline.

○ eXit

This option exits the Fit Data menu and returns to the main SPLINEDIT menu. It is the default option.

○ Close

This option in the main SPLINEDIT menu is available only for open (non-periodic) splines. While it performs the same function as the Close option in the Fit Data menu, it uses control points rather than fit points in closing a spline. Consequently, the shape of a spline closed through this option may be different than if it had been closed through its fit points. Also, this option causes the spline to lose its fit data.

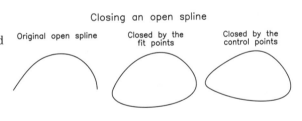

Closing an open spline

Original open spline

Closed by the fit points

Closed by the control points

• Open

This option, which will be offered only if the spline is closed (periodic), removes the last segment of a spline. Although it performs the same function as the Open option in the Fit Data menu, it uses control points rather than fit points in opening the spline. The Fit Data's Open option applies the spline's closing tangent to the new endpoints and adjusts the shape of the curve accordingly. This option, on the other hand, discards the closing tangent and keeps the spline's original shape in the remaining segments. This option causes the spline's fit data to be lost.

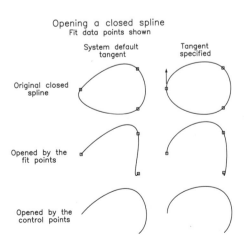

Opening a closed spline
Fit data points shown

System default tangent

Tangent specified

Original closed spline

Opened by the fit points

Opened by the control points

- Move Vertex

This option, which can be started by entering the letter *M* or the letter *V*, changes the location of control points. It also destroys the spline's fit data. The spline's first control point will be high-lighted, and the following submenu will be displayed:

```
Specify new location or [Next/Previous/Select Point/eXit] <N>:
Specify a point, select an option, or press Enter.
```

Use the Next, Previous, or Select Point options to highlight the control point you want moved. Then specify a new location for it, and enter an *X* (or the entire word *exit*) to fix its location and return to the main SPLINEDIT menu. The Next option highlights the next control point away from the spline's start point, and the Previous option highlights the next control point toward the spline's start point. The Select Point option permits you to go directly to the control point you wish to move.

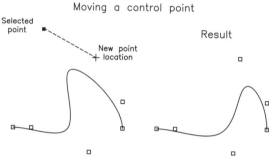

- Refine

You can add control points, elevate the order of the spline's equation, and change the weight of control points with this option. Any of these modifications will cause the spline to lose its fit point data. The option displays the following secondary menu:

```
Add control point/Elevate Order/Weight/eXit
```

- Add control point

This option adds a control point to the spline. The shape of the spline is not changed, and the locations of the other control points are changed as needed to maintain the original shape. The following prompt is issued:

```
Select a point on the spline:
  Select a point or press Enter.
```

This prompt is repeated until you press the Enter key to return to the Refine menu.

- Elevate Order

You may select this option by entering either *E* or *O*. It increases the order of the spline's equation. (When a spline is created, it always has an order of 4.) The option issues the following prompt:

```
Enter new order <current>:
Enter an integer number or press Enter.
```

Additional control points are added to the spline, but the shape of the spline is not changed. Once a spline's order has been increased, it cannot be reduced.

110

- Weight

  When a spline is created, all control points have a weight of 1 and have an equal effect on the shape of the spline. This option enables you to change the weight of control points. When the weight of a control point is increased, the spline will be pulled closer to it. When the weight of a control point is decreased, the spline will move away from it. This option highlights the spline's first control point and displays the following submenu:

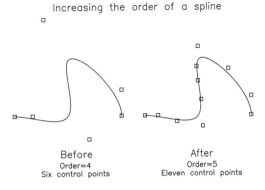

Increasing the order of a spline

Before
Order=4
Six control points

After
Order=5
Eleven control points

```
Enter new weight (current = 1.0000) or [Next/Previous/Select Point/eXit]
<N>: Enter a value, select an option, or press Enter.
```

Use the Next, Previous, or Select Point options to highlight the control point whose weight you want changed. AutoCAD will display its current weight, and you can enter a new value. The Next option highlights the next control point away from the spline's start point, and the Previous option highlights the next control point toward the spline's start point. The Select Point option permits you to go directly to the control point whose weight you wish modified. The eXit option returns to the Refine option's menu.

  - eXit

    This option exits the Refine menu and returns to the main SPLINEDIT menu.

- rEverse

  By default, the order in which AutoCAD lists the fit points and control points is the same as the order in which the fit points were specified. This option reverses the order—the last point becomes the first point, and the first point becomes the last point.

Selected point
Weight=1.0

Weight=3.25

Result

Changing the weight of a control point

- Undo

  This option cancels the last spline editing operation. You can repeatedly use the option to undo all modifications made during a SPLINEDIT session.

- eXit

  This option ends the SPLINEDIT command.

Exercise One

We will finish the wireframe model of an automobile oil pan that we started in Exercise Two of Chapter Four. You can use your model, or use the one in file mfe04207.dwg on the CD-ROM that accompanies this book. Your model should look similar to the one in the next figure. In this exercise, we will use the SPLINE command to connect the two existing sections of the oil pan wireframe.

Zoom in for a closer look at the missing flange area near the X axis. You will recall that the oil pan flange is drawn on the WCS X-Y plane. Be certain that the WCS is in effect and draw a spline between the outside corners in the missing section of the flange. The command line sequence to draw this spline is

```
Command: SPLINE (Enter)
Specify first point or [Object]: (Pick point A.)
Specify next point: (Pick point B.)
Specify next point or [Close/Fit Tolerance] <start tangent>: (Enter)
Specify start tangent: @1<180 (Enter)
Specify end tangent: @1<0 (Enter)
```

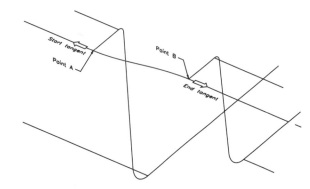

It is important that you use these tangent directions. Otherwise, the spline will not be properly curved. Although we used relative coordinates to specify the tangents, object snaps or simply picking points somewhere along the flange outside edge would work equally well. Use the same steps to draw a spline on the other edge of the flange, or make a copy of the one you just drew. The copy would be located 1 inch in the WCS Y direction from the original.

A 2D polyline could have been used to draw these curves since they are planar, but making them as splines requires less work. The next curve we will make, though, could not be made as a 2D polyline because it does not conveniently fit on a plane. The command line input to draw this curve is identical to that for the previous curve. Use endpoint

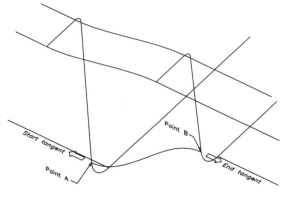

object snaps in locating points A and B, and use typed-in relative coordinates to establish the tangent directions (since there is nothing conveniently close to use as object snaps).

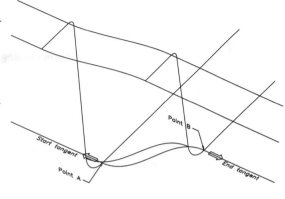

The curve connecting the other ends of the lower two arcs does not have the same shape as the one you just drew, so you will have to again use the SPLINE command. The command line input is the same. This time, though, you can use object midpoint snaps in establishing the spline's tangents.

You can now either make mirror-image copies (by using AutoCAD's MIRROR command) of these four splines for the other half of the oil pan, or use the SPLINE command to draw four new ones. Either way, your wireframe model should look like the one shown in the figure on the right. On the CD-ROM that accompanies this book, the wireframe model is in file mfe05105.dwg. In Section Two of this book, we will add surfaces to the wireframe.

Exercise Two

In our second exercise, we will build the wireframe for a surface model airplane propeller. Start a new drawing, and set up some layers, having names such as WF01 and WF02, for the wireframe objects. You should also set up some layers having a CENTERLINE linetype and a layer for temporary construction lines.

We will make just one propeller blade. After the wireframe is given surfaces, we can then use the polar option of AutoCAD's ARRAY command to make as many blades as we want for the completed propeller. The axis of the propeller is in the Z direction, and the propeller blade will extend in the X axis direction. We will make wireframes of the start and end cross-sections of the blade, and we will connect them with a spline to make the blade's leading and trailing edges.

The start cross-section will lay on the WCS Y-Z plane. Due to the requirements of the command we will use to surface the propeller blade, we will make the cross-sections in two pieces—a top half and a bottom half. Make sure that the WCS is in effect, then use the following command line input to set up the UCS X-Y plane for the first cross-section:

```
Command: UCS (Enter)
Current UCS name: *WORLD*
Enter an option [New/Move/orthoGraphic/Prev/Restore/Save/Del/Apply/?/World] <World>:
  ZA (Enter)
Specify new origin point <0,0,0>: (Enter)
Specify point on positive portion of Z-axis <0.0000,0.0000,0.0000>: 1,0,0 (Enter)
```

Since the orientation of the UCS relative to the WCS is not obvious in the first few figures for this exercise, the preceding command line input for the UCS command will ensure that we all start out with the X-Y plane in the same position. Switch to a plan view of the UCS and use the SPLINE command to draw the top half of the propeller blade cross-section. Use the coordinates given in the first figure below as fit point locations for the spline. Use the default tangent on the left end of the spline, and a tangent in the minus Y direction for the right end of the spline.

You may find it helpful to draw a line with a noncontinuous linetype (such as a CENTER-LINE linetype) along the UCS X axis to help you distinguish the division between the two halves of the cross-section. Now, use the SPLINE command to draw the bottom half of the propeller cross-section, with the coordinates in the figure as the spline's fit point locations. Use the default tangent on the left end of the spline, and a tangent in the positive Y direction for the right end.

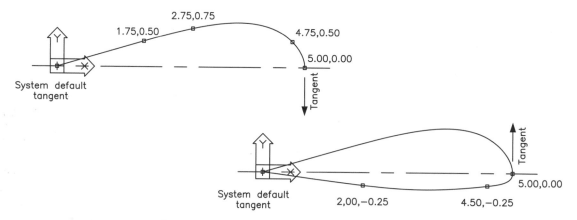

The cross-section for the other end of the propeller will be 30 units in the WCS positive X direction from the cross-section you just drew. Therefore, use the Origin option of the UCS command to move the X-Y plane 30 units in the current Z direction. Your current plan view will continue to be satisfactory, even though you have moved the X-Y plane. You will, however, want to turn off the layers used to draw the first cross-section (including the one for the center line) and use different layers for drawing the next one. Otherwise, the objects in the other plane will tend to clutter and confuse your view.

Just as with the previous cross-section, draw this one as two splines, using the coordinates in the figure on the next page for their fit points. Accept the system default tangents for the left side of the splines, and use the tangents shown in the figure for the right side of the splines. You may also find it useful to draw a horizontal center line between the two splines.

Next we will draw the profile of the propeller's tip, which adjoins the cross-section we just drew. This will be more complicated than you might think it would be, because the AutoCAD command (which will be EDGESURF) we will use to surface this section of the propeller requires four wireframe objects for a boundary. The objects can be in different planes (in fact, they do not even have to be planar objects), but their endpoints must exactly touch. Each of the two cross-section halves we just drew will serve as one boundary, so we need to draw three

114

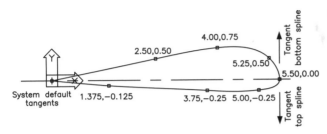

more. While arcs could be used to draw these three boundaries, we will use splines since we can easily control their end tangents. Change from a plan view to an isometric-type view, and zoom in on the tip of the propeller blade. Twist the UCS so that it is on the WCS X-Y plane but its origin is unchanged (at the narrow end of the cross-section). You can do this

Note: these objects are on a plane 30 units in the WCS positive X direction from the other cross-section.

in one step when you use the ZAxis option of the UCS command. Leave the origin as it is, and point in the current Y axis direction for the new Z axis direction. Then use the SPLINE command to draw the two new curves shown in the figure below left. Use the given coordinates for fit point locations, and use command line input to point the spline's end tangents as shown. As an example, the command line input for the lower curve is

```
SPLINE (Enter)
Specify first point or [Object]: 0,0 (Enter)
Specify next point: .25,0 (Enter)
Specify next point or [Close/Fit tolerance] <start tangent>: 1,.625 (Enter)
Specify next point or [Close/Fit tolerance] <start tangent>: (Enter)
Specify start tangent: @1<180 (Enter)
Specify end tangent: @1<60 (Enter)
```

After the two end curves have been drawn, draw a spline between them, using the fit point coordinates and end tangents shown in the figure below right. Notice that the tangents are 180 degrees from those of the adjacent splines—this makes the three curves appear to be a single smoothly blended curve.

We want the surface of the propeller to twist through space, and we will accomplish that by rotating the five splines we have just drawn. This is most conveniently done, with the UCS in its current position, by the ROTATE3D command. After selecting the objects to be rotated (include

115

the centerline if you drew it), pick a point 2.50 units in the Y direction from the UCS origin as the first point on the rotation axis, and a point to its right (having the same Y coordinate) as the second axis point. Enter 15 as the rotation angle.

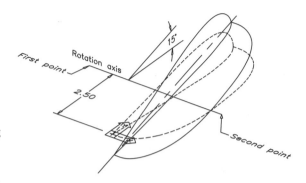

We will make the leading and trailing edge of the propeller blade by connecting the front and back ends of the two cross-sections with two splines. But first, since we want the surface of the propeller to be slightly wider in its middle than at its ends, we need to draw a construction line. Then the spline for each edge of the propeller blade will have three fit points—one on each cross-section endpoint and one on the construction line endpoint.

Turn on the layers you used for the first cross-section, and Zoom back so that you can see the entire propeller blade. Draw a line 6.5 units long positioned as shown in the next figure.

Use the ROTATE3D command to rotate the line you just drew 10 degrees about the rotation axis shown in the figure on the right. (It will be the same axis you used earlier to rotate the propeller end cross-section and tip.)

Finish the wireframe by drawing the leading and trailing edges of the propeller blade. Use the SPLINE command with the ends of the cross-sections as the ends of the splines and the endpoints of the construction line as their interior fit point. You can use object endpoint snaps to locate these points for the splines. You may find it helpful to have the graphics area divided into two viewports, with close-up views of the two cross-sections, when you draw the splines. On the left end of the splines, the end tangents should be in the WCS minus X direction, and they should be in the positive X direction on the right end. Your wireframe model should now look similar to the one shown in the next figure.

Adding surfaces to this wireframe will be almost trivially easy, but we will not do that until Section Two of this book. The completed wireframe propeller blade is in file mfe05209.dwg on the CD-ROM.

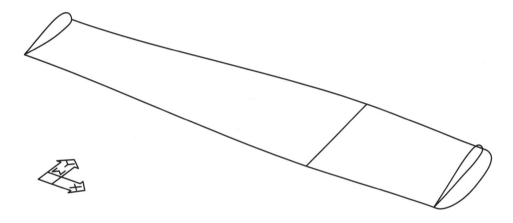

Building Surface Models

Extruded and Planar Surfaces

O ur exploration of surfaces will begin with this chapter.
In it we will

- *describe the AutoCAD object types that can be utilized for surfaces;*
- *discuss the use of extrusion thickness as a surface;*
- *explain how to make three- and four-sided planar surfaces with the 3DFACE command;*
- *add planar surfaces to the 3D wireframe house and oil pan models started as exercises in earlier chapters;*
- *explain how to use the PFACE command to make surface models with multiple planar surfaces.*

3D wireframe models are often useful, but they are seldom realistic looking. You must imagine that surfaces exist between their edges, and there is no way to hide objects that you would not be able to see if the model was opaque. When you need a 3D model that is closer to reality, you will make it as a surface model or as a solid model, rather than as a wireframe model. Either of those types of 3D models can be made to look reasonably realistic, especially when they are rendered.

Deciding whether a particular object should be built as a solid model or as a surface model will depend on the geometry of the object as well as on your intended use of the model. Objects based on fundamental geometric shapes such as prisms, spheres, cones, and cylinders are likely candidates for solid models. Also, most objects that are typically made in machine shops with lathes and milling machines will be modeled as solids.

Objects made from basic geometric shapes
are good candidates for solid models.

However, objects having sculpted, smooth, and flowing surfaces are beyond the capabilities of AutoCAD's solid modeler. For instance, the automobile fender shown in the figure on the right cannot be made in Auto-CAD as a solid model. It is easily made as a surface model, though. In this figure, the surface model is shown in its wireframe mode in the three left-hand viewports, and is shown rendered in the large viewport on the right. The model of an oil pan that we started in Chapter Four and the airplane propeller we started in Chapter Five will also have geometries that can be made only as surface models.

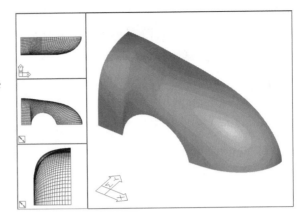

Although the 3D house that we started in Chapter Four could be made as a solid model, it is better to make it as a surface model since we intend to use it for renderings. Surface models usually give you more flexibility in setting and controlling surface appearance properties, such as color and texture, than solid models. For example, AutoCAD's renderer considers all six sides of a 3D solid cube to be a single object: you can attach only one material to the cube. A surface model cube, though, will have six different surfaces, and you can treat each surface differently.

We will begin our explorations of surface modeling in this chapter. First, we will look at the types of AutoCAD objects that can create surfaces, then we will examine extruded surfaces. Most of the chapter, however, will be devoted to planar surfacesÑsurfaces that are flat. Even though this is a specialized surface form, it is an extremely important form because so many objects and surfaces in the real world are flat.

AutoCAD Surface Object Types

An AutoCAD surface is an opaque object that has length and width but no thickness. Since it is opaque, it is able to hide objects that lie behind it relative to the current viewing direction (although a special command such as HIDE must be invoked before those objects are actually hidden). The object types that conform to this definition are listed in Table 6-1.

AutoCAD 3D solids are also opaque, and they have surfaces. But their surfaces represent the outside boundaries of 3D objects—the surface is not a separate object. Therefore, they are not listed in Table 6-1. We will discuss AutoCAD 3D solids extensively in Section Three of this book.

2D solids (made with the SOLID command) and traces (made with the TRACE command) meet our definition of an AutoCAD surface and are therefore included in Table 6-1, but you are not likely to ever use them for surfaces. (AutoCAD, nevertheless, displays 2D solids in its Surfaces pull-down menu and on its Surfaces toolbar.) AutoCAD objects that are intended specifically to be used as surfaces can easily handle the geometry that these commands can make and will give you more flexibility and control.

TABLE 6-1 AUTOCAD OBJECT TYPES FOR SURFACES		
Object Type	**Command**	**Remarks**
2D polyline	PLINE	2D polylines are surface objects only when they have width.
3D face	3DFACE	A fundamental AutoCAD object type, 3D faces always have either three or four edges.
Body	None	Bodies are nonplanar surfaces created when 3D solids are exploded.
Circle	CIRCLE	A fundamental AutoCAD object type.
Thickness	ELEV	Thickness is a property that imparts surfacelike characteristics to certain wireframe objects.
Polygon mesh	Various	Polygon mesh surfaces are made through the 3DMESH, EDGESURF, REVSURF, TABSURF, and RULESURF commands. They are a special polyline form that can create a wide variety of surface shapes.
Polyface mesh	PFACE	A special polyline form, in which a set of three- and four-sided faces are united to make one object.
Region	REGION	A planar object that has no thickness yet has some properties similar to those of 3D solids.
2D solid	SOLID	A 2D object that has width.
Trace	TRACE	A 2D object that has width.

You will not often use 2D polylines that have width as surfaces, but since you conveniently can make some unusual planar shapes with them, you may occasionally make a surface using a 2D polyline. When you do, you can turn off AutoCAD's **fillmode** system variable to avoid having the polyline being filled with its object color when it is seen from a plan view. Fill automatically goes away anytime you are looking at the polyline from a viewpoint that is not a plan view.

The inclusion of circle objects in Table 6-1 may surprise you. This common, often-used wireframe object is also a planar opaque surface—it is a disk. Sometimes, such as when you want to close the end of a tube, this property of circles is handy. At other times, such as when you need to use a circle as a surface boundary to create an open tube, it can be a nuisance.

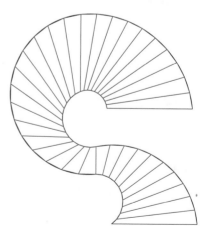

2D polylines that have width can be used to make planar surfaces that have unusual shapes.

If you need a circular wireframe object that is not a surface, you can use two 180-degree arcs rather than one circle.

A region is a surface object type that acts like a 3D solid. It is created with the REGION command, or by exploding 3D solid objects that have flat sides. Since regions share properties with 3D solids, we will not describe them until Section Three of this book. Nevertheless, you should keep them in mind since they can occasionally be useful as planar surfaces, especially when you need one that has interior holes or a curvy edge.

Bodies are an object type that is created when a 3D solid is exploded. You cannot make them directly. The nonplanar surfaces of exploded 3D solids become bodies, while the flat surfaces become regions. Thus, if you use the EXPLODE command on a cylindrical 3D solid, the ends of the cylinder will become regions, and the side of the cylinder will become a body. You will seldom, if ever, need to deliberately make a body object.

Circle for end boundary

Two arcs for an end boundary

Circles are disk-shaped planar surface objects.

Using Thickness as a Surface

Table 6-1 includes one surface type—thickness—that is an object property rather than an object type. When a wireframe object has thickness, it is stretched in the Z direction, as if it were forced through a die, to form a wall-like surface. These surfaces are sometimes referred to as *extruded surfaces*, and the property is often called *extrusion thickness*.

The direction of the extrusion is always in the direction the Z-axis was pointing when the object was created. AutoCAD keeps track of this direction, regardless of how the UCS is currently oriented, even if the object has an extrusion thickness of 0. The LIST command reports an object's extrusion direction.

Three lines   Same three lines with thickness

Extrusion thickness is controlled by the **thickness** system variable. When **thickness** has a positive value, extrusion direction is in the positive Z direction; when it has a negative value, extrusion direction is in the minus Z direction. This system variable can be set directly or through the ELEV command. This command is described in Chapter One. You can also set thickness through a dialog box by selecting Thickness from the Format pull-down menu.

When the value of **thickness** is changed, new objects will be drawn with the new value, but the thickness of existing objects will not change. An existing object's extrusion thickness can be changed, though, through the CHANGE, CHGPROP, and PROPERTIES commands. In fact, unless all of your objects are to have the same thickness, a good practice is to leave thickness at 0 and use one of these change property commands to assign a specific thickness to selected objects.

As you would expect, since they can twist and turn through space, and therefore may not have a constant Z direction, splines and 3D polylines cannot have thickness. Most 2D wireframe objects, on the other hand, can. Exceptions are dimensions, leaders, mlines, mtext, rays, viewports, and xlines. Moreover, spline-based ellipses cannot be given a thickness, although polyline-based ellipses can. (Polyline ellipses are made when the system variable **pellipse** is set to 1.)

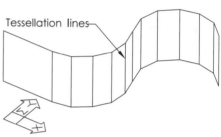

High **VIEWRES** setting

A 3D face, which we will discuss extensively later in this chapter, is another AutoCAD object type that does not accept thickness. If it could, the result would presumably be a hollow boxlike object. However, AutoCAD does have a command, named AI_BOX, that makes such an object, so extruded 3D faces are not really needed. We will describe that command in Chapter Eight.

Low **VIEWRES** setting

Text based on any of the shape file fonts (which have an .SHX filename extension) cannot initially have thickness, but you can give it thickness through any of the commands previously listed for changing properties. AutoCAD accepts a thickness for TrueType fonts (which have a .TTF filename extension), but it does not use it; the text retains its 0 thickness.

Even point objects can have thickness. The result is a vertical line in the Z direction. Although you are not likely to ever have any reason to assign thickness to a point, in early versions of AutoCAD this was the only way to draw a line that was perpendicular to the X-Y plane.

Extruded arcs and circles will have a set of evenly spaced and vertical parallel lines that are referred to as *tessellation* lines. The spacing of tessellation lines is controlled by the VIEWRES command, with the number and density of tessellation lines increasing as VIEWRES increases. These lines occur in printed output as well as on the computer display, and their relative density is seldom the same. The printed version usually has denser tessellation line spacing than the computer display.

Objects that have width become 3D surface objects when they also have extrusion thickness. This enables you to quickly make 3D boxes, wedges, and ductlike objects from 2D polylines that have thickness as well as width. A disadvantage with this technique is that you can-

2D polylines that have width and thickness

124

not control individual surfaces, and the objects are always closed. You cannot, for instance, make a box having an open side. You can use the DONUT command (which makes specialized 2D polylines) to make 3D washers. And, since a circle is a surfacelike disk, extruded circles become cylinders.

When one end of a line has a different Z coordinate than the other end, the extruded surface shape is that of a rhomboid (a parallelogram with oblique corner angles) rather than a rectangle. An object can have only one thickness at a time. Consequently you cannot have extruded lines in which the opposite sides have different lengths—their vertical shape is always that of a parallelogram. When grips are activated on an object that has thickness, grips will be located on both edges of the extrusion surface. You can use these grips to move the object and to change its length (or radius for arcs and circles), but you cannot use grips to change its thickness.

Exercises

We will use a couple of exercises to give you some experience in using thickness and to point out some of its advantages and disadvantages. These exercises will not create any models that you will want to keep, so the setup and the file names you use for them are not important.

Exercise One

On the X-Y plane of the WCS, draw the floor plan of a small house, similar to the one shown in the figure on the right. This is strictly a 2D drawing, and you should leave **thickness** at 0. The hatches and dimensions are intended to help you draw the floor plan and should not be included in your drawing. This floor plan is simply a suggestion, and you may choose to draw one that has different dimensions, or a different arrangement and complexity.

When you have drawn your floor plan, switch to a SE isometric view, invoke one of the commands that change object property (such as PROPERTIES), select all, and set object thickness

Circles that have thickness

Grips on lines that have thickness

DO NOT INCLUDE THE DIMENSIONS OR HATCHES.

to 8 feet. The result, as shown in the figure on the right when the HIDE command has been invoked, is an almost instant 3D model from a 2D drawing. (Although we have not discussed the HIDE command, you only have to call it—by entering HIDE on the command line—to use it. REGEN will restore the wireframe viewing mode.) But there are problems with the model. The door openings go completely up to the ceiling; furthermore, there is no good way to make openings for windows.

On the CD-ROM that accompanies this book, the file mfe06102.dwg contains this model.

Exercise Two

Our second exercise will build a half-round table that has three legs. Since we will be drawing some wide polylines within a plan view, you may want to turn object fill off by setting the system variable **fillmode** to 0. Leave the **thickness** system variable set to its default value of 0. We will add thickness to the objects after they have been drawn.

Use the following command line input to draw a 2D polyline 180-degree arc on the WCS X-Y plane that has a 2.0-unit width.

```
Command:  PLINE (Enter)
Specify start point:  0,1 (Enter)
Specify next point or [Arc/Close/Halfwidth/Length/Undo/Width]: W (Enter)
Specify starting width <0.0000>: 2 (Enter)
Specify ending width <2.0000>: 2 (Enter)
Specify next point or [Arc/Close/Halfwidth/Length/Undo/Width]: A (Enter)
Specify endpoint of arc or [Angle/CEnter/Close/Direction/Halfwidth/Line/Radius/Second
   pt/Undo/Width]: CE (Enter)
Specify center point of arc: 0,2 (Enter)
Specify endpoint of arc or [Angle/Length]: 0,3 (Enter)
Specify endpoint of arc or
   [Angle/CEnter/Close/Direction/Halfwidth/Line/Radius/Second pt/Undo/Width]: (Enter)
```

Switch to a SE isometric view and zoom back to give yourself working room. Use any of the property editing commands to set the thickness of this 2D polyline to 0.1. Then use the MOVE command to move the table top 3.0 units in the positive Z direction. Your table top should be similar to the one shown in the figure on the next page, top left.

Now, rotate the UCS so that its X-Y plane is on the WCS Y-Z plane while leaving its origin location unchanged. An easy way to do this is with the ZAxis option of the UCS command—accept the default origin location and point in the X direction when you are prompted for the new Z axis direction. You may also want to switch to a plan view of the new UCS.

Next, use a 2D polyline with a width varying from approximately 0.1875 to 0.3125 to draw a curved table leg similar to the one shown in the figure on the top right. This figure is only partially dimensioned since the 3.00-unit length is the only one that is important. You should start

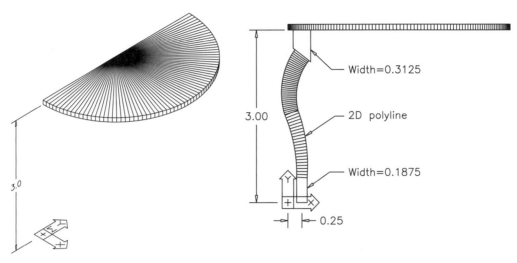

and stop with straight segments and have a couple of large radius curves in between. (A fairly low VIEWRES setting was used to make this figure. This is the reason for the apparent discontin-
uity near the top of the leg.)

When the table leg has been drawn, return to your SE isometric viewpoint. Then assign a thickness of 0.125 units to the leg. Restore the WCS, and use a 180-degree polar array with a center at point 0.0625,2.0 to make a total of three legs. Your completed 3D model should look similar to the one in the figure on the right. On the CD-ROM that accompanies this book, this model is in file mfe06203.dwg.

In Chapter Eight you will learn how to revolve a wireframe object about an axis to create surfaces that appear to have been turned in a lathe. That process can make better-looking table legs.

Making 3DFACE Surfaces

3DFACE is one of the oldest AutoCAD commands for making surfaces, but it still cannot be beat for making three- and four-sided flat surfaces. Clean, unmeshed surfaces, along with the ability to have invisible edges, give 3D faces a visual advantage over AutoCAD's newer surface object types, which generally have mesh lines running across their surfaces. If you are making 3D architectural models, you will use the 3DFACE command extensively as you make walls, roofs, floors, siding, and so forth. Even most furniture objects contain numerous flat areas that are conveniently made with 3DFACE.

127

3DFACE issues command line prompts for points to serve as the vertices of three- or four-sided 3D faces. The input, for example, to make one three-sided 3D face is

```
Command:  3DFACE (Enter)
Specify first point or [Invisible]:  (Specify
    point 1.)
Specify second point or [Invisible]: (Specify
    point 2.)
Specify third point or [Invisible]<exit>:
    (Specify point 3.)
Specify fourth point or [Invisible]<create three-
    sided face>:  (Enter)
Specify third point or [Invisible]<exit>:
    (Enter)
```

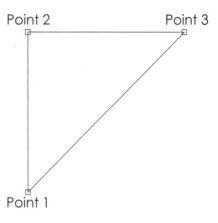

Point 2   Point 3

Point 1

The input to make a 3D face with four edges is

```
Command:  3DFACE (Enter)
Specify first point or [Invisible]:  (Specify
    point 1.)
Specify second point or [Invisible]: (Specify
    point 2.)
Specify third point or [Invisible]<exit>:
    (Specify point 3.)
Specify fourth point or [Invisible]<create three-
    sided face>:  (Specify point 4.)
Specify third point or [Invisible]<exit>:
    (Enter)
```

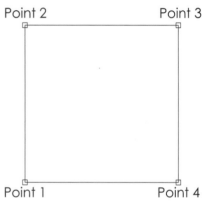

Point 2   Point 3

Point 1   Point 4

The points for four-sided 3D faces must be entered in order, but the order can be either clockwise or counter-clockwise. It is even possible to locate the corners of a four-sided 3D face so that its surface is folded diagonally. For example:

```
Command:  3DFACE (Enter)
Specify first point or [Invisible]:  0,0,1
    (Enter)
Specify second point or [Invisible]: 1,0,0
    (Enter)
Specify third point or [Invisible]<exit>:
    1,1,1 (Enter)
Specify fourth point or [Invisible]<create
    three-sided face>:  0,1,0 (Enter)
Specify third point or [Invisible]<exit>:
    (Enter)
```

The adjacent corners have different elevations, which causes the 3D face to be folded across the second and fourth points. You are not likely to ever

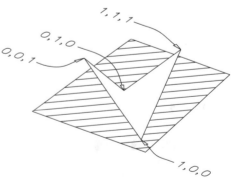

Folded 3D face

need to do this since you could make the same surface configuration more conventionally by using two 3D faces.

More than one 3D face can be made during a single call to the 3DFACE command, and the individual 3D faces can be in different planes. The following input, for example, will make three square 3D faces, each in a different plane:

```
Command:  3DFACE (Enter)
Specify first point or [Invisible]:  0,0,0 (Enter)
Specify second point or [Invisible]: 1,0,0 (Enter)
Specify third point or [Invisible]<exit>:  1,1,0 (Enter)
Specify fourth point or [Invisible]<create three-sided face>:  0,1,0 (Enter)
   (This completes the first 3D face.)
Specify third point or [Invisible]<exit>:  0,1,1 (Enter)
Specify fourth point or [Invisible]<create three-sided face>:  1,1,1 (Enter)
   (This completes the second 3D face.)
Specify third point or [Invisible]<exit>:  1,2,1 (Enter)
Specify fourth point or [Invisible]<create three-sided face>:  0,2,1 (Enter)
   (This completes the third 3D face.)
Specify third point or [Invisible]<exit>:
   (Enter)
```

The resulting 3D faces are individual objects that can be moved, modified, or erased individually. Notice that the input direction for each 3D face alternated between counterclockwise and clockwise and that after the first 3D face was completed an edge was drawn from each new fourth point to the third point of the previous 3D face.

Edges are normally visible, being drawn in the current color, but you can make an edge invisible by entering the letter *i* prior to specifying the first point of the edge. Our final example will make four four-sided faces, around an interior hole. Each face will have two invisible edges. The result will be similar to a wall that has a cutout for a window.

```
Command:  3DFACE (Enter)
Specify first point or [Invisible]:  i (Enter)
Specify first point or [Invisible]:  (Specify Pt 1)
Specify second point or [Invisible]:  (Specify Pt 2)
Specify third point or [Invisible]<exit>:  i (Enter)
Specify third point or [Invisible]<exit>:  (Specify Pt 3)
Specify fourth point or [Invisible]<create three-sided face>:  (Specify Pt 4)
Specify third point or [Invisible]<exit>:  i (Enter)
Specify third point or [Invisible]<exit> (Specify Pt 3a)
Specify fourth point or [Invisible]<create three-sided face>:  (Specify Pt 4a)
Specify third point or [Invisible]<exit>:  i (Enter)
Specify third point or [Invisible]<exit>: (Specify Pt 3b)
Specify fourth point or [Invisible]<create three-sided face>:  (Specify Pt 4b)
Specify third point or [Invisible]<exit>:  i (Enter)
```

```
Specify third point or [Invisible]<exit>:  (Specify Pt 3c)
Specify fourth point or [Invisible]<create three-sided face>:  (Specify Pt 4c)
Specify third point or [Invisible]<exit>:  (Enter)
```

In the above diagram for these faces, the letter *i* within a circle indicates the start of an invisible edge, and the locations of invisible edges are indicated by dashed lines. Notice that the direction of the input alternates between clockwise and counterclockwise for each face. We started with a counterclockwise direction, but a clockwise direction would have worked just as well.

Even though these four 3D faces were made during the same session of the 3DFACE command, they are not connected, and they could have been made through four separate calls to 3DFACE. Generally, you will be better off making one or two faces at a time than trying to make numerous faces during one session of 3DFACE.

There is no undo option for 3DFACE. If you specify the wrong location for a point, you will either have to cancel the command or finish the face and modify it. If you cancel, the edges of the current 3D face are deleted, but the previous 3D faces are left as they are. 3D faces can be stretched through their grips, which will appear on each vertex, or by the STRETCH command.

Creating invisible edges on 3D faces is not easy because you must act one step ahead of the edge that is to be invisible. AutoCAD comes with an AutoLISP program named EDGE.LSP that allows you to change visible edges into invisible edges, as well as invisible edges into visible edges. This program is automatically loaded and acts like a built-in AutoCAD command. It is so convenient to use that you may prefer to ignore invisible edges when you are creating 3D faces, then use EDGE to change the edges you want to be invisible.

130

Command: 3DFACE

Purpose: The 3DFACE command
               makes planar surfaces that
               have either three or four edges.

Initiate with:

- On the command line enter 3DFACE.
- From the Draw pull-down menu, select Surfaces, then 3D Face from the resulting flyout menu.
- Select the 3DFACE button from the Surfaces toolbar.

Implementation:

3DFACE operates from the command line using the following format:

```
Specify first point or [Invisible]:
   (Enter an I or specify a point.)
Specify second point or [Invisible]: (Enter an I or specify a point.)
Specify third point or [Invisible]<exit>:  (Enter an I or specify a point.)
   Specify fourth point or [Invisible]<create three-sided face>:  (Enter an I,
   specify a point, or press Enter.)
Specify third point or [Invisible]<exit>:  (Enter an I, specify a point, or
   press Enter.)
```

If you press the Enter key when prompted for a fourth point, AutoCAD will draw an edge back to the first point to make a three-sided face and prompt for another third point. Pressing the Enter key at that point will end the command, leaving one three-sided 3D face. If you do specify a fourth point, AutoCAD will draw an edge from it back to the first point and prompt for another third point. If you press Enter at that prompt, AutoCAD will end the command leaving a four-sided 3D face.

When you add points after the fourth point, the prompts alternate between Third Point and Fourth Point, and AutoCAD draws an edge from each new fourth point back to the third point in the previous pair of prompts to make another 3D face. Pressing the Enter key when prompted for a point will end the command.

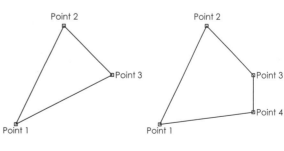

3D face with   3D face with
three sides   four sides

131

If you press the Enter key in response to a new fourth point, AutoCAD will draw an edge from the current third point back to the previous third point, making a three-sided face, and prompt for a new third point.

Edges are drawn in the current color. It is possible, though, to make an edge invisible by entering the letter *i*, or the entire word *invisible*, prior to specifying the first point for the edge.

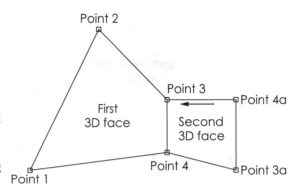

Specifying two additional points

Notes:

- Since each three- or four-sided 3D face is an individual object, there is seldom any advantage in making multiple faces with one call to the command. The results are the same, for instance, whether you use 3DFACE once to make five faces, or repeat 3DFACE five times in making them.

- Invisible edges cannot even be seen by AutoCAD. Consequently, if you need to select a 3D face, perhaps for moving or copying, you must include a visible edge in the selection set.

- An Autodesk-supplied AutoLISP program named EDGE.LSP can be used to permanently make visible edges invisible, as well as to make invisible edges visible.

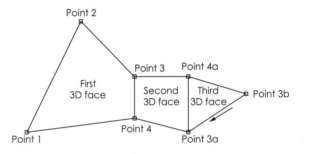

Pressing the Enter key when prompted for a third point makes a three-sided face.

Related system variables:

- **splframe**

  Invisible edges of 3D faces are displayed when **splframe** is set to 1. When **spl-frame** is set to 0 (its default value), invisible edges are not displayed. A regen is required for a change in visibility to take effect.

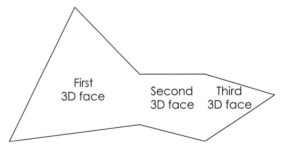

Three 3D faces with invisible edges between them

Command: EDGE

Purpose: EDGE allows you to make selected visible edges of 3D faces become invisible, and selected invisible edges visible.

Initiate with:

- On the command line enter EDGE.

- From the Draw pull-down menu, select Surfaces, then Edge from the resulting fly-out menu.

- Select the EDGE button from the Surfaces toolbar.

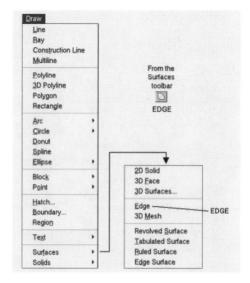

Options:

This command applies to any 3D face currently on the screen—you do not need to first specify a particular 3D face in order to modify the visibility of its edges. The following command line menu is displayed:

```
Specify edge of 3dface to toggle visibility or [Display]: (Enter D, select a 3D
    face edge, or press Enter.)
```

- Specify edge

This, the default option, causes the selected visible edge to become invisible. You must select an edge by picking a point on it—crossing and window selections are not allowed. Beginning with Release 14, AutoCAD automatically displays the midpoint object snap symbol when your pointing device is on an edge. If two edges are coincident (one edge is on top of another edge), they are both changed. As soon as an edge is picked, the main command line menu is repeated.

When you select an edge, it will be highlighted, and any invisible edges on the 3D face it belongs to will also be highlighted. If you select one of those highlighted invisible edges, they will become visible.

- Display

This option causes invisible edges to be displayed as highlighted lines. It brings up the secondary menu:

```
Enter selection method for display of hidden edges [Select/All] <All>: (Enter an
    option, or press Enter.)
```

○ All

This option will cause all invisible edges on all 3D faces currently on the screen to be visible and highlighted. The main EDGE menu will be redisplayed.

○ elect

This option allows you to view the invisible edges on specific 3D faces rather than globally. It uses the prompt:

`Select objects:` *(Select one or more 3D faces.)*

You may use any object selection method in choosing the 3D faces. The invisible edges on those 3D faces will be highlighted, and the main EDGE menu will be redisplayed.

○ Enter

When you press the Enter key in response to the main EDGE menu, the command will end, with the edge visibility changes taking effect.

Notes:

- You should leave the system variable **splframe** set to 0 when you are using EDGE because it is impossible to distinguish invisible edges from visible edges when **splframe** is set to 1.

- This is such an easy command to use, you may prefer to use it in making 3D face edges invisible, rather than directly through the 3DFACE command.

- EDGE is based on an Autodesk-supplied AutoLISP program. It is not a built-in AutoCAD command.

Before EDGE

Selected edges are highlighted.

During EDGE

Visibility of selected edges is reversed.

After EDGE

Exercises

To give you some practical experience in using the 3DFACE command, we will add 3D faces to the two models we started as wireframes in Chapter Four. We will continue to add features to these models in some of the following chapters, so you will want to work through these exercises and save your work.

Exercise Three

Open your drawing of the 3D wireframe house you began in Exercise One of Chapter Four. If you prefer, you can start with the model in file mfe04110.dwg on the CD-ROM that accompanies this book rather than the wireframe you constructed.

We will add 3D faces to the outside walls of the house, to its rooftop, to its roof ends, and to its eaves. Before you actually make any of these 3D faces, you should establish some layers for them. You should set up layers for surface models so you can selectively turn them off to get objects out of the way and to improve visualization. An additional consideration for layers is that AutoCAD's renderer can attach materials by layer. Therefore, if you think that particular surfaces might be rendered in a specific color, or material type, you may want to have their objects reside in a specific layer. I used the names SID01, ROOF01, and EAVES for the layers that the 3D faces will be drawn in. Also, while you will probably want to use a different color for each of these layers, the actual colors you use is not important.

As we make the 3D faces for the walls, we will leave some openings for windows and doors, which will be added in a later chapter. You should draw wireframe outlines of the doors and windows so that you can see their locations when you have the layer you use for the 3D faces turned off. I used a layer for these doors and window outlines that was different from the layers used to draw the wireframe objects of the house corners and roof.

Conceptually, there will be nothing difficult in making these 3D faces, but you will have to be systematic and careful. Otherwise, you may miss covering some areas or incorrectly position a 3D face. You will probably want your AutoCAD graphics area divided into several viewports as you work, even though the figures used for this exercise will show only one view at a time. The dimensions we are using for the house are such that you will be able to draw most of the 3D faces while using AutoCAD's snap mode.

We will start on the right side of the house. Align the X-Y plane of the UCS on the right side of the house as shown in the figure on the right. The viewpoint for this figure is 355 degrees (or minus 5 degrees) from the X axis in the WCS X-Y plane, and 12 degrees from the X-Y plane. Use a layer you have reserved for wireframe objects to draw the rectangular window borders shown in the figure. The dimensions are for your guidance and should not be added to your model.

Now, switch to the layer you intend to use for the side surfaces of the house (such as SIDE01) and make six 3D faces as shown in the figure on the right. Do not bother to make any of the 3D face edges invisible. The faces numbered 1 through 4 in this figure can be easily made when you activate the snap mode, with the snap spacing set to 12 (1 foot). However, you will have to use object endpoint snaps to establish the top corners for face number 5 and for each of the three corners of face number 6.

This figure shows the right side of the house when the HIDE command has been invoked. To use this command, enter HIDE on the command line. Use the REGEN command to restore hidden lines. You can also enter SHADEMODE on the command line and select the Flat option to verify the 3D face locations. This option, which fills the faces in with their object color, is useful when there is nothing behind a surface to be hidden. Although you can work in SHADEMODE's shaded views, the shaded faces occasionally get in the way, so you should again invoke SHADEMODE once you have verified your 3D face locations, and select the command's 2D wireframe option. (We will completely describe the SHADEMODE command in Chapter Seven.)

Move and reorient the UCS so that its X-Y plane is on the front of the house as shown in the top-left figure. This figure shows the right half of the front of the house. Its view point is 280 degrees from the X axis in the X-Y plane, and 0 degrees from the X-Y plane. Then, in the layer you use for wireframe objects draw an outline of a garage door, a front door, and a window using the dimensions given in the figure.

Change to the layer you use for the surface of the house siding, and make six four-sided 3D faces, as shown in the top-right figure. Do not make any of the 3D face edges invisible. The numbers and notes in the figure are to help you in drawing the 3D faces. The lengths and widths of these faces are such that you can easily draw them in AutoCAD's snap mode with a snap spacing of 6 inches. The top edge of face 5 is 10 feet from the bottom of the wall. When you have drawn the six 3D faces, use the SHADEMODE command to verify they are correct.

Move the UCS origin to the front extension of the house and draw (using a layer you've reserved for wireframe objects) the outline of the 8-by-6-foot window as shown in the figure on the right. You may recall from Chapter Four that this section extends 7 feet from the main front of the house. The viewpoint for the next figure is 275 degrees from the X axis in the X-Y plane, and 2 degrees from the X-Y plane.

After switching back to the layer you have been using for the house siding, make the seven 3D faces

136

shown in the figure on the right. Notice that 3D faces 1 and 2 are perpendicular to the other five. To make them, you can either position the UCS X-Y plane on their plane, or use object endpoint snaps without changing the UCS. You should make those two faces first and use the SHADEMODE command to ensure that they are correct. Making the other five 3D faces is a straightforward process, although you will have to use object endpoint snaps to locate the top edge of 3D face 6, and all three vertices of 3D face 7.

Finish covering the front of the house by moving the UCS as shown in the side-by-side central figures. The viewpoint for these figures is 260 degrees from the X axis in the X-Y plane, and 0 degrees from the X-Y plane. Draw the window outline using the dimensions given in the left figure, then make the four 3D faces shown in the right figure. You can most easily make the 3D faces by using Auto-CAD's snap mode with a snap spacing of 12 inches.

Cover the left side of the house with a copy of the six 3D faces and two window outlines you used for the right side of the house. After selecting those objects, use object endpoint snaps to establish the base and destination points for the copies. A quick check using the SHADEMODE command will help you verify that the copies were correctly made and positioned.

Now switch to a view of the back side of the house. The figure on the right shows the house from a viewpoint that is 70 degrees from the X axis in the X-Y plane, and 2 degrees from the X-Y plane. Set the UCS as shown in the figure. (The 3point option of the UCS command works well in doing this.) The house is beginning to be cluttered, which makes it difficult to visualize its surfaces and

to select points. Since at this time we are only interested in the 40-by-10-foot rectangle that makes up the back wall of the house, we will make the 3D faces for it in an area that is in the same plane but is located away from the house. That will give us a clear, clean view of our work. When we are finished, we will move the 3D faces onto the house.

Move the UCS origin 45 feet in the X direction as shown in the figure on the upper right. Then draw the out lines of one door and three windows using the dimensions in the figure.

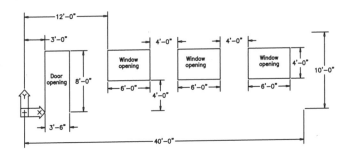

Make seven 3D faces similar to those shown in the figure on the lower right figure. Other arrangements of these 3D faces would be equally satisfactory. Be sure to draw them in the layer you have been using for the house's siding.

After checking the correct placement of your 3D faces with the SHADEMODE command, move them along with the wireframes for the door and windows 45 feet in the minus X direction so that they are on the back of the house.

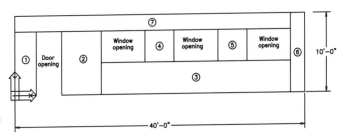

That finishes the surfaces for the sides of the house. We will now begin adding 3D faces to the eaves of the roof. Start on the right side of the house as shown in the figure below. We have turned off the layer that was used to make the 3D faces for the siding as well as the layer used for the window and door outlines. The figure uses a viewpoint that is rotated 315 degrees from the X axis in the X-Y plane and 55 degrees from the X-Y plane.

Make four 3D faces to cover the surfaces on the lower part of the roof overhang. The areas to be covered are shown hatched in the figure. Use a unique layer, having a name such as EAVES, for the 3D faces. Since you can use object endpoint snaps to locate the vertices of the 3D faces, the location and orientation of the UCS is not important.

Then, make four 3D faces on the outside edge of the roof end. The areas to be covered are shown hatched in the top-left figure on the next page. Here also, you can conveniently use object endpoint snaps to locate the vertices of the 3D faces. Use the SHADE-MODE command to verify that all eight 3D faces on this end of the roof are correctly positioned.

Use the same techniques to make 3D faces on the other end of the house (or else copy or mirror the ones you have just drawn) and on the front extension of the house. Then cover the bottom of the eaves on the left-front side of the house. This area, which can be covered with two 3D faces, is shown hatched in the

138

upper half of the top-right figure. Also, cover the vertical sides of these eaves with two 3D faces, as shown (hatched) in the lower half of the figure.

After checking these 3D faces with the SHADE—ODE command, cover the remaining eaves with 3D faces using the same techniques. You will probably want to use two viewports, zoomed in on opposite ends of the roof, to cover the 40-foot-long eaves on the back of the house. Check your 3D face locations with the SHADEMODE command.

Only the top of the roof remains to be covered. In this exercise we will make only the three 3D faces shown in the figure below. We will cover the remaining area of the roof later in this chapter in an exercise for the PFACE command. The viewpoint for the figure is 290 degrees in the X-Y plane from the X axis, and 60 degrees from the X-Y plane. Switch to the layer you intend to use for the rooftop and make the three 3D faces, using object snaps at the vertex points shown in the figure. If you use object endpoint snaps, the orientation of the UCS is not important.

Your house is now fully covered, except for the doors, windows, and part of the roof. It should look similar to the one shown in the figure on the top of the next page. when the viewpoint is 305 degrees in the X-Y plane from the X axis and 5 degrees from the X-Y plane. In this figure the HIDE command is active. Even so, at this stage the house doesn't look any better than the wireframe version did, but it is covered with surfaces that can make the house realistic looking when it is rendered.

You should save the file of your 3D model. We will finish covering its roof in Exercise Six of this chapter. This

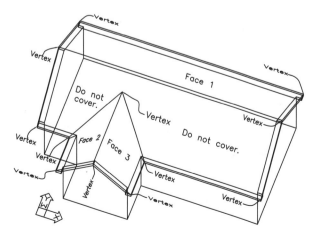

stage of the model is in the CD-ROM that accompanies this book as file mfe06315.dwg.

Exercise Four

Our next exercise in using the 3DFACE command will be much less involved than the first exercise. We will add seven 3D faces to the oil pan we started as a wireframe model in Chapter Four and added to in Chapter

Five. The wireframe model is on the CD-ROM that accompanies this book as file MFE05105.DWG. The next figure shows the model with the areas in which we will add the 3D faces labeled. Six of them are on the flange, and one is on the rectangular area of the raised bot-

tom of the oil pan. Although there are other planar areas on the oil pan, those areas have curved rather than straight edges, so we will use other types of surfaces for them. Also, we plan to make a domelike surface in the large rectangular area on the bottom of the oil pan.

Set up a layer for surfaces and use it to make all seven of the 3D faces. Now that you are experienced in using the 3DFACE command, we will not give you detailed guidance. The areas are bounded by wireframe objects so you can use object endpoint snaps to locate the vertices of the 3D faces. There is no need to make any of the edges invisible. Your model with the 3D faces should look similar to the one shown on the bottom when the SHADEMODE command has been invoked. On the CD-ROM that comes with this book, the partially surfaced oil pan model is in file mfe06402.dwg.

Making Surfaces with the PFACE Command

The PFACE command is similar to the 3DFACE command in that it makes three- and four-sided planar surfaces. Another similarity with 3DFACE is that the PFACE command can make any number of faces each time it is used. The faces made with PFACE, however, are joined so that they form one object having multiple faces rather than a set of individual objects. Also, edges between the three- and four-sided faces are normally invisible.

↑ "PFACE"

140

Surfaces made by the PFACE command are called *polyface meshes*. This is a unique AutoCAD object type. Although it is a variation of the polyline object type, it is not recognized by the PEDIT command. AutoCAD has another object type for surfaces, which we will describe in Chapter Eight, called a *polygon mesh*. The similarity in their names makes it easy to confuse these two object types, but they are different. Polygon meshes are a surface version of polylines that can be edited by PEDIT. To add to the possible confusion, when a polyface mesh is exploded, it turns into a set of 3D faces rather than a set of polylines.

Although both PFACE and 3DFACE make three- and four-sided faces, the input for PFACE is entirely different than it is for 3DFACE. In fact, it is a method that is unlike the input for any other AutoCAD command. PFACE first asks you to pick points in space to serve as the vertices of the faces, and as you pick those points AutoCAD internally assigns a number to each vertex. When you have selected the locations of all of the vertices, AutoCAD then asks you to enter the vertex numbers that go with which face.

To get an idea as to how the PFACE command works, consider the six points shown on the left in the next figure. These points are all on the same plane. The input to make a polyface mesh having these points as its vertices is

```
Command:   PFACE (Enter)
Specify location for vertex 1: 0,0,0 (Enter)
Specify location for vertex 2 or <define faces>: 0,2,0 (Enter)
Specify location for vertex 3 or <define faces>: 1,2,0 (Enter)
Specify location for vertex 4 or <define faces>: 1,1,0 (Enter)
Specify location for vertex 5 or <define faces>: 2,1,0 (Enter)
Specify location for vertex 6 or <define faces>: 2,0,0 (Enter)
Specify location for vertex 7 or <define faces>: (Enter)
Face 1, vertex 1: Enter a vertex number or [Color/Layer]: 1 (Enter)
Face 1. vertex 2: Enter a vertex number or [Color/Layer]<next face>: 2 (Enter)
Face 1. vertex 3: Enter a vertex number or [Color/Layer]<next face>: 3 (Enter)
Face 1. vertex 4: Enter a vertex number or [Color/Layer]<next face>: 4 (Enter)
Face 1. vertex 5: Enter a vertex number or [Color/Layer]<next face>: 5 (Enter)
Face 1. vertex 6: Enter a vertex number or [Color/Layer]<next face>: 6 (Enter)
Face 1. vertex 7: Enter a vertex number or [Color/Layer]<next face>: (Enter)
Face 2. vertex 1: Enter a vertex number or [Color/Layer]: (Enter)
```

The resulting polyface mesh is shown on the right in the figure. As is generally true with AutoCAD surfaces, only the edges of the surface show up in a wireframe mode view such as this. We specified the vertex numbers in the same order that we used to specify the point locations, but we did not have to. The following input sequence during the second phase of the PFACE command would have worked equally well.

Coordinates of six points in space and the AutoCAD assigned vertex numbers

Polyface mesh using the points as vertices

```
Face 1. vertex 1: Enter a vertex number or [Color/Layer]: 4 (Enter)
Face 1. vertex 2: Enter a vertex number or [Color/Layer]<next face>: 3 (Enter)
Face 1. vertex 3: Enter a vertex number or [Color/Layer]<next face>: 2 (Enter)
Face 1. vertex 4: Enter a vertex number or [Color/Layer]<next face>: 1 (Enter)
Face 1. vertex 5: Enter a vertex number or [Color/Layer]<next face>: 6 (Enter)
Face 1. vertex 6: Enter a vertex number or [Color/Layer]<next face>: 5 (Enter)
Face 1. vertex 7: Enter a vertex number or [Color/Layer]<next face>: (Enter)
Face 2. vertex 1: Enter a vertex number or [Color/Layer]: (Enter)
```

SPLFRAME

Although outwardly these two different input sequences seem to produce the same results, the two polyface mesh surfaces are subtly different. If you were to turn on the **splframe** system variable (by setting it to a value of 1), the polyface mesh from the first vertex input order would look like the one on the left side of the next figure, while the one using the second vertex input order would be like the one on the right.

Notice that both polyface meshes are internally composed of three subfaces, even though AutoCAD referred to this area as one face during the PFACE command. The first subface always has four edges, provided the entire face has at least four vertices, and the remaining subfaces always have just three edges. These subfaces are similar to those you might make with the 3DFACE command. Unlike 3D faces though, these three subfaces are

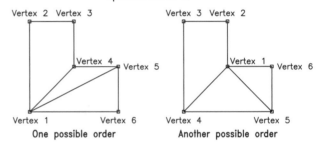

Same vertex locations, but entered in a different order. Splframe set to 1.

One possible order   Another possible order

joined to form a single object—if you move one, they all move, and if you erase one they are all erased. Moreover, AutoCAD automatically makes the edges between the subfaces invisible.

Notice also in the preceding figure that one edge of each subface originates from the first vertex that was specified during the second phase of the PFACE command. As a result, the internal arrangement of the subfaces on these two polyface meshes is different, even though they appear to be identical when **splframe** is set to 0.

This means that the location of the vertex you specify for the first vertex is very important. The next figure shows a polyface mesh surface made using an improper input order for these same vertices—one that requires an edge from the first vertex to cut across the straight-line border between vertex points. The face vertex input was clockwise, starting with vertex 1.

In a wireframe mode, as shown on the left, the surface appears to be all right. If you were to set **splframe** to 1, however, you would see, as shown in the middle of the figure, that one subface edge extends beyond the apparent boundary of the surface. The actual area covered by the surface is shown

Results of an improper vertex input order

Splframe set to 0   Splframe set to 1   Actual area surfaced

142

hatched on the right in the figure. This area would be evident when you used the SHADEMODE command.

If you were to explode that polyface mesh, it would be transformed into three 3D faces as shown on the right in the next figure. In this figure, the 3D faces have been moved away from each other. Notice that one of these 3D faces, which has four vertices, crosses over itself. The edges of 3D faces created by exploding a polyface mesh retain the original subface edge visibility. As a result, all of the edges on the 3D faces that originally represented interior edges of subfaces will be invisible. In the figure, **splframe** has been set to 1, so all of the edges on the 3D faces are shown.

Splframe set to 1   Polyface mesh exploded into three 3D faces

Its cumbersome input has severely limited the popularity of PFACE, and Autodesk now even seems to be trying to ignore the command. Since Release 13, PFACE has not been included in any of the menus or toolbars, and the Command Reference manual, as well as on-screen help, suggests that you use 3DFACE or one of the commands that make polygon meshes instead of PFACE.

Nevertheless, it is a handy command for certain situations. You may prefer to use PFACE for making planar surfaces having five to seven sides instead of 3DFACE since you don't have to bother with making invisible edges. Furthermore, the interface isn't that bad when you get used to it. Most likely, though, you will need to make yourself a diagram of the area, or areas, you want surfaced to ensure that the vertex numbers match the face input.

Command:	PFACE
Purpose:	PFACE makes a single object consisting of multiple three- and four-sided planar surfaces.

Initiate with:

• On the command line enter PFACE.

Implementation:

PFACE has two separate phases. First, the command prompts you for the vertices, the corners, of the surfaces you want to create. In this phase you specify points in space, one at a time, to be surface vertices, and AutoCAD consecutively assigns a vertex number to each point. In the second phase of the command, AutoCAD creates surface faces as you enter the appropriate vertex numbers.

The command line sequence of prompts and input for the first phase of PFACE is

```
Command:    PFACE
Specify location for vertex 1:  Specify a point.
Specify location for vertex 2 or <define faces>:  Specify a point.
Specify location for vertex 3 or <define faces>:  Specify a point or press
   Enter.
Specify location for vertex n or <define faces>:  Specify a point or press
   Enter.
```

You can specify as many points, using any input method, as you want. When you press the Enter key in response to a vertex point, AutoCAD moves to the second phase of the command:

```
Face 1, vertex 1: Enter a vertex number or [Color/Layer]: Enter the letter L or
   C, or a vertex number.
Face 1, vertex 2: Enter a vertex number or [Color/Layer]<next face>: Enter the
   letter L or C, or a vertex number.
Face 1, vertex n: Enter a vertex number or [Color/Layer]<next face>: Enter the
   letter L or C, a vertex number, or press Enter.
Face 2, vertex 1: Enter a vertex number or [Color/Layer]:  Enter the letter L or
   C, a vertex number, or press Enter.
Face m, vertex n: Enter a vertex number or [Color/Layer]<next face>: Enter the
   letter L or C, a vertex number, or press Enter.
```

Whenever the Enter key is pressed, AutoCAD moves to the next face, prompting for the number of the first vertex on the face. These faces do not have to be in the same plane. Pressing the Enter key twice in succession ends the command.

Options:

Edges between faces are normally visible, but you can make them invisible if you enter the first vertex on the edge as a negative number.

If you enter the letter *c* or the word *color* when prompted for a vertex number, AutoCAD will issue a prompt for a color. After you specify a color, either by number or name, Auto-CAD will resume with a prompt for another vertex number.

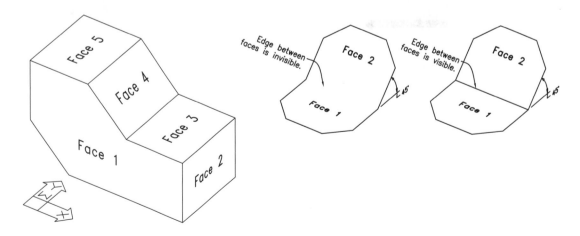

144

All edges of the current face, and of the faces that follow, will be drawn in the specified color.

```
Face m, vertex n: Enter a vertex number or [Color/Layer]: color (Enter)
Enter a color number or a standard color name <CURRENT>: Enter a color number or
    name.
Face m, vertex n: Enter a vertex number or [Color/Name]:Enter a vertex number.
```

If you enter the letter *l* or the word *layer* when prompted for a vertex number, AutoCAD will issue a prompt for a layer name. The current face, as well as the faces that follow, will be in the specified layer. After you specify a layer, AutoCAD will resume the prompts for vertex numbers.

```
Face m, vertex n: Enter a vertex number or [Color/Layer]:layer (Enter)
Enter a layer name<CURRENT>: Enter the name of a layer.
Face m, vertex n: Enter a vertex number or [Color/Layer]:Enter a vertex number.
```

Notes:

- If a face has more than four vertices, it will be divided into subfaces having three or four vertices that are similar in shape to 3D faces. The edges between these subfaces are invisible.

- The type of object created by this command is a polyface mesh. While this object type is within the polyline family, it cannot be edited by PEDIT. Moreover, when a polyface mesh is exploded, it becomes a set of individual 3D faces.

- AutoCAD does not draw any faces until you signal an end to the second phase of the command by pressing the Enter key twice in succession. If you cancel the command, no faces will be drawn, even if their vertex numbers have already been entered.

Related system variables:

- **splframe**

  If the system variable **splframe** is set to 1, invisible edges between faces and between subfaces will be displayed. The default value of **splframe** is 0. A regen is required before changes in splframe have any effect.

- **pfacevmax**

  This is a curious system variable that sets the maximum number of vertices per face. However, it is a read-only variable, so you cannot do anything with it. Its value is fixed at 4.

Using AutoLISP to Make Polyface Meshes

Autodesk intended PFACE to be used primarily by applications, such as AutoLISP programs, and when PFACE first appeared in Release 11, Autodesk supplied an AutoLISP program as an example. This program, named MFACE.LSP, worked well in Release 11, but unfortunately, the Release 12 version of the program contained an error that prevented it from running, and subsequent releases of AutoCAD do not even include MFACE.LSP.

The CD-ROM that accompanies this book contains a corrected version of MFACE.LSP that works in AutoCAD 2000. Once the program has been loaded, it uses the following command line input:

```
Command: MFACE
Layer/Color/<Select vertex>: Enter an option or specify a point.
```

If you select the Layer option, the command prompts for a layer name to be used in drawing the face, with the current layer presented as a default. After a name is entered, or the Enter key is pressed to accept the default, the main menu is repeated.

If you select the Color option, the command prompts for a color name or number (with the current color offered as a default) to be used for drawing the face. After a color is specified, the main menu will be repeated.

When you select a point in response to the main menu, it serves as the first vertex of a face, and the program prompts for additional vertex points:

```
Select vertex: Specify a point or press Enter.
```

This prompt is repeated until you press the Enter key. When you specify the fourth vertex, AutoCAD will draw a highlighted line (representing the inside edge of the first subface) to it, and as each additional vertex is specified, AutoCAD will draw a highlighted line (representing the edge of a three-cornered subface) to it.

Whenever you press the Enter key in response to a point, the current face is completed, and the original menu is repeated so that you can make another face:

```
Layer/Color/<Select vertex>: Enter an option, specify a point, or press Enter.
```

Pressing the Enter key will terminate the command. The *Layer* and *Color* options allow the next face to be drawn in a different layer or with a different color than the previous face, and specifying a point will establish the first vertex of the next face.

The edges between the subfaces will always be invisible (provided **splframe** is set to 0), while edges between faces will always be visible—there is no provision for making invisible face edges, as there is in the PFACE command itself.

Converting 3D Faces to Polyface Meshes

As we have seen, when you explode a polyface mesh, it is transformed into a set of individual 3D faces, with the invisible edges between faces remaining invisible. Beginning with Release 13, you can reverse the transformation, to make polyface meshes from 3D faces, although the process is not direct. You must first use AutoCAD's 3DSOUT command to export the 3D faces to a 3D Studio format file, then import the 3D Studio file back into AutoCAD by way of the 3DSIN command. (3D Studio is a stand-alone rendering and animation program.)

The process is easy. When you invoke the 3DSOUT command, you will be asked to select the objects to be exported and then for a name and location for the exported file. This will be followed by a dialog box named 3D Studio File Export Options. You can safely accept the default options in this dialog box, and press its OK button to save the file. The original 3D faces will remain as they were.

As soon as the file has been saved, you can start the 3DSIN command to import the 3D Studio version of the 3D faces. A standard file location dialog box will be presented so that you can find and specify the 3D Studio file—it will have a 3DS file name extension. As soon as you specify the file, a dialog box named 3D Studio File Import Options will appear. A list of 3D Studio objects types available for import will be shown in a list box located on the left side of this dialog box. Press the *Add All* button below this list box to select these object types, and move their names to a list box on the right side of the dialog box. Then press the OK button to import the objects into AutoCAD.

The imported objects, which are now a single polyface mesh, are inserted in the same spot as the original objects. This process can be useful when you want to join a set of 3D faces so that you can treat them as a single object. One drawback, however, is that edges on the original 3D faces that were originally invisible will be visible on the resulting polyface mesh. Actually, this transformation also works for other AutoCAD objects having surfaces, such as polygon meshes, regions, 3D solids, and even circles and extruded wireframe objects. You are not likely, however, to ever want to convert those objects to polyface meshes.

Exercise Five

As an exercise in using PFACE, we will make the surface model of a sheet-metal air duct that has a 90-degree bend. We will not use this model in the future, and you may not want to keep it. Therefore, the setup for the drawing file and its name is not especially important. You will need at least two layers, though. On the CD-ROM, this surface model is in the file mfe06503.dwg.

We will use a wireframe to establish the vertex points of the polyface mesh. Start by rotating the UCS about the X axis so that the UCS X-Y plane is on the WCS Z-X plane. Then draw the seven lines that represent the edges of one side of the duct, using the dimensions given in the next figure. When you have completed the one side, copy all seven lines 12 units in the WCS Y direction. Your finished wireframe should look similar to the one shown in the figure on the lower left.

The dashed lines in this figure are to give you an idea as to where the edges of the polyface mesh faces will be—you should not draw the dashed lines. You should now switch to a layer

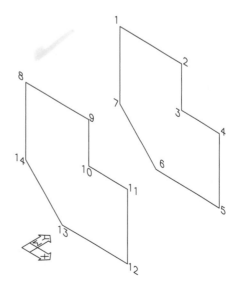

that is different from the one you used for the wireframe. Although you could do this during the PFACE command, it will probably be less confusing if you do it now.

Set up a running endpoint object snap, through the OSNAP command, then start the PFACE command. In the first phase of the command, pick the numbered line endpoints shown in the lower-right figure on the previous page in response to AutoCAD's prompts for Vertex 1, Vertex 2, Vertex 3, and so forth. When you have specified the location of 14 vertex points, press the Enter key when AutoCAD prompts for Vertex 15. Other equally suitable arrangements of the vertex numbers could be used, but this one is as good as any. You could even assign numbers randomly, as long as the numbers match the face vertices during the second phase of the command.

When you press the Enter key in response to a vertex point, AutoCAD will move to the second phase of the command in which you specify which vertex numbers correspond to which face. We will make a total of seven different faces on the duct. The top of the duct, represented by vertexes 1, 2, 9, and 8, will be left open. We will also leave the front of the duct—the space between vertexes 4, 5, 12, and 11—open.

Enter vertexes 1, 7, 14, and 8 for the first face. Alternately, you could start with any of those vertex numbers, and you can traverse either clockwise or counterclockwise, but if you skip diagonally (such as 1, 14, 7, and 8), the face will cross over itself. Press the Enter key when you are prompted for Vertex 5 of Face 1. AutoCAD will then ask for the vertexes that will define Face 2.

For Face 2, enter vertexes 6, 7, 14, and 13. Press the Enter key when AutoCAD prompts for Vertex 5 of Face 2, to move to the next face. Complete the PFACE command using the following vertex numbers for the remaining five faces:

Face 3   Vertex numbers 5, 6, 13, and 12
Face 4   Vertex numbers 2, 3, 10, and 9
Face 5   Vertex numbers 3, 4, 11, and 10
Face 6   Vertex numbers 3, 4, 5, 6, 7, 1, and 2
Face 7   Vertex numbers 10, 11, 12, 13, 14, 8, and 9

When AutoCAD prompts for Vertex 7 of Face 8, press the Enter key twice to finish PFACE. At this time AutoCAD will draw the seven faces. It is important that you start Face 6 with Vertex 3, and Face 7 starts with Vertex 10. Otherwise, the surface may extend beyond our intended outline. Your completed surface model should look similar to the one shown on the right. HIDE has been activated for this figure, and the viewpoint is 325 degrees from the X axis in the X-Y plane and 10 degrees from the X-Y plane.

Exercise Six

We will finish the roof of our 3D surface model house with the PFACE command. The area we will cover has seven vertices. Although you could easily surface this area with three 3D faces, we will use a single polyface mesh instead. The reason for this is that when we set up a rendering of the house in Chapter Nineteen, we will want that surface to be a single object rather than three separate objects.

Open your file of the surface model house, or retrieve and open file mfe06315.dwg on the CD-ROM that comes with this book. Set a viewpoint that is rotated approximately 300 degrees in the X-Y plane from the X axis and approximately 50 degrees from the X-Y plane. If your model is too cluttered, you can freeze the layers used for the house siding and windows. Your model should look similar to the one in the next figure.

Switch to the same layer you used for the 3D face surfaces on the roof, then start the PFACE command. When you are prompted in the first phase of PFACE to select vertex locations, pick the points labeled in the previous figure. If you use a running object endpoint snap, you can do this without changing the UCS location or orientation. In the second phase of PFACE, specify the vertices in the same order that you entered them. After specifying Vertex 7, press the Enter key twice to end PFACE. That finishes the roof of the house. On the accompanying CD-ROM, the file mfe06601.dwg contains the house at this stage.

PFace = (MFACE .LSP)

Visualizing Surface Models

V isualizing the 3D objects on your computer's 2D display can be a major problem when you build surface models. Fortunately, AutoCAD provides several commands that help. We will demonstrate what those commands can do and how they work in this chapter. Specifically, we will

- *discuss hidden-line removal with the HIDE command;*
- *describe the wireframe, hidden line, and shaded options of the SHADEMODE command;*
- *explain how to remove view obstructing objects and how to make perspective views with DVIEW and with the commands related to 3DORBIT.*

Even though surface models are a step up in reality from wireframe models, their increased complexity can make them harder to visualize. This is especially true for models with polymesh surfaces, which we will discuss in Chapter Eight, but even models surfaced with 3D faces become cluttered with extra lines and edges, as you undoubtedly noticed in Chapter Six when we added surfaces to our 3D house. Furthermore, you can see completely through the surfaces most of the time. This makes it difficult to tell where the surfaces are located, to distinguish between surfaces, to determine where a particular object is located on a model, and to pick points on a model.

AutoCAD's HIDE, SHADEMODE, DVIEW, and 3DORBIT commands can help you obtain clearer, more understandable, and more realistic pictures of your 3D models. We will examine those commands in this chapter to see how they work, how they differ, and how you can best use them.

Wireframe 3D model

Surface model in wireframe mode   Surface model in hidden-line mode

Using The Hide Command

Often, surface models (as well as solid models) are referred to as wireframes when they are displayed in a nonopaque form. In this book, though, we will refer to the nonopaque form of surface models and solid models as their *wireframe mode* rather than as wireframes. This will distinguish them from models made solely from wireframe objects.

The most frequently used method for making surfaces opaque is to invoke the HIDE command. HIDE requires no object selection and has no options. After performing some calculations, AutoCAD will redraw the current viewport so that all objects, and parts of objects, that are behind surface objects are no longer shown. The result is often referred to as a *hidden-line image*, or as the *hidden-line mode*. The surfaces will continue to be opaque until some operation causes a viewport screen regeneration. As you would presume, which objects are hidden is dependent upon the view direction. Objects may simultaneously be hidden in one viewport and visible in another.

If two objects are in the same plane, they will not hide each other. The figure on the right shows the 3D model of a simple building made from 3D faces. The top edges of the walls show through the roof in hidden-line views since they are in the same plane as the roof, as can be seen on the right side of the figure. These

Edges of 3D faces are still shown.

Before HIDE   After HIDE

edges will not show up in a rendering, so they may not really be a problem. If it is important that the edges are not to appear in hidden-line views, however, you have two options. The best one is to make the edges invisible, perhaps with the EDGE command. A more complicated and possibly less desirable option (since it affects the accuracy and preciseness of your model), is to move, or remake, the objects so that they are no longer in the same plane.

As you can imagine, AutoCAD must perform extensive calculations in determining which objects are to be hidden. Normally, AutoCAD uses single precision arithmetic in performing these calculations, and this can affect the accuracy of the hidden line removal. The next figure

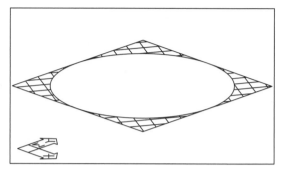

The circle is 0.0005 units above the hatch. HIDE does not work properly.

The circle is still 0.0005 units above the hatch, but **hideprecision** has been set to 1. HIDE now works properly.

shows a circle that is 0.0005 units above a hatch pattern. With single precision arithmetic, AutoCAD has problems and the hatch is only partly hidden.

However, when AutoCAD uses double precision arithmetic (which means that it uses more digits to the right of the decimal point), the HIDE command works properly in hiding the hatch, as shown in the upper-right figure. The system variable **hideprecision** controls whether Auto-CAD uses single or double precision arithmetic. When **hideprecision** is set to 0, single precision arithmetic is used; when it is set to 1, AutoCAD uses double precision arithmetic.

In practice, the problem we have used as an example seldom occurs, and you will seldom have any reason to change **hideprecision** from its default value of zero. This system variable was a late addition to AutoCAD Release 14, so you may not find any references to it in the AutoCAD manuals or in on-screen help.

Surface model in hidden-line mode. All layers for surfaces are ON.

Surface model in hidden-line mode. Some layers for surfaces are OFF.

Surface objects in layers that have been turned off continue to hide objects that are behind them. In some cases you can use this characteristic to obtain hidden-line views without the clutter of mesh lines. More likely, though, the result will be mysterious-looking gaps in your model. The left side of the figure of two boats shows the hidden-line view of a model in which all layers for surfaces are on. The right side of the figure shows a hidden-line view of the same model but with the layers for the deck and cabin surfaces turned off. This phenomenon does not occur with layers that have been frozen, and it does not affect plots.

Command: HIDE

Purpose: This command causes all objects that have surfaces to be opaque in the current viewport.
Objects, and parts of objects, that are behind surfaces, relative to the current viewing direction,
are hidden from view.

Initiate with:

- On the command line enter HIDE.

- From the View pull-down menu, select Hide.

- Select the HIDE button from the Render toolbar.

Implementation:

This command requires input and has no options. As soon as it is invoked, it begins its work
of finding objects that are behind surfaces in the current viewport and removing them from
the screen. The screen will remain in its hidden-line mode until some operation—such as
REGEN, ZOOM, or VPOINT—causes the screen to regenerate. The REDRAW command does
not affect the hidden-line mode.

Notes:

- Text will not be hidden unless it has
thickness.

- Objects in layers that are frozen are completely transparent, and therefore have
no effect on hidden-line displays.
However, surface objects in layers that
are turned off are still considered to be
opaque by the HIDE command, and consequently will hide objects that are
behind them.

Before HIDE   After HIDE

- The HIDE command has no effect on hidden-lines during plotting. That is handled by the
Hide Lines option of the PLOT command, or (better) through paper space and the MVIEW
command. (We will discuss this command in Section Four.)

- The Advanced Modeling Extension (AME), an Autodesk solid modeling program that ran
with AutoCAD Releases 11 and 12, required that a special AME command be used to create surfacelike faces on solids before the HIDE command had any effect on them. Such a
step is not necessary with AutoCAD's 3D solids. Whenever the HIDE command is invoked,
all 3D solids currently on the screen are automatically changed into a faceted format that
has opaque surfaces. (We will discuss the details of hidden-line removal on 3D solids in
Section Three.)

- Real-time zoom and pan is disabled when the hidden-line mode is in effect.

Related system variable:

- **hideprecision**

    This system variable determines whether hide calculations are performed in single or double precision arithmetic. When **hideprecision** is set to 0, its default setting, hidden-line calculations are performed in single precision, while double precision arithmetic is used when **hideprecision** is set to 1.

    Double precision arithmetic requires more memory, and it may slow performance (especially when hiding 3D solids). Although double precision calculation can result in more accurate hidden-line displays when objects are very close together, single precision calculations generally yield satisfactory results, and you will probably never need to change **hideprecision** from its default value of zero. This system variable was a late addition to Release 14 and is not mentioned in AutoCAD's on-screen help.

Creating Shaded Images

Surfaces shaded by the SHADEMODE command are colored in with their object color, and the relative brightness of each surface face depends on its orientation to the beam of a single light that is positioned over the left shoulder of the viewer and pointed toward the center of the viewport. Faces directly facing this incoming light are the brightest, and their relative brightness decreases as their angle to the light beam increases.

Wireframe

Hidden

Shaded

You will have two reasons for shading surfaces as you construct surface models. The first is that shading can help you verify that a newly added surface is properly located and correctly shaped. The HIDE command can also be used to do this, but only if there is something behind the surface to hide. Shading, on the other hand, leaves no doubt as to the precise shape and location of a surface. We used the SHADEMODE command several times for this purpose in Chapter Six as we added 3D faces to the 3D model house.

A second reason for using shaded images is that they often give you a clearer picture of your model's shape than hidden line views. This can be especially useful as you set viewpoints with the 3DORBIT command, which we will discuss later in this chapter.

The SHADEMODE command offers four different types of shading. While Gouraud shading, which is named for the person who developed the computer technique for smoothly shading surfaces, creates the most realistic images, you are often more interested in the basic shape of a model than in having a realistic image of it. Also, there is no practical difference between flat shading and Gouraud shading for models that have no rounded or curved surfaces.

154

In addition to its shading modes, SHADEMODE has a hidden-line viewing mode. SHADE-MODE's hidden-line views differ from those of the HIDE command in that they are not affected by screen regenerations, they can be used for real time zooms and pans, and circles are transparent.

SHADEMODE also has options for two wireframe viewing modes. One of these, the 2D wireframe viewing mode, is AutoCAD's default viewing mode. You will select this option to return to your usual way of viewing objects. The most obvious difference between SHADEMODE's other wireframe viewing mode (3D wireframe) and the 2D wireframe mode is that the UCS icon consists of three mutually perpendicular, cone-shaped arrows on cylindrical shafts. Not so obvious differences are that raster, OLE, and line weights are not displayed in the 3D wireframe mode. Also, noncontinuous line types—such as center lines and dashed lines—are displayed as continuous.

An aid for setting viewpoints, called the *compass,* can be displayed in all viewing modes, except the 2D wireframe mode. The compass consists of three circular arrays of short lines representing the three principal UCS planes that are located in the center of the current viewport. Also, the positive X, Y, and Z directions are labeled. Similar to the UCS icon, the compass is invisible to object selection and cannot be printed. The compass is displayed when the system variable **compass** is set to a value of 1, and it is not displayed when **compass** is set to 0.

Unlike the views of the SHADE command that it replaced, you can freely work in any of SHADEMODE's viewing modes, even in shaded views. Generally, though, you will prefer to work in wireframe views because object selection is easier.

Command: SHADEMODE

Purpose: SHADEMODE creates shaded images of solid and surface models, as well as special wireframe and hidden-line viewing modes.

Initiate with:

- On the command line enter SHADEMODE.
- From the View pull-down menu, select Shade, and then select an option.

Options:

- 2D wireframe

  This option restores the default AutoCAD 2D wireframe viewing mode. The UCS icon is displayed as wide 2D arrows pointing in the X and Y directions, and all surface objects are transparent. The compass icon cannot be displayed.

2D wireframe

3D wireframe

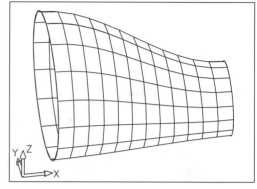

Hidden

- 3D wireframe

   Just as in the 2D wireframe viewing mode, all surface objects are transparent when this option is in effect. The UCS icon, though, appears as three mutually perpendicular cone-shaped arrows on round shafts. Raster and OLE objects are not displayed. Lineweights, also, are not displayed, and non-continuous linetypes are displayed as continuous. The compass is displayed when the system variable **compass** has a value of 1.

- Hidden

   Surface objects are opaque, with the exception of circles. Unlike the hidden line mode of the HIDE command, real time pan and zoom may be used, and a screen regeneration does not cause the wireframe viewing mode to be restored.

Flat shaded

Gouraud shaded

- Flat shaded

   Surfaces are shaded according to their object color and their orientation with the viewport's line of sight. Rounded and curved surfaces are divided into distinct three- and four-sided facets.

- Gouraud shaded

   Surfaces are shaded according to their object color and their orientation with the viewport's line of sight. Rounded and curved surfaces are not divided into facets, and therefore, have a smooth appearance. This is true even for polygon mesh surfaces that have facets in wireframe and hidden-line viewing modes.

- fLat + edges

  Surfaces are shaded, with rounded and curved surfaces being divided into facets as in Flat shading. In addition, the edges of all visible faces are shown in their object color.

- gOuraud + edges

  Surfaces are shaded without dividing rounded and curved surfaces into facets. Edges are shown in their object color, and the edges of facets on surfaces having a mesh will be displayed in their object color, even though the surface is smooth and rounded.

Notes:

Flat shaded plus edges

Gouraud shaded plus edges

- SHADEMODE replaces the SHADE command. Although the SHADE command is no longer documented, you can still invoke it from the command line. The resulting viewing mode will be one of the SHADEMODE viewing modes, as determined by the setting of the **shadedge** system variable.

- You can also initiate SHADEMODE and set its options through the right-click shortcut menus of PAN, ZOOM, and 3DORBIT.

Related system variables:

- **shadedge**

  This system variable controls the shading mode used by the SHADE command. It can be set to an integer value of 0, 1, 2, or 3, with the following results:

- **shadedif**

  This system variable controlled the contrast between the brightest and dimmest shaded faces for the SHADE command. It no longer has any effect.

Value	Viewing Mode
0	Gouraud shading
1	Gouraud shading plus edges
2	Hidden
3	Flat shading plus edges

- **compass**

  When this system variable is set to 1, a visual aid named the compass that depicts the principal planes of the UCS will be displayed in all SHADEMODE viewing modes, except 2D wireframe. When **compass** is set to 0, the compass will not be displayed.

Using the DVIEW Command

DVIEW, which stands for Dynamic VIEW, is a multipurpose viewing command that gives you a preview before you actually commit to its view parameters. For instance, when you set a view direction with DVIEW, you can rotate the line of sight in real time to see what your model looks like from various view angles until you find one that suits you. Its zooms and pans are also real time operations.

DVIEW has twelve different command line options, and many of those options have suboptions, which makes DVIEW one of AutoCAD's more complicated and involved commands. It is a powerful command that can create unique views, but it can also be a confusing and intimidating command. With DVIEW, you can

- Set viewpoints in 3D space. While the DVIEW options for doing this produce the same results as the VPOINT command, they work in different ways.

- Set perspective views. Perspective views simulate those of the human eye and of photographs, in which objects appear to become smaller as their distance from the viewer, or camera, increases.

AutoCAD's perspective view mode

AutoCAD's parallel projection view mode

- Remove objects that obstruct or confuse your view of a model. If walls or ceilings prevent you from seeing inside a room, for instance, DVIEW can, in effect, slice through the walls and ceilings. It does this with a clipping plane that makes everything in front of the plane disappear. You can also install a clipping plane that removes everything behind the plane.

Room interior is obscured by walls.

Clipping planes allow you to see inside the room.

Although AutoCAD 2000 has a set of commands, such as 3DORBIT, 3DCLIP and 3DDISTANCE, that can do everything that DVIEW can do, you may still prefer to use DVIEW for setting clipping planes, and sometimes for establishing perspective views. DVIEW's twist option is also useful for straightening views that have become tilted when view directions have been set in real time. The new commands for establishing views commands will be discussed later in this chapter.

Since DVIEW uses previews in helping to set viewing parameters, it starts by prompting you to select the objects that are to be shown in the previews. All other objects then disappear from the screen for the duration of the command. When you exit DVIEW, all objects are restored and reflect the new view parameters.

Your choice of preview objects is important. Too many objects can make the previews slow and confusing. On the other hand, you will not obtain a representative preview if you do not have enough objects, or you do not select the proper objects. If you do not select any objects at all, AutoCAD automatically creates a simple 3D surface model house for the previews. It is not a good choice for previews, however, since few of the parameters you establish with it will be suitable for your model.

The DVIEW command often uses the words *target* and *camera* in its options. Target, as you would surmise, refers to the point in space in which the view direction, or line of sight, is pointing; camera refers to the point on the opposite end of the line of sight. For the DVIEW options that establish general view directions (the Camera, Target, and Point Selection options), these two points indicate only a viewing direction. Their actual location in space is not important, but the direction defined by a line drawn between them is important. However, for the DVIEW options related to perspective views (the Points and Distance options) and clipping planes (the Points and Clip options), the point locations of the target and camera are very important.

Command: DVIEW

Purpose: DVIEW is a general-purpose viewing command. Within the current viewport, it can set 3D view directions, eliminate portions of 3D models from the view that are in front of or in back of clipping planes, create perspective views, and rotate the view about the view direction.

Initiate with:

- On the command line enter DVIEW.

Options:

DVIEW starts with a prompt for you to select the objects that are to be viewed dynamically:

`Select objects or <use DVIEWBLOCK>:` *Select objects or press the Enter key.*

Objects that are not included in the selection set will disappear from the screen during the DVIEW command. Objects that are included will be viewed in real time during the various options of DVIEW. Upon exiting DVIEW, all objects within the viewing area will be restored with the selected DVIEW options in effect.

AutoCAD often uses the terms *camera* and *target* in DVIEW's options. Initially, the target is positioned approximately in the center of the viewport, and the camera is located somewhere along the line of sight.

If you press the Enter key when prompted to select objects, AutoCAD will display a 3D surface model house that you can view dynamically as you set various DVIEW options instead of objects from your own model.

After you specify the objects to be shown in the previews or press the Enter key to display the preview house, AutoCAD will switch to the WCS (provided the system variable **worldview** is set to its default value of 1) and display the following menu of DVIEW options on the command line:

The DVIEW preview house

CAmera/TArget/Distance/POints/PAn/Zoom/TWist/CLip/Hide/Off/Undo *(Select an
    option, press Enter, or pick a point.)*

When you select an option, this menu will be redisplayed when you have finished the
option. Cancelling a partially completed option also returns control to this menu. Press the
Enter key to end the command. The current viewport will be redrawn to reflect the
parameters established through DVIEW.

• Point Selection

This option rotates the preview objects about the selected point. It takes effect when you pick
a point with your pointing device in response to the main DVIEW menu. You cannot enter
point coordinates on the command line, and you cannot use an object snap in specifying the
point. The option displays the prompt

Enter direction and magnitude angles: *(Enter two angles, between 0 and 360
    degrees, separated by a comma, or specify a point with your pointing device.)*

The direction angle represents a rotation angle about an axis that is through the picked
point and parallel with the horizontal sides of the viewport. The magnitude angle is a rotation angle about an axis that is through the picked point and parallel with the vertical sides
of the viewport.

AutoCAD will anchor a rubberband line on the picked point and will dynamically rotate
the preview objects about the point as you move your pointing device. Horizontal
movement of your pointing device rotates the view about a vertical axis, while vertical
movement rotates the view about a horizontal axis.

• CAmera

This option sets a view direction based on a horizontal angle in the X-Y plane from the
WCS X axis and a vertical angle from the X-Y plane. It is basically the same as VPOINT's
rotate option, even though its prompts and input sequence are entirely different. Despite
its name, the CAmera option does not set an exact camera location.

CAmera option of DVIEW

Resulting view

You can specify the view direction rotation angles by entering them on the command line or by picking a point as the preview objects appear to rotate on the screen. When you move your pointing device sideways, the screen cursor will move horizontally and the preview objects will rotate in the X-Y plane. When you move the cursor vertically, the preview objects will rotate from the X-Y plane.

- ### TArget

  Like the Camera option, the Target option sets a viewing direction through the input of two angles. The angle directions, however, are from the camera to the target, rather than from the target to the camera. Despite its name, this option does not set the target location. You can specify the view direction by entering the angles on the command line or by picking a point as the preview objects appear to rotate on the screen. The preview objects will be a mirror image of those shown in the Camera option.

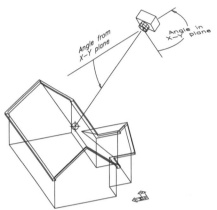

TArget option of DVIEW

- ### Distance

  This option performs two functions: it sets the camera's distance from the target, and it changes the viewing mode from a parallel projection to a perspective view. The viewer's eye point for the perspective view will be at the camera point. This option displays the command line prompt:

  ```
  Specify new camera-target distance <current>:
      (Enter a distance or press Enter.)
  ```

  The camera will be located on the current line of sight (the viewing direction). A slider bar will be positioned at the top of the screen and can be used to specify a distance. This slider bar will be graduated from 0x to 16x, with 1x representing the current distance.

Distance option of DVIEW

Parallel projection view

Perspective view

- **POints**

  The target and camera points are set through this option. It first issues a command line prompt for the target location:

  ```
  Specify target point <current>: (Specify a point or press Enter.)
  ```

  AutoCAD will anchor a rubberband line on the new target point and prompt for a camera point:

  ```
  Specify camera point <current>: (Specify a point or press Enter.)
  ```

  If the perspective mode is active, Auto-CAD will temporarily turn it off as you specify the target and camera points. Any method may be used to specify the points. In the figure on the right, the absolute coordinates shown were used for the target's point, and relative polar coordinates were used to establish the camera's point. The parallel projection and perspective views shown in the figure on the bottom of the previous page are based on the target and camera points shown in this figure.

Setting a target and camera point

- **PAn**

  This option shifts the view image without changing the viewing direction or zoom level. It performs a real-time pan, based on the command line prompts:

  ```
  Specify displacement base point: (Specify a point.)
  Specify second point: (Specify a point.)
  ```

- **Zoom**

  DVIEW's Zoom option performs a real-time zoom. A slider bar, graduated from 0x to 16x, is displayed near the top of the viewport and can be used to set the zoom level. Pressing your pointing device's pick button will select the indicated zoom level. The current zoom level is 1x. A command line prompt is also shown. For parallel projection views, the command line prompt will be

  ```
  Specify zoom scale factor <1>:
     (Enter a value or press Enter.)
  ```

  Values less than 1 zoom back, while values greater than 1 zoom in. You do not have to include an *x* with the value, as you do with AutoCAD's standard ZOOM command.

162

If the perspective mode is active, the command line prompt will be

`Specify lens length <current>:` *(Enter a value or press Enter.)*

AutoCAD expresses lens length in millimeters. 50mm gives a view similar to that of a normal lens on a 35mm camera. Entering a value less than 50mm zooms in, acting like a wide-angle camera lens, while values greater than 50mm zooms back, similar to the telephoto lens of a camera.

- **TWist**

This option rotates the view about the line of sight. It issues the prompt

`Specify view twist angle <current>:` *(Enter a value, specify a rotation angle, or press Enter.)*

AutoCAD will anchor a rubber-band line at the center of the viewport, and the view will rotate about the viewport center as you move your pointing device. Picking a point will fix the view as it is shown. You can also enter an angle value, ranging from 0 to 360 degrees. This value is not a relative angle from the current one. A twist

Before DVIEW's TWist option

View with a DVIEW's TWist angle of 0

angle of 0 will cause the vertical lines on the model to be vertical in the view, and a 90-degree twist angle will cause the vertical lines on the model to be horizontal.

- **CLip**

This option enables you to locate planes, called *clipping planes*, that will hide sections of your model. These planes are invisible, have an infinite size, and are always perpendicular to the line of sight. There are two types of clipping planes—*front* clipping planes, which hide everything from the plane toward the camera, and *back* clipping planes, which hide everything from the plane away from the camera.

The option uses the following command line prompt:

`Enter clipping option [Back/Front/Off] <Off>:` *(Enter an option or press Enter)*

- **Off**

This option turns off all clipping planes. (When the perspective viewing mode is being used, AutoCAD automatically places a front clipping plane at the camera. This option has no effect on that clipping plane.)

- **Back**

This option establishes and controls back clipping planes. AutoCAD will display a non-graduated slider bar at the top of the viewport that can be used to set the clipping plane location. As you move the slider, the appearance of the DVIEW preview objects will reflect the effect of the clipping plane. Pressing the pick button on your pointing device will fix the location of the clipping plane. The option also displays the command line prompt:

Specify distance from target or [ON/OFF] < <current>: *(Enter an option, enter a distance, or press Enter)*

The OFF option turns off the back clipping plane, but it remains in place. The ON option turns the back clipping plane on again, at the current location. Entering a distance specifies the location of the back clipping plane along the line of sight, from the target. Positive values locate the plane toward the camera, while negative numbers locate it away from the camera (behind the target).

A back chipping plane between the target and the camera

Resulting view

- ○ Front

This option manages front clipping planes. A slider bar, with no graduations, will be displayed at the top of the viewport. As you move your pointing device sideways, the slider will move and the display of the DVIEW preview objects will indicate the location of the front clipping plane. Pressing your pointing device's pick button will fix the clipping plane position. The option also displays the following command line prompt:

Specify distance from target or [set to Eye(camera)/ON/OFF] <current>: *(Enter an option, enter a distance, or press Enter)*

The Eye option places the front clipping plane at the camera point. OFF turns off the front clipping plane, and ON turns a previously turned off clipping plane on again. You cannot turn the front clipping plane off if the perspective view mode is active. Positive distance values will place the front clipping plane toward the camera, and negative values place it behind the target (from the camera).

A front chipping plane between the target and the camera

Resulting view

- ● Hide

This DVIEW option suppresses the view of objects behind opaque objects. Upon exiting the DVIEW command, or the implementation of another DVIEW option, hidden objects will be restored.

- ● Off

The perspective view mode is turned off, and parallel projection is restored, by this option.

- Undo

  This option cancels the results of the last DVIEW option. You can repeatedly use Undo to step back through all of the DVIEW operations to the start of the command.

Notes:

- The 3D surface model house that DVIEW displays when you press the Enter key in response to the Select objects prompt is an internal block named DVIEWBLOCK. You can create your own DVIEWBLOCK block. If you do, it should fit in a 1-by-1-by-1-unit cube, and its insert point should be in its lower-left corner.

- Your selection set of preview objects is important. If you select too many objects, the dynamic previews of the DVIEW options and settings will be slow and may be confusing. On the other hand, if you do not select enough objects, or if you do not select representative objects, the previews may not display the information you need.

- Most of the time you will use DVIEW to set up perspective views and clipping planes, rather than to establish view directions. In the process of setting perspective views and clipping planes, though, you may need to set a view direction within DVIEW. Then, you will probably use the Camera option when you want to set specific viewpoint rotation angles, and the Point Selection option for dynamically setting a viewpoint. When you use the Point Selection option, you should pick a point near the geometric center of your preview objects to minimize skewing.

- The view direction angles in the Camera and Target options are from opposite directions. Thus, the Camera view direction angles of 30 degrees from the X-Y plane and -55 degrees in the X-Y plane from the X axis result in the same view direction as the Target angles of -30 degrees from the X-Y plane and 125 degrees in the X-Y plane. You are not likely to find the Target option helpful.

- DVIEW's Twist option is useful for straightening out views that became skewed during the Camera, Target, or Point Selection options. It is also useful for setting up auxiliary views in paper space floating viewports. See Section Four for a description of paper space floating viewports.

- The start and stop points for rendering fog are based on the distance from the camera to the back clipping plane. See Chapter Twenty for a discussion of rendering fog.

Related system variables:

- **backz**

  This read-only system variable stores the distance of the back clipping plane from the target. This distance is along the line of sight.

- **frontz**

  The distance from the front clipping plane to the target is stored in this read-only system variable. The distance is along the line of sight.

- **lenslength**

  The current zoom level for perspective views is stored in this read-only system variable. The units are in millimeters, with the effects similar to those of a camera lens.

- **target**

  This read-only system variable holds the 3D point location of the target.

- **viewdir**

  The view direction of the current viewport is stored in this read-only system variable. It is a 3D point location that represents an offset from the target point.

- **viewmode**

  The integer number in this read-only variable is the sum of the following bit values:

Bit Value	Condition
1	Perspective viewing mode is on.
2	Front clipping plane is on.
4	Back clipping plane is on.
8	UCS follow mode is on (**ucsfollow** is set to 1).
16	The front clipping plane is not at the camera (eye).

- **viewtwist**

  This read-only system variable stores the twist angle within the current viewport.

- **worldview**

  When **worldview** is set to its default value of 1, the DVIEW command will temporarily restore the WCS, and all view directions will be based on WCS coordinates and directions. When **worldview** is set to 0, view directions will be set according to the current UCS.

Using the 3D Orbit Commands

AutoCAD 2000 introduced a set of seven commands for dynamically establishing views in 3D space. They are 3DORBIT, 3DCORBIT, 3DSWIVEL, 3DDISTANCE, 3DCLIP, 3DPAN, and 3DZOOM. You can initiate any of them through the 3D Orbit toolbar, as well as by entering their name on the command line. Even though they are separate commands, you will often use them as if they were options of a single command, and since they are linked to 3DORBIT, they are often referred to as the 3D Orbit commands.

The 3D Orbit commands work in conjunction with the SHADEMODE viewing options. When any of SHADEMODE's shaded options or its hidden option is in effect, that viewing mode is retained during the 3D Orbit operations; if the 2D wireframe mode is in effect, the viewing mode will automatically switch to SHADEMODE's 3D wireframe mode.

Parameters for the 3D Orbit commands are set dynamically in real time, even for shaded viewing modes. Complex models, however, will often degrade to a bounding box image. How complex a model must be before its image degrades depends largely on the power of your computer system. If objects have been selected prior to initiating a 3D orbit operation, only the selected objects will be displayed, which may improve dynamic viewing.

Once any 3D Orbit command has been started, you can press the return button of your pointing device to display shortcut menus that allow you to invoke another view-related command or operation. With the options in these menus, you can do anything that the DVIEW command can do, except twist the view. Moreover, they are generally easier to work with than DVIEW.

The options in the 3D Orbit shortcut menu are described in the following paragraphs.

Exit	Returns to the AutoCAD editing mode.
Pan	Initiates 3DPAN.
Zoom	Initiates 3DZOOM.
Orbit	Initiates 3DORBIT.
More	Opens a menu for initiating 3DDISTANCE, 3DSWIVEL, 3DCORBIT, Zoom Window, and Zoom Extents. The menu also initiates specific options of 3DCLIP.
Projection	Opens a menu for toggling between the parallel and perspective viewing modes. A check mark indicates which mode is current.
Shading Modes	Opens a menu for setting all of the SHADEMODE viewing modes, except 2D wireframe.
Visual Aids	Opens a menu for turning AutoCAD's compass, grid, and UCS icon on and off. The grid is displayed as a grid of lines, rather than dots.
Reset View	Restores the view that was current when the 3D Orbit operation started.
Preset Views	Opens a menu for setting one of the six orthographic views or one of the four isometric views that look down on the XY plane. The views are based on the WCS, and they do not affect the current UCS.
Saved Views	This option, which is available only if one or more user-saved views exist, opens a secondary menu that lists all user-saved views. Click a view name to restore the view.

We will also include the CAMERA command in this discussion of the 3D Orbit commands, even though it does not appear on the 3D Orbit toolbar or in the 3D Orbit shortcut menus. Nevertheless, the CAMERA command is an important part of the 3D Orbit commands because it sets exact camera and target points—both of which are critical in setting perspective views and in positioning clipping planes.

Command: 3DORBIT

Purpose: Dynamically sets viewpoints in 3D space.

Initiate with:

- On the command line enter 3DORBIT.
- From the View pull-down menu, select 3D Orbit.
- Select Orbit from the 3D Orbit shortcut menu.
- Select 3D Orbit from the 3D Orbit toolbar or the Standard toolbar.

Implementation:

When 3DORBIT starts, AutoCAD will display a large circle in the center of the current viewport. This circle is called the *arcball*, and small circles are centered on its quadrants. The compass, if it is displayed, will coincide with the arcball.

You set view directions in 3DORBIT by moving the screen cursor with your pointing device as you hold down its pick button. Your model will appear to revolve as you move the screen cursor, and when you have a view direction you like, you release the pick button to set the view direction. To exit the command, select Exit from the 3D Orbit shortcut menu, or press the Enter or Esc keys.

The orientation of the axis about which your model appears to rotate depends on where the screen cursor is located when you press the pick button. Also, the form of the screen cursor changes to indicate the rotation axis orientation. The screen cursor forms and orientations of the axis of rotation are described in the following paragraphs.

- When the cursor is within the arcball, its form is that of a sphere encircled by a horizontal and a vertical circle. The viewpoint rotation angle axis is 90 degrees to the direction that the cursor is moved. For example, if you move the cursor down and to the right 45 degrees, the image will rotate about an axis that passes through the center of the viewport and is tilted 45 degrees from the edges of the viewport.

- When the cursor is outside the arcball, the screen cursor will become a dot within a circular arrow, and the 3D model will rotate about the viewport's line of sight.

- When the cursor is within either of the small circles at the top and bottom of the arcball, it assumes the form of a horizontal line that serves as an axis for a circular arrow. The view rotation axis will pass through the center of the viewport and be parallel with its horizontal sides.

168

- When the cursor is within either of the small circles on the right and left quadrants of the arcball, it takes on the shape of a vertical line that serves as the axis of a circular arrow. The view then rotates about an axis that passes through the center of the viewport and is parallel with its vertical sides.

Command: 3DCORBIT

Purpose: Continually rotates the viewpoint in 3D space.

Initiate with:

- On the command line enter 3DCORBIT
- From the 3D Orbit shortcut menu, select more, and then select Continuous Orbit
- From the 3D Orbit toolbar, select 3D Continuous Orbit

Implementation:

The arcball will disappear and the screen cursor will change to a sphere encircled by two arc-shaped arrows having axes that are 45 degrees to the edges of the viewport. Click the pick button of your pointing device, drag the cursor, and release the pick button. The model will rotate about an axis that passes through the center of the viewport and is perpendicular to the direction that the cursor was moved. Moreover, the rate of rotation is proportional to the speed of the cursor movement. To stop the rotation, click the pointing device pick button again. Press Enter or Esc to end the command.

Command: 3DSWIVEL

Purpose: Sets a viewpoint by swiveling the camera about a fixed point.

Initiate with:

- On the command line enter 3DSWIVEL.
- From the 3D Orbit shortcut menu, select more, and then select Swivel Camera.
- From the 3D Orbit toolbar, select 3D Swivel.

Implementation:

Unlike 3DORBIT, which sets a view direction by moving the camera about in 3D space as it is pointed toward a fixed target, 3DSWIVEL sets a view direction by locking the camera in a fixed location and swiveling it toward a movable target. The effect is as if you were looking through the viewfinder of a camera that is on a tripod; when you swivel the camera to the right, objects in the viewfinder shift to the left, and when you swivel the camera upward, objects appear to shift downward. Similarly, when you move the screen cursor to the left, objects on the screen move to the right; when you move the screen cursor up, the screen objects move down. Press Enter or Esc to end the command.

Command: 3DZOOM

Purpose: Dynamically increases or decreases the apparent size of objects in the current viewport.

Initiate with:

- On the command line enter 3DZOOM.
- From the 3D Orbit shortcut menu, select Zoom.
- From the 3D Orbit toolbar, select 3D Zoom.

Implementation:

This command is similar to the real time option of the ZOOM command. The screen cursor changes to a magnifying glass with + and - signs. Press the pick button of your pointing device and drag the screen cursor up to magnify objects, and drag it down to make them smaller. Release the pick button to set the view, and press Enter or Esc to end the command.

The most important difference between real time ZOOM and 3DZOOM is that 3DZOOM works in perspective views, while real time ZOOM, along with the other ZOOM options, does not. 3DZOOM differs from 3DDISTANCE in that it does not change the distance from the camera to the target.

Command: 3DPAN

Purpose: Dynamically moves objects in the current viewport without changing their apparent size.

Initiate with:

- On the command line enter 3DPAN.
- From the 3D Orbit shortcut menu, select Pan.
- From the 3D Orbit toolbar, select 3D Pan.

Implementation:

Similar to the real time version of PAN, the screen cursor will assume the shape of a hand. Press the pick button of your pointing device and drag the screen cursor in the direction that you want the objects in the current viewport to move. Release the pick button to set the view, and press Enter or Esc to end the command.

The most important difference between real time PAN and 3DPAN is that 3DPAN works in perspective views, while real time PAN does not. In perspective views, the line of sight may appear to rotate as the view is panned.

Command: CAMERA

Purpose: Sets exact camera and target points.

Initiate with:

- On the command line enter CAMERA.

- From the View toolbar, select Camera.

Implementation:

This command is equivalent to the Points option of the DVIEW command. You will be prompted from the command line to first specify a camera point, and then to specify a target point.

Command: 3DDISTANCE

Purpose: Dynamically moves the camera along the line of sight toward or away from the target.

Initiate with:

- On the command line enter 3DDISTANCE.

- From the 3D Orbit shortcut menu, select More, and then select Adjust Distance.

- From the 3D Orbit toolbar, select 3D Adjust distance.

Implementation:

Although 3DDISTANCE dynamically changes the apparent size of the model in a manner that seems to be equivalent to 3DZOOM, it makes the size changes by moving the camera, rather than by using a zoom camera–like lens. When you drag the screen cursor up, the camera moves along the line of sight closer to the target; when you drag the cursor down, the camera moves away from the target. Release the pick button to set the distance, and press Enter or Esc to end the command.

The distance between the camera and the target is important in

The camera is too close to the target.   The camera-to-target distance is about right.   The camera is too far from the target.

perspective views. If the camera is too close to the target, the model will be overly distorted; and, if it is too far from the target, the perspective mode will not be evident.

Command: 3DCLIP

Purpose: 3DCLIP turns front and back clipping planes on and off, and moves their location along the line of sight.

Initiate with:

- On the command line enter 3DCLIP.

- From the 3D Orbit shortcut menu, select More, and then select Adjust Clipping Planes.

- From the 3D Orbit toolbar, select Adjust Clipping Planes.

Options:

Clipping planes are two invisible, infinitely sized planes that are perpendicular to a viewport's line of sight. One of these planes is called the front clipping plane, and when it is activated everything from it to the camera is hidden. The other is called the back clipping plane, and it is able to hide everything that is from the plane away from the camera. You can independently move these planes along the line of sight, and you can individually turn them on and off.

3DCLIP opens a small, square window titled Adjust Clipping Planes over the AutoCAD window. In this window, your 3D model will be shown from a view direction that is perpendicular to the view direction of the current AutoCAD viewport. Also in the window are two horizontal lines that represent the edges of the clipping planes. The target is in the center of the viewport. Near the top of the window is a toolbar for selecting the options of 3DCLIP. You can also right-click anywhere within the window to bring up a shortcut menu that has these same 3DCLIP options.

- Adjust Front Clipping

Use this option to move the front clipping plane. Press the pick button of your pointing device, and move the screen cursor vertically up or down to drag the front clipping along the line of sight. As you drag the clipping plane, the effect of the clipping plane location is dynamically shown in the current AutoCAD viewport.

- Adjust Back Clipping

You move the back clipping plane with this option. Press the pick button of your pointing device, and drag the back clipping plane along the line of sight by moving the screen cursor up or down. The effect of the clipping plane location is dynamically shown in the current AutoCAD viewport as you drag the back clipping plane.

172

- Create Slice

  This option locks the current positions of the front and back clipping planes relative to each other, and allows you to drag them in tandem along the line of sight.

- Front Clipping On/Off

  This option activates or deactivates the front clipping plane.

- Back Clipping On/Off

  Use this option to activate or deactivate the back clipping plane.

Notes:

- The front and back clipping planes can be in the same location, but the front clipping plane cannot be further away from the camera than the back clipping plane.

- When any of the tool bar buttons are active, its outline is drawn to give the button the appearance of being depressed. Moreover, the shortcut menu will have a check mark beside each active option.

- You can also turn the clipping planes on or off through options on the 3D orbit toolbar and in the More shortcut menu.

- When you start the 3DCLIP command, the front clipping plane is automatically turned on. Depending on the location of the front clipping plane, this can cause portions, or even all, of your model to disappear.

Setting Up Perspective Views

Often, especially with models of structures and rooms, you will set up a perspective view as preparation for a rendering. AutoCAD perspective views are strictly for viewing because you cannot use your pointing device in them. If your model needs some editing or additions, you must do it in a viewport that shows the model in a parallel projection viewing mode. Also, you cannot use AutoCAD's ZOOM and PAN commands in viewports with perspective views—you must use DVIEW's versions of those operations or 3DZOOM and 3DPAN to adjust the view. And, you should not use VPOINT or PLAN for changing the view direction since these commands change the mode back to the parallel projection mode.

If they are not set up correctly, perspective views can be grossly distorted.

Creating a perspective view is not an especially complicated operation, but it does require some forethought, and you should expect to make changes and adjustments before you achieve the results you want. The parameters involved in setting up a perspective view are (1) the view direction, (2) the distance from the target to the camera, and (3) the zoom level. The distance between the target and the camera is especially important. If it is too long, the perspective view will look like a parallel projection view, and if it is too close, the view will be grossly distorted.

In AutoCAD 2000, you can create perspective views with either DVIEW or the 3D Orbit options. When you use DVIEW, the steps you will most likely use in setting up a perspective view are as follows:

- Establish the view direction. You can do this before you start DVIEW through the VPOINT or 3DORBIT commands, or within DVIEW with its Camera, Target, or Point Selection options.

- Use DVIEW's Distance option to establish the initial zoom level and turn on the perspective viewing mode. You may possibly, or even probably, change the distance value after you see what your perspective view looks like, but a distance that is roughly equal to twice the width of the model section or side that will be shown is a good distance for the first try.

- Use DVIEW's Zoom and Pan options to adjust the view, and use its Hide option for a clearer look at the model. If the model is severely distorted, go back to the Distance option and increase the distance between the target and the camera. If the model looks too much like it does in a parallel projection view, decrease the distance.

Differences in personal preferences means that there are no right or wrong target-to-camera distances or zoom levels. Many people tend to favor a distance that gives a perspective zoom level of about 50mm (you will recall that AutoCAD uses the analogy of camera lens focal lengths, in units of millimeters, when referring to zoom levels for perspective views), but many people prefer a smaller one—perhaps even 35mm.

Setting up perspective views with the 3D Orbit commands and options is generally easier than with DVIEW. The steps in using them to create a perspective view are

- Establish a view direction with 3DORBIT.

- Use the Zoom and Pan options from 3DORBIT's shortcut menu to adjust the size and position of the model's image.

- Open 3DORBIT's Projection shortcut menu and select Perspective. AutoCAD automatically sets an appropriate camera-to-target distance.

If you would like to increase or decrease the angle at which parallel edges on the model appear to converge, use the 3DDISTANCE command to move the camera toward or away from the target. Use 3DPAN and 3DZOOM to adjust the size and position of the model in the perspective view.

Controlling DVIEW's Clipping Planes

Clipping planes are invisible walls of infinite size that are perpendicular to the view direction. There are two of them. The front clipping plane hides everything between the clipping plane and the camera. The back clipping plane hides everything from the clipping plane away from the camera. You will find them to be especially useful when you are working with building interiors.

You have full control over both clipping planes. They can be turned on and off independently so that they can be used singly or together. You can also move each of them independently. It would sometimes be convenient to be able to tilt the clipping planes, but you cannot do that. They are always perpendicular to the line of sight (the view direction). The parameters to consider when setting up a clipping plane are (1) the target location, (2) the view direction, (3) whether the plane is a front or back clipping plane, and (4) the plane's distance from the target.

Once a clipping plane has been turned on, it remains in effect even if the view direction changes. Clipping planes can be used in perspective views. In fact, AutoCAD automatically positions a front clipping plane at the camera when the perspective mode is active. This is to

174

prevent objects behind the camera from showing up when extremely close zooms are in effect.

Just as in setting up perspective views, setting up clipping planes requires some planning along with a knowledge of the dimensions and locations of key points on your model. The steps to set up a clipping plane are as follows:

- Establish the target point with DVIEW's Points option or with the CAMERA command.

- Establish the view direction. Within DVIEW this can be conveniently done at the same time you set the target location within the Points option, by using relative coordinates in setting the camera point. Otherwise, use 3DORBIT to set the view direction. This will cause the camera to move, but the target will remain where it was placed by the CAMERA command.

- Use 3DCLIP or DVIEW's Clip option to select the type of clipping plane (front or back) and set its distance from the target. If, when you use 3DCLIP, the entire model is not within the Adjust Clippping Plane window, temporarily return to the 3DORBIT mode and zoom away from the model. This will increase the area covered by the Adjust Clipping Planes window.

Exercises

We will use two exercises to give you some experience in setting up perspective views and clipping planes. The first exercise will set up a perspective view of the 3D surface model house we have been working with. The second exercise will use a 3D surface model kitchen in setting up a cutting plane and a perspective view. Neither of these exercises requires you to draw anything.

Exercise One

In this exercise you will create a perspective view of the 3D house we started as a wireframe model in Chapter Four. While we added 3D face surfaces to the walls and roof of the house in Chapter Six, it still contained holes where the doors and windows were to be installed. A more complete version of the model is in file mfe07101.dwg on the CD-ROM, and you should retrieve and use that model for this perspective view exercise.

This version of the house has doors and windows. No object types or techniques that you are not familiar with were used in making the doors and windows. They are made primarily from 3D faces, although a few polyface meshes and extrusions were also used.

We will first describe how to use DVIEW in setting the perspective view. Once you have opened the file, start the DVIEW command. For preview objects, you can select just the roof, and the siding, but selecting everything will not cause any problems, since most of our previews will be for zooms and pans.

Our surface model house, with doors and windows

We will first set the view direction. From the main DVIEW menu, choose the Camera option by entering the letters *ca* or the entire word *camera*. AutoCAD will first prompt for an angle from the X-Y plane and then for one in the X-Y plane (the reverse of the sequence used by the VPOINT command).

```
Specify camera angle location, or enter angle from XY plane [Toggle (angle in)]
   <35.2655>:  0 (Enter)
Specify camera angle location, or enter angle in XY plane from X axis, or [Toggle
   (angle from)] <-45.0000>: -115 (Enter)
```

In VPOINT, you would most likely enter the angle in the X-Y plane as 245 degrees, but DVIEW does not permit horizontal angles greater than 180 degrees, so you must enter a negative number.

The view will change to one looking edge-on to the X-Y plane showing the front-left side of the house. The main DVIEW menu will be displayed again. This time select the Distance option by entering the letter *d* or the entire word *distance*. DVIEW will prompt for a new target to camera distance:

```
Specify new camera-target distance
   <0'-1 3/4">: 960 (Enter)
```

View of house after using DVIEW's camera option
to set the view direction to 0 degrees from the X-Y plane,
and -115 degrees in the X-Y plane from the X axis.

If you are using architectural units, you can enter 960 as 80' (do not overlook the apostrophe). Before you enter this value, you may want to observe the screen as you move the slider bar back and forth. However, your target-to-camera distance is probably so close that no meaningful image is displayed. Therefore, our command line numerical input is the best way to set the distance.

The image of the house will most likely recede into the distance. To bring it in closer, choose DVIEW's Zoom option. A slider bar will appear at the top of the screen, and as you move the slider to the right, the house will become larger. The zoom level, in millimeters, is updated on the status line as you move the slider bar. Also, the the zoom level currently in effect will be displayed in a command line prompt, and you can enter a new lens length value.

```
Specify lens length <11.888>: 50 (Enter) (Or, move the slider until the house looks
   right to you.)
```

Lastly, use DVIEW's Pan option to center the house, and use Hide to make sure the house looks as you want it to look. When you are satisfied, exit the DVIEW command. Your house should look similar to the one shown on the next page when HIDE is on.

Now use the following steps to use the 3D Orbit commands and options to set a perspective view.

- Invoke VPOINT, and enter the view coordinates of 1,-1,1. In addition to establishing a SE isometric viewpoint, this turns off the perspective mode.

- Invoke 3DORBIT. Starting from the small circle on the bottom quadrant of the arcball, rotate the view direction to about 0 degrees from the X-Y plane. Then, start from the small circle on the left quadrant of the arcball, and rotate the view direction to about minus 45 degrees from the X axis. Rotating the view direction in this manner will minimize twist.

- From 3DORBIT's shortcut menu, turn on the perspective projection mode.

- Use the Pan, Zoom, and Adjust Distance options from the shortcut menus until you are satisfied with

Perspective view of the house, with a DVIEW zoom level of 50mm

the view. You will probably have to alternate several times between the Zoom and Adjust Distance options before you get the view you want.

Exercise Two

In this exercise, you will set up a perspective view of a 3D surface model kitchen. Since the kitchen has walls, you will also need to set up a front clipping plane so you can see inside the kitchen. This model is on the CD-ROM that accompanies this book in a file named mfe07201.dwg. Architectural feet and inch units are in effect for this model.

The inside dimensions for this kitchen are 24 feet long (in the X direction), 16 feet wide (in the Y direction), and 9 feet high (in the Z direction). The walls are 6 inches thick. The WCS origin is on the inside lower-left corner of the kitchen. The left half of the kitchen, which is for dining, is not furnished in this model.

Our plan is to make a perspective view of the right half—the cooking half—of the kitchen. We will position the target slightly outside the room, behind the sink and the window, at a height of 6 feet. Its coordinates will be 18′,18′,6′. The view direction will be rotated 15 degrees from the Y axis (equivalent to the view rotation angle of 105 degrees clockwise from the X axis), and we will place a front clipping plane 15 feet in front of the target. These locations are shown in the figure on the next page. The section of the room that we want to show is roughly 16 feet wide, so we will place the camera 32 feet from the target. (In the figure, the target-to-camera distance is not to scale.) It will be outside the room, but the front clipping plane will allow us to see the kitchen interior.

Surface model kitchen

We will first use DVIEW to set up the front clipping plane. Open the file, invoke the DVIEW command, and select most of the objects on the right side of the room for preview objects. For our purposes, you can even select everything in the model. Then, choose DVIEW's Points option by entering the letters *po*, or the entire word *points*. AutoCAD will issue prompts for the target point and the camera point.

Points →

```
Specify target point <10'-0.0000", 8'-4.0000", 2'-11.0000">: 18',18',6' (Enter)
Specify camera point <9'-11.4375", 8'-3.3725", 2'-11.5736">: @32'<-105 (Enter)
```

Be certain to include the apostrophes, which signify that the input is in units of feet, when entering the coordinates. Notice that we used relative polar coordinates to specify the camera location. AutoCAD will keep the elevation of the resulting view direction at 6 feet. As soon as you enter the camera's location, AutoCAD will switch to an edge-on view of the X-Y plane. Choose DVIEW's Clip option next by entering the letters *cl,* or the entire word *clip*, on the command line. AutoCAD will ask you what type of clipping plane you want and for its distance from the target.

```
Enter Clipping Option [Back/Front/Off] <Off>: F (Enter)
Specify distance from target or [set to [Eye (camera)/ON/OFF] <31'-11.9996">: 15'
(Enter)
```

You can use the slider at the top of the viewport to set the clipping plane distance from the target, but with our viewpoint you will not be able to see where it actually is or its effects, so our command line input of 15 feet is the best way to locate the clipping plane.

Now choose DVIEW's Distance option to turn on the perspective viewing mode. Enter the letter *d,* or the entire word *distance*. AutoCAD will prompt for a new camera-to-target distance.

```
Specify new camera-target distance <32'-0.0000">: (Enter)
```

Since we previously established the camera-to-target distance that we wanted through the Points option, we accepted the default of 32 feet. AutoCAD will zoom in and switch to the perspective viewing mode. You should not have to change the zoom level, but you probably will need to use DVIEW's Pan option to center the view, and you will want to use its Hide option to ensure that your view is as you want it. Lastly, exit the DVIEW command. Your view should be similar to the one shown in the figure on the next page.

Next, we will use the 3D Orbit commands to set up a front clipping plane and a perspective view. Use the VPOINT coordinates of -1,-1,1 to set a SW isometric view of the room and simultaneously turn off the perspective mode. Then take the following steps to set up a front clipping plane and perspective view.

- Invoke the CAMERA command. In response to the command line prompt for a camera position, enter 10',-13',6'; in response to the prompt for a target position, enter 18',18',6'.

- Invoke the 3DORBIT command. Select Zoom from its shortcut menu, and zoom back until the width of the model fills about one-half of

Target and front cutting plane locations

178

the viewport length. This is to ensure that the entire model will be shown in 3DCLIP's Adjust Clipping Planes window.

- From 3DORBITs Shading Modes shortcut menu, select Hidden.
- From 3DORBIT's More shortcut menu, select Adjust Clipping Planes.
- By default, the front clipping plane will be turned on, and the Adjust Front Clipping option will be active. Drag the front clipping plane down in the Adjust Clipping Planes window until it is between the refrigerator and the front wall of the room. Close the Adjust Clipping Planes window.

- From 3DORBIT's Projection shortcut menu, select Perspective.
- Use the shortcut menu options of Zoom and Pan to size and position the image until the room looks similar to the one shown in the figure on the right.

Perspective view with front clipping plane

3D Polygon Mesh Surfaces

*I*n this chapter we will discuss surfaces that, unlike the planar surfaces of 3DFACE and PFACE, can curve and twist through space, can be rounded, and can have irregular edges. These are polygon mesh surfaces. Specifically, we will

- *describe the characteristics and properties of polygon mesh surfaces;*
- *explain how each of the five AutoCAD commands that make polygon mesh surfaces work, what they can and cannot do, and how they differ from each other;*
- *add surfaces to the automobile oil pan model we started in Chapter Four;*
- *surface the airplane propeller model we started in Chapter Five;*
- *describe AutoCAD's premade surface objects.*

Properties of Polygon Mesh Surfaces

With a little ingenuity and imagination you can use AutoCAD to make surfaces in a surprisingly wide variety of shapes, including shapes that cannot be made as solid models. Generally, these surfaces will be made by the RULESURF, TABSURF, EDGESURF, REVSURF, or 3DMESH command.

While these five commands have different requirements and use different input methods, they make the same type of AutoCAD object—a polygon mesh surface that has the following characteristics:

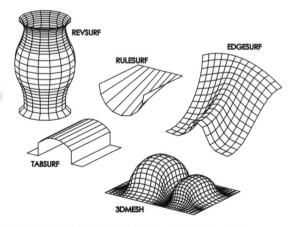

180

- The surface is mostly composed of flat faces. (Sometimes, depending on how the surface was created, some of the faces may be warped.) Most of these faces have four sides, although a few have only three sides. Each face is not only similar to a 3D face object (made with the 3DFACE command)—if the surface mesh is exploded, it becomes a set of 3D faces.
- The faces form a grid of rows and columns, although the rows and columns may bend and turn as they conform to the surface, and the faces are not necessarily uniform in size or shape. Moreover, some surface meshes will have only a single row or a single column of faces.

3-sided face

4-sided face

- To identify the position of each face in the surface grid, AutoCAD establishes an origin on the surface and directions from this origin. AutoCAD calls one the *M direction* and the other the *N direction*. These directions have no relationship to the coordinate system directions, and often they are not even perpendicular to each other.
- Except for the 3DMESH command, AutoCAD controls the number of faces in the M and N directions through system variables **surftab1** and **surftab2.** With the 3DMESH command, the number of faces in both directions are specified as the command is implemented.

- When a surface mesh is wrapped around so that one edge is joined with its opposite edge, it is called a *closed mesh*. A mesh can be closed in the M direction or in the N direction, and if the surface forms a torus it will be closed in both directions.
- Even though Autodesk's documentation often refers to ruled surfaces, tabulated surfaces, and revolved surfaces, all five commands make the same type of AutoCAD database object. They are polygon mesh surfaces, which are a variation of 2D polylines. As a result, they can be edited on a basic level with the PEDIT command (which we will discuss in the next chapter).

With the exception of those made through the 3DMESH command, polygon mesh surfaces are based on wireframe boundary objects. RULESURF, for example, makes a surface between two wireframe objects; EDGESURF makes a surface between four wireframe objects; TABSURF extrudes a wireframe object; and REVSURF revolves a wireframe object. When the 3DMESH command is used, each vertex, or node, on the surface mesh must be specified.

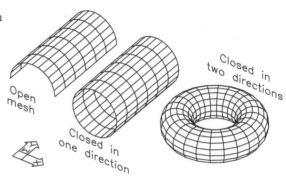

Polygon mesh surfaces are drawn using the current layer, and the boundary objects are retained. You should always use separate layers for surfaces and wireframe objects so you can get one or the other out of the way (by freezing or turning off its layer) as you work with the model.

Polygon mesh directions are potentially confusing because AutoCAD is not consistent with its names and labels. You would think, for instance, that the **surftab1** system variable would apply to either the M or N direction, while **surftab2** would apply to the other direction, but that isn't the way it is. **Surftab1** sets the number of faces in the M direction for REVSURF and EDGESURF, but it sets the number of faces in the N direction for RULESURF and TABSURF.

Surftab2, on the other hand, sets the number of faces in the N direction for REVSURF and EDGESURF and has no effect on RULESURF and TABSURF (which have only one face in the M direction). You may find it less confusing when you ignore the M and N directions when setting mesh sizes and concentrate on the actual edges affected by **surftab1** and **surftab2** instead. You will, however, need to know which direction is which when you edit a mesh with PEDIT.

Now that you are familiar with the properties of polygon mesh surfaces, we will take a closer look at each of the five commands that create them. We will see how each command works, what it can and cannot do, and how it differs from the others. After we have looked at all five commands for making polygon mesh surfaces, we will lead you through some exercises in using the commands.

Command:	RULESURF
Purpose:	Creates a polygon mesh surface between two wireframe boundaries.

Initiate with:

- On the command line enter RULESURF.
- From the Draw pull-down menu, select Surfaces, then Ruled Surface from the resulting flyout menu.

- Select the Ruled Surface button from the Surfaces toolbar.

Implementation:

RULESURF will report the current value of **tabsurf1** and issue command line prompts for two boundary objects:

```
Current wireframe density: SURFTAB1=6
Specify first defining curve: (Select a wireframe object.)
Specify second defining curve: (Select a wireframe object.)
```

You must select the boundary objects by picking a point on them—window and crossing selection methods are not allowed. AutoCAD proceeds as soon as you pick an object—you do not have to press the Enter key. Despite the wording of the prompts, boundary objects do not have to be curved. Arcs, circles, 2D and 3D polylines, splines, lines, and even points can be used as boundaries. The boundaries can be open, such as those made with a line or an arc or they can be closed, such as those made with a circle. Polylines are considered to be open boundaries even if their start points and endpoints are in the same location, unless they were closed with the Close option of their command or of the PEDIT command. Splines, on the other hand, are considered to be closed when the start points and endpoints are in the same location, even if the Close option of the SPLINE or SPLINEDIT command was not used.

You cannot mix open and closed boundaries—if one boundary is closed, the other boundary must be closed also. If a point is selected as a defining curve, the other curve cannot be a point. The other defining curve can be either open or closed.

As soon as the two defining curves are picked, AutoCAD will construct a polygon mesh surface between them. Each face on the surface will have four sides, and the number of faces will equal the value stored in the **surftab1** system variable. The N direction of the surface is along the boundary curves.

The pick point is important for open boundaries, because AutoCAD considers the end of the boundary closest to the pick point to be the leading edge of the polygon mesh surface. Therefore, you must pick corresponding ends to avoid making a surface that crosses itself.

For closed boundaries, the location of the pick point is not important because AutoCAD starts the surface at a predetermined point. If the boundary is a circle, the edge of the first face starts at the first quadrant of the circle and the surface is built counterclockwise (as viewed from the positive Z direction). In most cases, therefore, the surface will start at the 3 o'clock point and proceed counterclockwise. If, however, the **snapang**

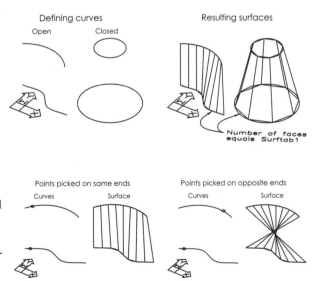

Defining curves
Open   Closed

Resulting surfaces

Number of faces equals Surftab1

Points picked on same ends
Curves   Surface

Points picked on opposite ends
Curves   Surface

system variable contains a value other than 0, the start point will be different.

For closed polylines, on the other hand, the surface starts at the last vertex and proceeds toward the first vertex. When a closed spline is used for a boundary curve, the surface will begin at the first fit point of the spline and proceed in the direction of the spline.

Notes:

- As a result of the differences in the surface start points and directions, the surface between a polyline and a circle is seldom satisfactory. In fact, boundaries made from closed polylines are often difficult to work with, and you are generally better off not closing polylines when they are to be used as RULESURF boundary curves.

Related system variables:

- **surftab1**

  The number of faces in a surface made by RULESURF is equal to the value of **surftab1**. Its initial value is 6.

- **snapang**

  This system variable sets the snap/grid rotation angle, and along with that the orientation of the 0 quadrant of circles and arcs. Its default value is 0.0.

Using RULESURF

As shown in the figure on the right, the M direction of surfaces made with RULESURF is from one boundary curve to the other. In this direction there is an edge at the beginning of the surface and another edge at its end. There are no further divisions, or any mesh lines in the M direction. The N direction is along the boundary curves, with the number of mesh divisions being controlled by the **surftab1** system variable. Since the edges of each individual face on the surface are straight, the ends of the surface consist of short straight lines that will deviate from the boundaries, unless the boundaries are straight. Since there is only one face in the M direction, the surface will have straight sides in that direction.

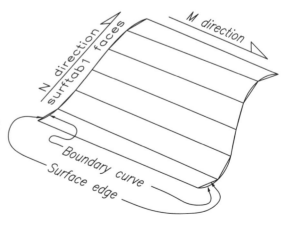

You will use RULESURF any time one end of the surface is to have a different shape than the other end and the sides of the surface can be straight. Often you can combine several surfaces, made with RULESURF or another surfacing command, to create a complex surface.

The figure on the right shows the steps to make a surface that changes from a round cross-section to a square cross-section. Four surfaces were used to make this surface. You might think that you could make the surface as a single surface using a circle for one boundary and a 2D polyline square for the other, but it is extremely difficult to match circle and polyline boundaries when you use RULESURF.

Boundary Curves   After RULESURF   Polar array copies to make a circular-to-square transition

Command: TABSURF

Purpose: Creates a polygon mesh surface by extruding a wireframe boundary in a straight-line direction.

Initiate with:

- On the command line enter TABSURF.
- From the Draw pull-down menu, select Surfaces, then Tabulated Surface from the resulting flyout menu.
- Select the Tabulated Surface button from the Surfaces toolbar.

Implementation:

From the command line, TABSURF will prompt you to select two wireframe objects:

```
Select object for path curve: (Select a wireframe object.)
Select object for direction vector: (Select a line or an open polyline.)
```

You must pick a point on these objects to select them. The first object selected defines the shape of the surface. It can be any wireframe object, including 3D polylines and splines. Moreover, it may be either an open object, such a line or arc, or a closed object, such as a circle or closed polyline.

Defining curves   Resulting surfaces

The second object selected, the direction vector, must be a line, an open 2D polyline, or a single segment 3D polyline. This direction vector determines both the length and the direction of the resulting surface. The surface will start at the path curve.

Interior vertices of a 2D polyline direction vector are ignored, with the length and direction of the surface being the same as that of a straight line drawn between the first and last vertices of the polyline. This is also true if the 2D polyline consists of a single arc-shaped segment.

Defining curves   Resulting surface

185

The direction vector's end closest to the object selection pick point is the starting direction of the surface.

The N direction of the resulting surface is along the path curve, and the surface will always be composed of four-sided faces of equal length. When the path curve is any object other than a 2D polyline that has not been spline fit, the faces on the surface will be equal in size, and the number of faces will be the same as the value of the **surftab1** system variable. If, on the other hand, the path curve is a 2D polyline that has not been spline fit, each straight segment of the polyline will make one face while each arc segment will be divided into the number of faces that correspond to the value of **surftab1**. Thus, each polyline vertex will mark the corner of a face on the surface.

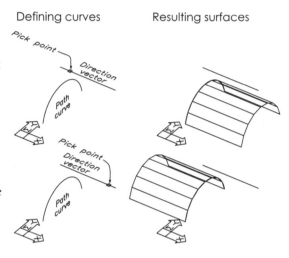

Defining curves   Resulting surfaces

Notes:

- When you want to make a linear surface that closely fits its defining curve, TABSURF combined with a 2D polyline path curve is a good choice.

Related system variable:

- **surftab1**

  This system variable determines the number of face divisions along the path curve on surfaces made with TABSURF.

Using TABSURF

TABSURF makes a surface by extruding a boundary curve, with both the direction and the length of the extrusion being controlled by a direction vector. Any existing line or open polyline can serve as a direction vector. AutoCAD calls the boundary curve the *path curve* in its command line prompts for TABSURF, which is potentially confusing since AutoCAD's prompts in the command for extruding solids—EXTRUDE—use the word *path* when referring to an object that sets the direction and length of solid extrusions. Thus, the word *path* has opposite meanings in TABSURF and EXTRUDE (we will discuss extruded solids in Section Three).

Defining curves   Resulting surface

Direction vector

2D polyline path curve

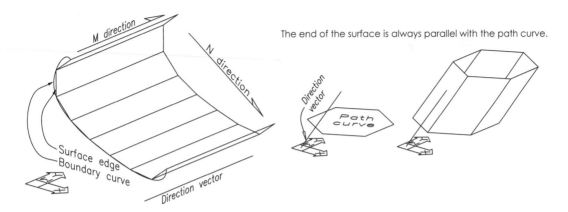

The end of the surface is always parallel with the path curve.

The M direction on surfaces made with TABSURF is in the direction of the direction vector, and the N direction is along the boundary curve. There will be only one face in the M direction, and the number of faces in the N direction will be equal to the value of the **surftab1** system variable.

The location of the direction vector is not important—it does not have to touch, or be centered with, the boundary curve. Also, the end of the surface will always be parallel with the boundary curve, even if the direction vector is not perpendicular to the boundary curve.

TABSURF is similar to RULESURF in that it makes linear surfaces having straight sides and in that the number of faces on the surface is controlled by the **surftab1** system variable. The surface shown in the figure on the right, for instance, could have been made with either RULESURF or TABSURF. Without the defining curves, you cannot tell which command was used.

However, when 2D polylines are used as boundary curves, TABSURF's surfaces can track the boundary much closer than those of RULESURF. RULESURF always divides the surface along the boundary curve into faces having the same width; the number of faces is equal to the value of **surftab1**. On the other hand, when a 2D polyline is used as a TABSURF boundary, each straight segment of the polyline makes one face on the surface, while each arc segment of the polyline is divided into the same number of faces as the value of **surftab1**.

The figure on the right shows two surfaces made from the same 2D polyline boundary. The polyline has four straight segments and one arc segment, and **surftab1** was set to 8. Notice that the surface made by TABSURF fits the boundary curve much more closely than the surface made by RULESURF.

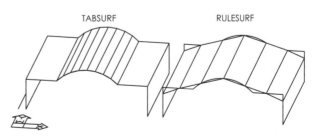

TABSURF   RULESURF

Command: REVSURF

Purpose: Creates a polygon mesh surface by revolving a wireframe boundary about an axis.

Initiate with:

- On the command line enter REVSURF.
- From the Draw pull-down menu, select Surfaces, then Revolved Surface from the resulting flyout menu.
- Select the Revolved Surface button from the Surfaces toolbar.

Implementation:

REVSURF reports the current value of **surftab1** and **surftab2**, and issues command line prompts for you to specify the boundary curve, the axis, the offset angle of the surface from the boundary curve, and the angle through which the boundary curve is to be rotated:

```
Current wire frame density: SURFTAB1=6  SURFTAB2=6

Select object to revolve: (Select a wireframe object.)
Select object that defines the axis of revolution: (Select a line or an open
    polyline.)
Specify start angle <0>: (Enter an angle or press Enter.)
Specify included angle (+=ccs, -=cw) <360>: (Enter an angle or press Enter.)
```

The object to be revolved can be any open or closed wireframe object, even if it is a 3D polyline or a spline. As soon as you pick a point on it, AutoCAD will prompt for the axis of revolution.

The axis of revolution must be a line, an open 2D polyline, or an open 3D polyline. You must select it by picking a point on it. If a polyline having multiple segments is selected as an axis, AutoCAD uses a straight line between the endpoints of the polyline as the rotation axis.

The start angle represents the angular offset from the object to be revolved at which the surface starts, while the included angle represents the number of degrees that the object is rotated.

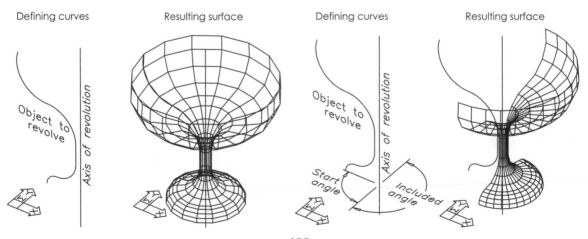

Defining curves   Resulting surface   Defining curves   Resulting surface

Rotation direction follows the right-hand rule, with the positive direction of the axis being determined by the location of its object selection point. The positive direction of the axis is from the end closest to the pick point to the opposite end. You can reverse the normal rotation direction by preceding the angle with a minus sign (-).

The number of surface faces around the axis (through the angle of revolution) is equal to the number of faces in the **surftab1** system variable, while the number of faces along the object that revolved is controlled by the value in **surftab2**. If the revolved object is any object type other than a 2D polyline that has not been spline fit, the number of faces on the surface along the object will be equal to the value in **surftab2**.

If, however, the revolved object is a 2D polyline that has not been spline fit, each line segment of the polyline will constitute one face while the number of faces of each arc segment of the polyline will equal the value of **surftab2**.

Notes:

The manner in which REVSURF divides 2D polyline path curves into polygon mesh faces is the same as TABSURF's.

• When the wireframe boundary object is revolved a full 360 degrees, the direction of revolution and the start angle are not important. Consequently, the pick point location for the axis is not important.

Related system variables:

• **surftab1**

The number of polygon mesh faces through the angle of revolution is controlled by this system variable.

• **surftab2**

The number of polygon mesh faces along the object that is revolved is controlled by **surftab2.**

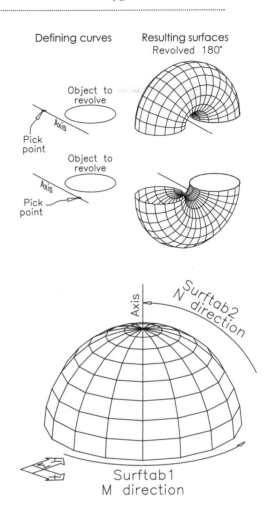

Defining curves   Resulting surfaces
Revolved 180°

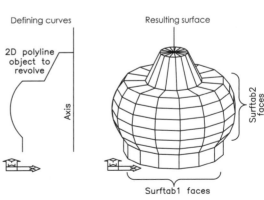

Defining curves   Resulting surface

189

Using REVSURF

REVSURF is a straightforward way to make a surface, especially if it is a full 360-degree surface of revolution. You simply pick a boundary curve (AutoCAD calls it the object to be revolved) and an axis, and AutoCAD generates the surface. The boundary curve can be any open or closed wireframe object, and while the axis is usually a line, it can be an open 2D or 3D polyline. Although you will generally have the axis either just touch the boundary curve, or be some distance from it, AutoCAD is not particular. It will create a surface even if the axis is in the middle of the boundary curve (which makes an impractical self-intersecting surface).

REVSURF shares some of TABSURF's characteristics. REVSURF uses the straight line direction between the endpoints of a crooked polyline (or one that has arc segments) for an axis, just as TABSURF does for a direction vector. Also in a manner similar to TABSURF, REVSURF makes a single face along flat segments of 2D polyline boundary curves, while the surface along the arc segments of a polyline is divided into the number of faces in one of the **surftab** system variables.

Unlike TABSURF, though, the number of faces along the boundary curve is controlled by the **surftab2** system variable, rather than by **surftab1**, even though this is the N direction of the surface in both instances. Around the axis of revolution, which is the M direction, the number of faces will be equal to the value of **surftab1**.

Making a revolved surface is slightly more complicated if you revolve the surface only part way around the axis, because the axis pick point determines the direction of revolution. The positive direction of the axis is from the end closest to the pick point to the other end. Rotation follows the right-hand rule, which is easily visualized by mentally grasping the axis with your right hand—your fingers will be curled in the positive rotation direction. You can reverse the direction by entering a negative angle value.

Normally, the surface starts at the boundary curve, but if you specify a start angle, the surface will begin at the specified angle from the boundary curve. This angle also follows the right-hand rule.

Command: EDGESURF

Purpose: Creates a polygon mesh surface between four wireframe boundary objects.

Initiate with:

- On the command line enter EDGESURF.

- From the Draw pull-down menu, select Surfaces, then Edge Surface from the resulting fly-out menu.

- Select the Edge Surface button from the Surfaces toolbar.

Implementation:

EDGESURF reports the current values of the **surftab1** and **surftab2** system variables and issues four command line prompts for you to specify the four edges of the surface:

```
Select object 1 for surface edge: (Select an open wireframe object.)
Select object 2 for surface edge: (Select an open wireframe object.)
Select object 3 for surface edge: (Select an open wireframe object.)
Select object 4 for surface edge: (Select an open wireframe object.)
```

Any mix-or-match combination of four open wireframe objects can be used as the surface boundary. A line, an arc, a 2D polyline, and a spline were used as edges in the figure below. Their endpoints, however, must exactly touch. Not even the smallest gap or overlap is allowed. If an edge does not touch an adjacent edge, EDGESURF will fail and AutoCAD will display a command line message that reports which edge did not touch another edge.

You must select the edges by picking a point on them. The M direction of the surface will be along the first edge that is selected, and the surface from that edge to the opposite edge will have a polygon mesh face division equal to the value in the **surftab1** system variable.

The N direction of the surface will be along the edges adjacent to the first edge, and in that direction the number of polygon mesh faces will be equal to the value of **surftab2.** Once the first edge has been selected, the order in which the other three edges are selected is of no consequence.

Notes:

- EDGESURF creates the surface by blending the opposite boundary edges as they sweep along the adjacent edges.

- AutoCAD's documentation sometimes calls the surface created by the EDGESURF command a *Coons patch*. The word *patch* refers to a specific surface area, while the name *Coons* refers to the person who developed the mathematics the surface is based on. The object created by EDGESURF is an AutoCAD polygon mesh.

Related system variables:

- **surftab1**

  The number of polygon mesh faces along the first boundary edge selected is equal to the value in **surftab1**.

- **surftab2**

  The number of faces along the edges adjacent to the first boundary edge selected is equal to the value in this system variable.

Using EDGESURF

When you get used to it, EDGESURF might just be your favorite command for making polygon mesh surfaces. Using the command is very easy: you simply pick four adjacent wireframe objects and AutoCAD generates the surface by sweeping and blending the boundary curves. The first edge you pick becomes the M surface direction, and the number of faces along that edge to the opposite edge will be equal to the value of **surftab1**. The order in which you pick the remaining three edges is of no consequence. The number of faces along the edges adjacent to the first edge is equal to the value of **surftab2**.

The key to mastering EDGESURF is in drawing the four wireframe boundary objects. First of all, their endpoints must exactly touch—absolutely no gaps or overlaps are allowed. Equally important in making the surface shape you want is your choice of the four boundary shapes and positions. Often you can use symmetry to make a complex surface that cannot be made in one piece. The tube intersection shown in the figure at the top of the page, for instance, is rather easily made with EDGESURF when it is divided into sections as shown in the next figure.

One 2D polyline

Command: 3DMESH

Purpose: A polygon mesh surface is created by specifying a point for each vertex of the mesh.

Initiate with:

- On the command line enter 3DMESH.

- From the Draw pull-down menu, select Surfaces, then 3D Mesh from the resulting flyout menu.

- Select the 3D Mesh button from the Surfaces toolbar.

Implementation:

AutoCAD first issues command line prompts for you to specify the number of surface mesh vertices, or nodes, in the M and N directions:

```
Enter size of mesh in M direction: (Enter an integer number between 2 and 256.)
Enter size of mesh in N direction: (Enter an integer number between 2 and 256.)
```

The total number of vertices on the surface will be equal to the M size multiplied by the N size, and the number of mesh faces in each direction will be one less than the specified size. Next, AutoCAD will issue a series of prompts for the location of each vertex in the surface mesh:

```
Specify location for vertex (0, 0): (Specify a point.)
Specify location for vertex (0, 1): (Specify a point.)
Specify location for vertex (0, 2): (Specify a point.)
  .
  .
Specify location for vertex (0, n): (Specify a point.)
Specify location for vertex (1, 0): (Specify a point.)
Specify location for vertex (1, 1): (Specify a point.)
  .
  .
Specify location for vertex (1, n): (Specify a point.)
  .
  .
Specify location for vertex (m, 0): (Specify a point.)
  .
  .
Specify location for vertex (m, n): (Specify a point.)
```

Point locations may be specified by entering coordinates on the command line or by pointing. Each vertex is identified by two integers that are separated by a comma. The first integer is the vertex number in the M direction, and the second is the vertex number in the N direction. Numbering starts with 0. Notice that the input sequence is row by row down a column, with the N direction representing rows and the M direction representing columns. The M and N directions relative to the WCS depend entirely upon the user's input. The resulting surface will be open (even if the surface wraps around so that one edge is adjacent to its opposite edge), and each face will have four sides.

The figure on the right shows a 4-by-3 polygon mesh surface. The numbers shown in this figure are vertex numbers, not point coordinates.

AutoCAD does not draw the surface until every vertex has been entered. There is no undo option, and if you cancel the command, nothing will be drawn.

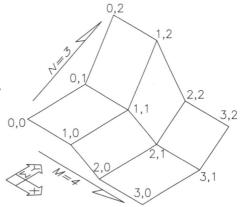

Notes:

- This command is seldom used due to its tedious input. Autodesk's original intent with the command was for use in applications, but only a few programs have been written. In AutoCAD 2000 some of the functions in 3d.lsp (which is the basis of the command named 3D) use 3DMESH.

Using 3DMESH

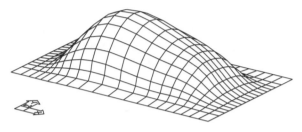

3DMESH is a command for making surfaces that you will most likely use only as a last resort, because you must specify the location of every vertex on the surface mesh. This can be extremely tedious and error prone. Nevertheless, 3DMESH can make some surfaces that no other AutoCAD command can make. The surface in the above figure, for example, could be made as a single surface only with 3DMESH.

For a do-it-yourself demonstration of how 3DMESH works, start a new AutoCAD drawing and use the following command line input to draw a simple surface. The settings for this drawing are not important, and neither is your initial viewpoint. Also, you will probably not want to save the drawing when you are finished.

```
Command: 3DMESH (Enter)
Enter size of mesh in M direction: 4 (Enter)
Enter size of mesh in N direction: 3 (Enter)
Specify location for vertex (0, 0): 0,0 (Enter)
Specify location for vertex (0, 1): 1,0 (Enter)
Specify location for vertex (0, 2): 2,0 (Enter)
Specify location for vertex (1, 0): 0,1 (Enter)
Specify location for vertex (1, 1): 1,1,-1 (Enter)
Specify location for vertex (1, 2): 2,1 (Enter)
Specify location for vertex (2, 0): 0,2,1 (Enter)
Specify location for vertex (2, 1): 1,2,-1 (Enter)
Specify location for vertex (2, 2): 2,2 (Enter)
Specify location for vertex (3, 0): 0,3,1 (Enter)
Specify location for vertex (3, 1): 1,3 (Enter)
Specify location for vertex (3, 2): 2,3 (Enter)
```

Although the numbers in the prompts look like point coordinates in that there are two numbers separated by a comma, they are not. They are vertex identification numbers. You did not need to enter Z coordinates for the eight vertex points that were on the X-Y plane. From a plan view, the surface will look like six squares. For a better look at the surface, switch to an isometric-type viewpoint with the following command line input:

```
Command: VPOINT (Enter)
Current view direction: VIEWDIR=0.0000,0.0000,1.0000
Specify a view point or [Rotate] display compass and tripod: 2,-3,4 (Enter)
```

194

Your surface should look similar to the one shown in the second figure on the previous page. Although this is a very simple surface, it illustrates many of the specific characteristics of 3DMESH surfaces, as well as some general characteristics of polygon mesh surfaces.

- Each vertex, or node, on the surface has an invisible two-digit identification number. The first number represents the vertex's position in the M direction on the surface, while the second number represents its position in the N direction. AutoCAD starts the numbers at 0, so vertex 3,1 is actually the fourth vertex in the M direction and the second vertex in the N direction.

- When 3DMESH starts, you must specify the number of vertices that the surface will have in both the M and N directions. The number of surface faces in these directions will be one less than the number of vertices.

- AutoCAD's command line prompts for 3DMESH vertex locations begin with vertex 0,0 and move in the N direction until the point of the last vertex is specified. Then, AutoCAD moves to the next vertex in the M direction (vertex 1,0) and again moves in the N direction. This is repeated until the location of the last vertex in the last row has been specified.

- Although the M direction of the demonstration surface you made is in the WCS Y axis direction and the N direction is in the WCS X axis direction, these directions could just as easily have been reversed. In fact, there is nothing to prevent either of these directions from being in the Z axis direction, or any angle in between. Furthermore, the M and N directions do not have to be mutually perpendicular.

- Every face on the surface mesh must have four sides. Often the faces will be flat, but only one of the six faces in the surface you made is flat, and the corner faces are severely warped.

3DMESH doesn't draw the surface until the location of the last vertex has been specified. If you cancel the command, nothing is drawn. Not even the surface up to the last specified vertex. Also, there is no undo option—once the location of a point has been specified, it is fixed.

Even though its vertex-by-vertex input enables you to make unique shapes, 3DMESH is seldom a practical method of making surfaces when it is implemented from the command line. Script files can reduce, or even eliminate, input errors, but determining the coordinates of each point is no small task.

If you must use 3DMESH, you may find that drawing profiles can help you visualize the surface and provide pick points at the same time. The next figure shows the wireframe that the 3DMESH surface shown earlier (in the description of the 3DMESH command) is based on. The wireframe is made entirely of lines. Although this figure has tick marks to show the end of each line, the tick marks are not really needed to construct the surface. Object endpoint snaps were used in specifying points for the surface.

Also, the 3DMESH surface can be made in a fairly crude and rough form, then smoothed with the PEDIT command. The 3DMESH surface shown earlier was smoothed with PEDIT. The same surface in its original, unsmoothed 3DMESH form is pictured on the next page.

We will explain how to smooth polygon surface meshes with the PEDIT command in
Chapter Nine.

Autodesk intended for 3DMESH to be
used with applications, rather than by user
input on the command line, and if you commonly make surfaces that can be defined by
equations or formulas, you should consider
making them through a program that uses 3DMESH.

The CD-ROM that comes with this book contains an AutoLISP program named fplot.lsp that
can be used as a front end for 3DMESH or as an example of how to write a program of your
own. This program, which was written by Autodesk and can be freely used and distributed, is
not included with Release 14, even though it works well in Release 14. Instructions for using
and adapting the program are included as remarks within fplot.lsp.

If you want an example of what can be done with fplot.lsp and 3DMESH, load the program
(the AutoCAD APPLOAD command is the easiest way to do this) and enter DEMO on the

command line. The result, which is shown in
the figure on the right, illustrates the interference pattern of two exponentially damped
cosine waves. Two other demonstrations in
the file, COSINE and EXPONENT, also plot
mathematical equations having two variables. Since each of these plots is centered at
the origin, you should erase one, or move it
away from the origin, before making another.

Exercises

We will try out each of the commands that make polygon mesh surfaces, except for 3DMESH.
All of the surfaces will be added to wireframes that we have already constructed. Since making
the wireframe boundary objects is the hardest and most time-consuming job in making surface
models of polygon meshes, adding these surfaces will seem almost trivial.

Exercise One

Retrieve file mfe08101.dwg from the CD-ROM that accompanies this book and open it. We
started this model, which is of an automobile oil pan, as a wireframe in Chapter Four and added
seven 3D faces to it in Chapter Six. You should use this version of the model because it includes
some wireframe objects, which will be used for polygon mesh boundaries, that your model will

not have. Also, the arc-line-arc objects at the
corners have been changed into 2D polylines
with the PEDIT command so that they can be
used to make one surface rather than three
separate surfaces. This version of the model
does include the 3D face surfaces that were
added in Chapter Six.

We will use the RULESURF command to make surfaces that have straight sides and are between two boundaries that have different shapes. The six remaining planar areas on the flange of the oil pan meet this criteria. Change to the layer named Surf_rule and set the **surftab1** system variable to 6. Start RULESURF, and pick two points on your wireframe corresponding to those labeled Pt1A and Pt1B in the next figure. It does not matter which of the two points you pick first. However, each pick location should be near one end of the curve rather than near the middle, and you should pick the corresponding end of both curves. As soon as you pick the second point, AutoCAD will draw the surface between the two curves.

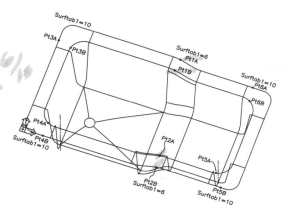

Start RULESURF again, and pick points on your wireframe corresponding to those labeled Pt2A and Pt2B in the figure to make the next surface. Then change the value of **surftab1** from 6 to 10, and use RULESURF four more times to add surfaces to the corners of the flange. Suggested pairs of point locations on the boundary curves are shown in the figure.

We will also use RULESURF to make three nonplanar surfaces near the middle of the oil pan. The boundary curve pick points are shown in the figure below. VPOINT, with the rotation angles of 190 degrees in the X-Y plane from the X axis and 60 degrees from the X-Y plane, was used to set the viewpoint for this figure. Since the curvature of the boundary curves is relatively large, we can use a relatively low **surftab1** value. Therefore, set **surftab1** back to 6. Then invoke RULESURF three times, and pick the point pairs shown in the figure for the boundary curves. If you happen to pick a pair of points such that the surface crosses over itself, use AutoCAD's UNDO command to back up, then remake the surface.

Next, we will use TABSURF to make the remaining sides of the oil pan. Switch to the layer named Surf_tab and reduce the value of **surftab1** to 4. Start TABSURF and pick the curve labeled Path A in the figure on the top of the next page as the path curve for TABSURF, and the line labeled Direction Vector A as the direction

vector of the surface. (Remember, in the prompts for TABSURF and REVSURF, AutoCAD refers to boundary curves as path curves.)

The viewpoint for this figure is 305 degrees in the X-Y plane from the X axis and 15 degrees from the X-Y plane. Be certain that your pick point on the direction vector is in the half of the line that is closest to the path curve.

Repeat TABSURF command and pick the curve labeled Path B in the figure as the path curve, and the line labeled Direction Vector B as the direction vector. And use TABSURF again with Path C and Direction Vector C to make a third surface.

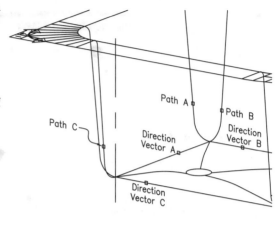

Then move to the opposite end of the oil pan and use TABSURF three times to make similar surfaces. Since a 3D face lies on top of the wireframe in this section, you may have problems picking the direction vectors. If AutoCAD displays the message "Object not usable as direction vector," hold your keyboard's Ctrl key down as you pick the line. When the line, rather than the edges of the 3D face, is highlighted, press the Enter key to signal acceptance. Your model should now look like the one in the figure on the right when HIDE is activated.

Next, we will use REVSURF to make the corners of the oil pan. Since the model is beginning to be cluttered with surface objects, you should switch to the layer named Surf_rev and freeze the Surf_face, Surf_rule, and Surf_tab layers. Set the **surftab1** system variable (which controls the number of faces around the axis of revolution) to 4, and set **surftab2** (which controls the number of faces along the boundary curve) also to 4.

Invoke REVSURF and pick the curve labeled Path A in the next figure for the boundary curve. Pick a point on the lower end of the centerline to specify the axis of rotation. Accept AutoCAD's 0 degree start angle by pressing the Enter key and enter 90 as the included angle. Invoke REVSURF again, picking Path B as the boundary curve, and the lower end of Axis B for the axis of revolution. Specify 0 degrees for the start angle and 90 degrees for the included angle.

The corners on the opposite side of the oil pan model do not have an axis that can be used by REVSURF. You can either copy the existing center lines to those corners and use them with REVSURF to make the corner surfaces, or use MIRROR to make copies of the two surfaces you just made. Either way works well.

Use VPOINT or 3DORBIT to rotate the viewpoint 190 degrees in the X-Y plane from the X axis and 60 degrees from the X-Y plane. This viewpoint will give you an unobstructed view of the remaining eight areas that are to be surfaced. We will use EDGESURF to make the surfaces. Leave **surftab1** set to 4, but change the value of **surftab2** from 4 to 6. Start the EDGESURF command; pick the point labeled A1 in the figure on the next page as edge one of the polygon mesh, and pick the objects labeled A for the other three edges of the mesh. The order in which you pick these three points as well as the location of the pick points on the curves is of no importance.

Repeat EDGESURF, selecting a point on the curve labeled B1 in the figure on the right as edge number one, and the three curves labeled B as the other edges of the surface. Make the two surfaces on the opposite side of the oil pan with two calls to EDGESURF, selecting the curve labeled C1 as the first edge of one surface, and curve D1 as the first edge of the other surface.

Set the value of **surftab1** to 6 and leave **surftab2** set to 6. Invoke EDGESURF four times, picking the curves labeled E in the previous figure for one surface, those labeled F for the second surface, those labeled G for the third polygon mesh surface, and those labeled H for the remaining surface. Four of the curves serve as edges for two surfaces, and you may have to hold down the Ctrl key as you pick those curves so that AutoCAD will cycle through the stacked objects until you find the one you want. For any one surface, the order in which you pick the curves and the pick point locations is not important.

You are now finished with the surface model oil pan. Thaw all of the layers used for the surfaces (Surf_face, Surf_rule, Surf_tab, Surf_rev, and Surf_edge) and freeze the layers used for wireframe objects (Wf01 and CL). Your model should look like the one shown in the figure above when you view it from an angle 300 degrees in the X-Y plane from the X axis and minus 20 degrees from the X-Y plane. The completed version of this model is in file mfe08108.dwg on the CD-ROM that comes with this book.

Exercise Two

In this exercise you will add surfaces to the wireframe airplane propeller you drew in Chapter Five. Open file mfe08201.dwg from the accompanying CD-ROM rather than the one you created. The wireframe in this file contains some additions for making a hub on the propeller.

All of the surfaces on this model will be made with the EDGESURF command. Zoom in to the tip section of the wireframe. Set the **surftab1** system variable to 12, set **surftab2** to 4, and switch to the layer named Surf01. Start the EDGESURF command and follow the directions in the figure on the top of the next page—when picking the surface edges. This figure uses tick marks to show where the three curves that make the propeller tip start and stop; the wireframe on your computer screen, however, will not have these tick marks. After you make the first surface, repeat EDGESURF and pick the points shown in the figure for the surface edges. Three of the curves serve as edges for both surfaces.

When HIDE is active, the tip of your propeller should look similar to the one in the second figure.

Change to the layer named Surf02 and freeze Surf01. (This will make picking edges easier.) Leave **surftab1** set to 12, but change **surftab2** from 4 to 16. Zoom out so that you can see the entire propeller. Start EDGESURF and pick the edges for the first (lower side) surface as shown in the third figure. The first edge must be on one of the cross-sections of the propeller (so that our **surftab1** and **surftab2** face divisions will be as we planned), but it does not matter which order you use in picking the other three edges. Repeat EDGESURF to make the second (upper side) surface on the propeller by picking the edges shown in the figure.

Zoom in close to the hub of the propeller as shown in the top-left figure on the next page. Change to layer Surf03 and freeze layers Surf02 and WF03. The first two surfaces in this area, which make a cross-section transition from an airfoil to elliptical shape, will be very short, so change **surftab2** from 16 to its minimum of 2. Leave **surftab1** at its current value of 12. Use EDGESURF and pick the points labeled Pt1, Pt2, Pt3, and Pt4 for the surface edges, with either Pt1 or Pt4 being picked first. Then repeat EDGESURF, using Pt2, Pt3, Pt5, and Pt6 as the edges, with Pt5 or Pt6 as the first edge.

The remaining six surfaces make the transition from an ellipse to one that will fit the side of a vertical cylinder. Change the layer of the two surfaces you just made from Surf03 to Surf02. (The AI_PROPCHK command, which can be called from the Standard toolbar, is a convenient way to do this.) Since Surf02 is frozen, the surface will disappear. Freeze layers WF01 and WF02, and thaw layer OBJ03. When you zoom in close to the hub area of the propeller, you will see just the eighteen wireframe objects that are in layer OBJ03, as shown in the top-right figure on the next page.

Set both **surftab1** and **surftab2** to 8. Verify that Surf03 is the current layer and invoke EDGESURF six times to make the six surfaces. Use the following table in conjunction with the

200

numbers shown on the objects in the previous figure as a guide in selecting the edges for EDGESURF. Since **surftab1** and **surftab2** are equal, it does not matter which edge you pick first.

Surface

Surface	Edge Objects
1	4, 10, 16, 17
2	5, 11, 17, 18
3	6, 12, 13, 18
4	3, 9, 15, 16
5	2, 8, 14, 15
6	1, 7, 13, 14

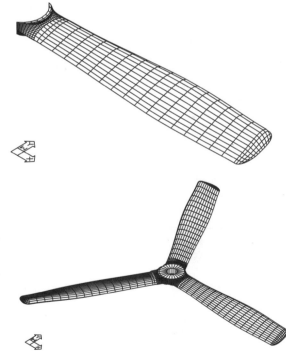

Notice that the sequence in creating the surfaces is to start in the back and work forward. This is to minimize visibility and selection problems. Since there will be edges on top of edges, you will probably have to hold down the Ctrl key as you pick the wireframe objects. When the wireframe object is highlighted, rather than the adjoining surface, press the Enter key for AutoCAD to accept the edge. When you have finished making the six surfaces, thaw layers Surf01 and Surf02, and freeze layer WF03. Your finished propeller blade should look like the one in the middle figure on the right. The completed propeller blade is in file mfe08207.dwg on the CD-ROM that comes with this book.

You can make polar array copies of this blade to create propeller assemblies having up to three blades. You will have to add to the hub area, but you now have all of the knowledge and skills to do this on your own. The bottom-right figure shows a three-bladed propeller. This surface model is on the CD-ROM in file mfe08208.dwg.

AutoCAD's Premade Surface Objects

AutoCAD has nine premade surface objects that can be used alone or in combination with other surface objects. They are comparable to the primitives in solid modeling (which we discuss in Chapter Ten), but since surface objects are unable to interact in any way, they are not nearly as useful. Nevertheless, they are handy when you need to make a basic geometric shape, such as a box or sphere.

The name of the command that makes these surface objects is simply 3D. If you invoke 3D from the command line, a command line menu will be displayed for you to select the geometric shape you want. A more direct route to the object you want to make is to select its button on the Surfaces toolbar. A shape not available from the toolbar is that of a four-sided mesh. You can, however, start that surface shape, as well as any of the other eight shapes, directly from the 3D Objects dialog box that is opened when you select Surfaces from the Draw pull-down menu, then select 3D Surfaces. This dialog box is an especially good way to start an object because it has image tiles that show an example of each one of them.

3D is not a built-in AutoCAD command—it is based on an AutoLISP program named 3d.lsp. The AutoCAD commands of RULESURF, REVSURF, and 3DMESH are used by this AutoLISP program in making the objects. Consequently, each object is a polygon mesh, and each object is a single entity. A box, for example, does not consist of six individual planar surface objects.

Command: 3D

Purpose: This command creates a polygon mesh surface object in any of nine different basic geometric shapes.

Initiate with:

- On the command line enter 3D.

- From the Draw pull-down menu, select Surfaces, then 3D Surfaces to bring up the 3D Objects dialog box.

- Select the Box, Pyramid, Sphere, Dish, Wedge, Cone, Dome, or Torus button from the Surface toolbar.

Options:

When 3D is initiated from the command line, nine command line options will be offered:

`Box/Cone/DIsh/Dome/Mesh/Pyramid/Sphere/Torus/Wedge:` *Specify an option.*

If you start the command from the Draw pull-down menu, these options will be shown in image tiles in the 3D Objects dialog box that you can select by double-clicking or by highlighting, then pressing the OK button.

The Surfaces toolbar has buttons for initiating any option directly, except for Mesh.

- Box

    This option makes a rectangular parallelepiped or a cube on the X-Y plane of the UCS. From the command line, AutoCAD will ask for the starting corner of the box, then prompt for its length, width, and height. When the box is drawn, AutoCAD will prompt for a rotation angle about the Z axis, based on the first corner of the box.

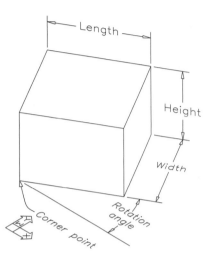

- Cone

    You can make either a sharp-tipped cone or a truncated cone. AutoCAD will first ask for the base center of the cone, then for the radius or the diameter of the base. The next prompt is for the top radius or diameter of the cone, with a default response of 0 to make a sharp-tipped cone. The third prompt is for the height of the cone (in the Z direction), and the last is for the number of segments, or faces, the cone is to have.

- Dish

    This option makes a half-sphere that is open in the positive Z direction. AutoCAD will issue command line prompts for the center of the dish, its diameter or radius, the number of longitudinal segments (around the edge of the dish), and the number of latitudinal segments (along the depth of the dish).

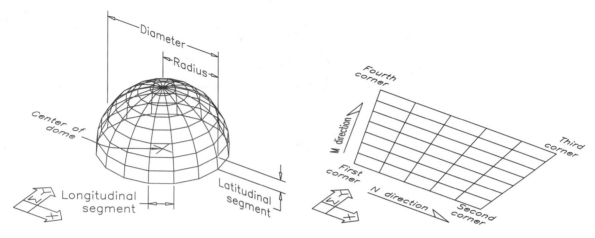

- DOme

  A half-sphere that is open in the negative Z direction is made with this option. Command line prompts are used to specify the center of the dome, its diameter or radius, the number of longitudinal segments (around the edge of the dome), and the number of latitudinal segments (along the height of the dome).

- Mesh

  This option makes a four-sided mesh surface. AutoCAD will issue command line prompts for the first, second, third, and fourth corners of the mesh. Although these corners do not have to be in the same plane, they must be specified in a clockwise or counterclockwise direction to prevent the mesh from crossing itself. As soon as the fourth corner is specified, AutoCAD will highlight an edge in the M direction and prompt for the number of vertices in that direction; then AutoCAD will prompt for the number of vertices in the N direction. The minimum allowable input for vertices is 2, and the maximum is 256. The number of faces in each direction will be one less than the specified number of vertices.

- Pyramid

  You can make pyramids (five sides, including the base), tetrahedrons (four sides), and ridge-shaped objects with this option. Furthermore, the pyramids and tetrahedrons can be truncated. All of these shapes are created through command line input.

- Sphere

  This option makes a hollow ball that has an axis perpendicular to the UCS X-Y plane. Command line prompts ask you to specify the center of the sphere, its radius or diameter, the

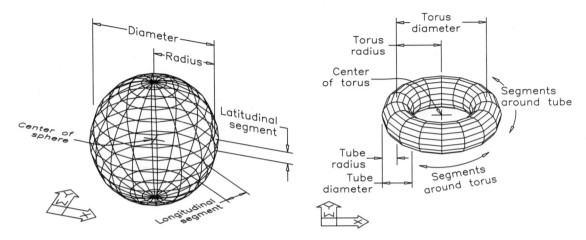

number of faces around the axis (longitudinal segments), and the number of faces along the axis (latitudinal segments).

- Torus

  A torus is the geometric shape obtained by revolving a circle about an axis that is in the plane of the circle and offset from its center line. The plane of the circle, and therefore the direction of the revolution axis, for tori made by 3D is always perpendicular to the UCS X-Y plane. The option uses command line prompts for you to specify the axis location, the distance to the center of the circle (the torus radius or diameter), the circle's radius or diameter (the tube radius or diameter), the number of segments (faces) around the axis of revolution, and the number of segments around the circle (the tube).

- Wedge

  A polygon mesh surface in the shape of a right-angle wedge is made by this option. Its first command line prompt is for a corner of the wedge on its high side. The next prompt is for the distance, or length, from the high side to the pointed side, a third prompt asks for the width of the wedge, and a fourth asks for the height of the high side of the wedge. The fifth, and last, prompt is for a rotation angle in the X-Y plane, with the first specified point as the rotation point.

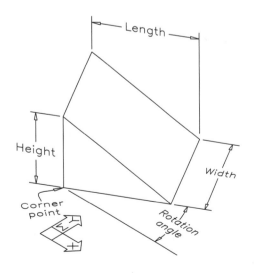

Notes:

- There is no tool bar button for the Mesh option.

- You can start each of the nine options directly from the command line by preceding its name with ai_. For example: ai_box will start the Box option, and ai_sphere will start the Sphere option.

- This command is based on an AutoLISP program named 3d.lsp, and each option is based on a function in this program. The program uses the 3DMESH command to make boxes, wedges, meshes, and pyramids; RULESURF to make cones; and REVSURF to make spheres, tori, domes, and dishes.

- Although the Pyramid option draws a variety of geometric shapes, its usefulness is impaired because you must supply points for the upper parts of the pyramids. You cannot simply specify their height. Therefore, you must know the point locations for the pyramid's peak, ridge, or upper corners of a truncated pyramid before you start the option.

Modifying Polygon Mesh Surfaces

W e will discuss AutoCAD's capabilities in modifying polygon mesh surfaces—those surfaces made with RULESURF, TABSURF, REVSURF, EDGESURF, and 3DMESH—in this chapter. Specifically, this chapter will

- describe AutoCAD's capabilities and limitations in modifying polygon mesh surfaces;
- explain how to move surface mesh vertices;
- describe how to change polygon mesh surfaces into B-spline and Bezier surfaces.

AutoCAD has respectable surface modeling capabilities, as you have seen in the last three chapters, even though Autodesk has not added to those capabilities since Release 11. The main deficiencies in AutoCAD as a surface modeler are related more to its surface modification and editing capabilities than to its surface creation abilities.

You cannot trim two overlapping surfaces (or even find the curve where they intersect), you cannot fillet two adjacent surfaces, and you cannot join adjacent surfaces. Furthermore, for all practical purposes you cannot break a surface into separate surfaces, you cannot make a hole in a surface, and you cannot make a surface longer or shorter. Actually, you can do some of these modifications on a limited basis if you have a little ingenuity and a lot of time, since you can work on individual nodes of a mesh. As a last resort (and certainly not recommended), you can even explode a polygon mesh surface down to its basic 3D faces and work on them one by one.

For the most part, modifications to polygon mesh surfaces—those surfaces made with RULESURF, TABSURF, REVSURF, EDGESURF, or 3DMESH— are limited to either moving vertices or fitting the mesh surface to a smooth curve. Since polygon mesh surfaces are a variation of 2D polylines, you can use the PEDIT command to do both of these operations.

Moving Vertices

When a polygon mesh is selected as a PEDIT object, AutoCAD recognizes its object type and displays a special command line menu for modifying surface meshes. Similar to the PEDIT menu for polylines, this menu contains an Edit Vertex option, but unlike the Edit Vertex option for polylines, you cannot remove or add vertices to a polygon mesh. The only vertex editing you can do is to move them.

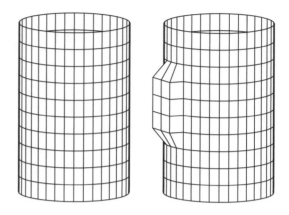

Moving vertices is sometimes useful when you need a specialized surface shape. You can, for instance, make a flat protrusion on a tube by moving vertices.

When you do need to move vertices of a polygon mesh, you will most likely prefer the STRETCH command or the mesh's grips (there is one on every vertex) over the PEDIT command. PEDIT requires you to move a vertex marker from node to node on the surface until you reach the vertex you want moved. Then you specify a new location for that vertex. If you use grips, on the other hand, you can go directly to the vertex you are interested in, highlight it, and move it to a new location. If you need to move several vertices at one time, the STRETCH command is useful.

No matter what method you use, it helps to know exactly where you want a vertex to be before you move it, and often object snaps are useful in establishing destination points. The flat face on the previous figure, for example, was made by drawing a temporary rectangular-shaped wireframe in front of the tube so that object snaps could be used to pick the destination points of the vertices.

Smoothing Surfaces

Probably your main use of PEDIT will be to smooth polygon mesh surfaces. Before you smooth a surface, though, you will want to check, and most likely change, the values of three system variables.

One of these system variables, **surftype**, controls the type of equation used in shaping the smoothed surface. Your choices for equation types are quadratic B-spline, cubic B-spline, and Bezier, with cubic B-spline being the default. From our discussion of PEDIT and 3D polylines in Chapter Five, you are already familiar with the characteristics of quadratic and cubic B-splines. Bezier (pronounced BAY-zee-a— the name of the person who developed the equation) curves and surfaces are an early version of B-splines, which are easily implemented in computer applications.

As shown in the following table, surfaces must have at least three vertices in both directions to be fit to a quadratic B-spline, and they must have at least four vertices in both directions to be fit to a cubic B-spline. Therefore, you cannot use those equation types in smoothing polygon mesh surfaces made with RULESURF or TABSURF. They can, however, be fit to a Bezier surface. The vertices of the original surface mesh are used as control points for the smoothed surface. Consequently, the surface will pull away from its original vertices, except for those on the edges of the surface. Bezier surfaces deviate the most from the original surface, cubic B-spline surfaces come closer, and quadratic B-spline surfaces come the closest to matching the original surface.

Surftype Value	Surface Type	Minimum Number of Mesh Vertices in Either Direction	Maximum Number of Mesh Vertices in Either Direction
5	Quadratic B-spline	3	None
6	Cubic B-spline	4	None
8	Bezier	2	11

One surface shape is not better than another—it just depends on what shape you are after. If you want the smoothest, least curving, and flattest surface, you will use the Bezier equation. If you want the surface to match the original surface as closely as possible, you will use a quadratic B-spline equation.

Despite the PEDIT option name of Smoothed Surface, the resulting surface will not be perfectly smooth—it will still be a mesh of (generally) flat faces. The number of faces on the smoothed surfaces is determined by **surfu** and **surfv**, which are the other two system variables you will want to set before you smooth a polygon mesh surface. **Surfu** sets the number of faces in the M direction on the surface, while **surfv** sets the number of faces in the N direction. The maximum value allowed for these system variables is 200, and the minimum is 2.

Just as it does for smoothed polylines, AutoCAD retains its information about the defining mesh of smoothed surfaces, and you can see the defining surface mesh by setting the **splframe** system variable to 1. (A regen is required for the change to take effect.) When **splframe** is set to 0, the default setting, only the smoothed surface is shown. When **splframe** is set to 1, the original surface is shown. The display would be too cluttered and confusing if both were shown simultaneously (as are smoothed polylines).

Furthermore, the original surface can be restored by selecting the Desmooth option from the PEDIT menu. This is a good feature—if you don't like the results of a smoothed surface, you can desmooth it and smooth it again with different parameters.

You can move the vertex location of smoothed surfaces with the Edit vertex option of PEDIT, but it can be a daunting task since AutoCAD uses the vertices of the original surface rather than the smoothed surface. Even though the smoothed mesh is the one shown, the PEDIT vertex position marker will always be located on one of the vertices of the invisible defining mesh. The marker appears to be jumping around in space, and it is difficult to tell where it actually is or what effect moving the vertex will have on the mesh. Using grips is slightly better. While just the original vertex locations are shown as grips, all of them are shown, which gives you a better picture of the defining mesh.

When a polygon mesh is selected, the dialog box of AutoCAD 2000's PROPERTIES command contains information about vertices and meshes.

Property names are listed in the left column of this dialog box and their value or setting is listed in the right column, as described in the following table.

Property	Description
Vertex	An AutoCAD assigned number representing the current vertex. By clicking in the right-hand column, you can move to the next vertex or to the previous one. An X marker is displayed on the mesh to show the location of the vertex.
Vertex X	The X coordinate of the current vertex. You can edit the coordinate.
Vertex Y	The Y coordinate of the current vertex. You can edit the coordinate.
Vertex Z	The Z coordinate of the current vertex. You can edit the coordinate.
M closed	Indicates by a Yes or No whether the mesh is open or closed in the M direction. You can open a closed mesh, and close an open mesh.
N closed	Indicates by a Yes or No whether the mesh is open or closed in the N direction. You can open a closed mesh, and close an open mesh.
M density	Indicates the number of vertices in the M direction for smoothed meshes. The value represents the value of **surfu** plus one. You can edit the number.
N density	Indicates the number of vertices in the N direction for smoothed meshes. The value represents the value of **surfv** plus one. You can edit the number.
M vertex count	Indicates the number of vertices in the M direction for meshes that are not smoothed. The value represents the value of **surftab1** or **surftab2** plus one. This number cannot be edited.
N vertex count	Indicates the number of vertices in the N direction for meshes that are not smoothed. The value represents the value of **surftab1** or **surftab2** plus one. This number cannot be edited.
Fit/Smooth	Shows the type of surface curve fit. It will be none, quadratic, cubic, or Bezier. You can change the curve fit type.

Surface M and N directions, and consequently the **surfu** and **surfv** directions, can be confusing because AutoCAD is not consistent with M and N directions and **surftab1** and **surftab2** relationships. The figure above shows the directions and controlling system variables for surfaces made with RULESURF, TABSURF, REVSURF, and EDGESURF. 3DMESH is not included since **surftab1** and **surftab2** have no effect on its mesh density, and the M and N directions are dependent upon user input.

Command:	PEDIT
Purpose:	PEDIT allows you to move individual vertex locations and to smooth the surface of polygon mesh surfaces, as well as to open a closed surface or close one that is open.

Initiate with:

- On the command line enter PEDIT.
- From the Modify pull-down menu, select Polyline.
- Select the Edit Polyline button from the Modify II toolbar.

Options:

The PEDIT command will ask you to select one object. If that object is a polygon mesh surface, AutoCAD will display the command line menu

```
Enter an option [Edit vertex/Smooth surface/Desmooth/
    Mclose/Nclose/Undo]: (Enter an option or press Enter.)
```

If the surface is closed in the M direction, the Mclose option will be replaced by the Mopen option; if the surface is closed in the N direction, the Nclose option will be replaced by the Nopen option. This menu reappears after an option is completed. Press Enter to end the command.

- Edit vertex

You can change the location of a vertex with this option. When it is selected, AutoCAD will display the following secondary menu on the command line:

```
Current vertex (M,N). Enter an option [Next/Previous/Left/
    Right/Up/Down/Move/REgen/eXit] <N>:
```

An X marker will be positioned on a vertex of the polygon mesh, and the current M and N mesh position of the marker will be shown on the left side of the menu. Most of the options in this secondary menu are for moving this marker. When the marker is on the vertex you want to move, select the Move option.

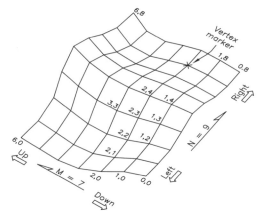

○ Next

This option moves the X marker to the next vertex in the N direction. Upon reaching the last vertex in the N direction, the M component of the vertex position number will increment by 1, and the N component will become 0. Using the mesh in the previous figure as an example, if the marker is on vertex (1,3), the next vertex will be (1,4); if it is on (1,8), the next vertex will be (2,0).

○ Previous

This option moves the X marker to the previous vertex in the N direction. Thus, if the marker is on vertex (1,3), the previous vertex is (1,2).

○ Left

The vertex marker is moved in the N direction to the previous vertex with this option. If, for example, the marker is on vertex (2,3), the Left vertex is (2,2). Unlike the marker movement of the Previous option, the marker will stop when the first vertex in the N direction is reached.

○ Right

The N component of the X marker's vertex number is incremented by 1 when this option is selected. It is similar to the Next option, but movement stops when the last vertex in the N direction is reached. Thus, on the mesh in the previous figure, Right will move the marker from (1,3) to (1,4), but if the marker is on (1,8), Right will have no effect.

○ Up

This option moves the X marker one vertex in the positive M direction. For example, if the marker is on vertex (2,3), Up will move it to vertex (3,3). Once the last vertex in the M direction is reached, Up will have no effect.

○ Down

The X marker is moved one vertex in the minus M direction with this option. If the marker is on vertex (2,4), for instance, Down will move it to (1,4). This option does not wrap the marker's movement.

○ Move

Selecting this option signals that you want to move the vertex that the X marker is currently on. AutoCAD will issue the prompt

```
Enter new location: (Specify a point.)
```

° REgen

This option regenerates the
polygon mesh.

° eXit

Select eXit to end the Edit Vertex option and return to the
main PEDIT menu.

Original surface   Smoothed surface

- Smooth surface

This option changes the shape of the surface into that of a quadratic B-spline, a cubic B-
spline, or a Bezier spline, depending upon the setting of the **surftype** system variable. The
number of faces on the smoothed surface is controlled by the **surfu** and **surfv** system variables.

- Desmooth

The original, unsmoothed version of
the polygon mesh surface can be
restored with this option.

- Mclose/Mopen

The Mclose option will be offered if
the polygon mesh surface is open
in the M direction, and the Mopen
option will be offered if the surface
is closed in the M direction. Mclose
will add a row of faces between the
first and last edges of the surface,
while Mopen will remove the last
row of faces along the N edge of
the surface.

Open in M direction   Closed in M direction

Closed in M direction   Opened in M direction

- Nclose/Nopen

If the polygon mesh surface is open in the N direction, the Nclose option will be displayed;
the Nopen option will be displayed if the surface is closed in the N direction. When Nclose
is selected, a row of faces will be added between the surface's first and last edges in the N
direction. When Nopen is selected, the last row of faces in the N direction will be removed.

- Undo

This option reverses the last PEDIT operation.

Notes:

- Unlike the Edit vertex options of PEDIT for polylines, you cannot remove or insert vertices
in a polygon mesh and you cannot break the mesh. You can only move vertices. Since you
can also move polygon mesh vertices by the STRETCH command, as well as with grips, you
will seldom use the Edit vertex option of PEDIT.

- Although you can move vertices of smoothed surfaces, this is not something you will want to do. First of all, you cannot move the vertices of the smoothed surface—you can move only the vertices of the original defining mesh. Second, AutoCAD moves the vertex marker from node to node on the original mesh, even though it is not visible. This makes the marker appear to be jumping about on invisible points in space.

- You can close an open polygon mesh even if the results are not logical. For instance, if you close a planar surface, a row of new faces is laid over the existing surface.

- If a mesh has more than eleven vertices in either its M or N direction, it cannot be smoothed to a Bezier surface.

- A mesh must have at least three vertices in both directions to be smoothed to a quadratic surface, and it must have at least four vertices in both directions to be smoothed to a cubic surface.

Related system variables:

- **surftype**

  This system variable determines the equation type used by PEDIT in smoothing surfaces. It takes an integer value of 5, 6, or 8. A quadratic B-spline equation is used when **surftype** is set to 5, a cubic B-spline equation is used when it is set to 6, and a Bezier equation is used when it is set to 8. The initial setting is 6.

- **surfu**

  This system variable controls the number of faces in the M direction of a smoothed polygon mesh surface. Its minimum value is 2, its maximum value is 200, and its initial setting is 6.

- **surfv**

  The number of faces on a smoothed polygon mesh surface in the N direction is equal to the value in this system variable. Its initial value is 6, and it will accept any integer from 2 through 200.

- **splframe**

  When **splframe** is set to its default value of 0, AutoCAD displays smoothed polygon mesh surfaces in their smoothed condition. When splframe is set to 1, the original unsmoothed form of the mesh is displayed. A regen is required to implement the change. This variable controls just the display of smoothed polygon meshes—if you want to permanently desmooth the mesh, you must use PEDIT.

Exercises

We will describe two exercises you can use for getting a feel for smoothing polygon mesh surfaces and seeing the effects of **surfu** and **surfv**. You should feel free to perform additional experiments with the objects in these exercises on your own.

Exercise One

Draw a 2D polyline on the X-Z plane of the WCS that has a shape similar to the one on the left side of the top figure. The dimensions of this polyline are not important. Also, draw a center line that can be used as an axis of revolution. If you do not want to draw this 2D polyline and the axis, you can use those that are in file mfe09101.dwg in the CD-ROM that comes with this book.

Make a copy of the polyline and center line, and use REVSURF on one pair of the objects to make a surface model stemware glass, as shown on the right side of the top figure. Use the default setting of 6 for both **surftab1** and **surftab2**.

Now, use PEDIT or DDMODIFY to fit the surface to various shapes by varying the surface type as well as the **surfu** and **surfv** values. Since there are more vertices in the N direction than permitted for Bezier surfaces, you can smooth the model only with quadratic and cubic equations. The middle figure shows the model smoothed to a cubic B-spline with a **surfu** value of 20 and two different **surfv** values. Notice that smoothing the surface cancels the REVSURF characteristic of dividing polyline curved segments into **surftab2** faces and of not dividing straight segments at all.

Use REVSURF, combined with a **surftab1** value of 3 and a **surftab2** value of 6, with the other polyline and center line to make a surface model that has a triangular cross-section, as shown on the left side of the bottom figure. Then use PEDIT or DDMODIFY to smooth the surface. A quadratic surface is your only choice, because there are too many vertices for a Bezier surface and not enough for a cubic B-spline. One example of the smoothed surface is shown on the right. Since the smoothed surface is based on the vertices of the original surface mesh, it is lobed rather than round in cross-section.

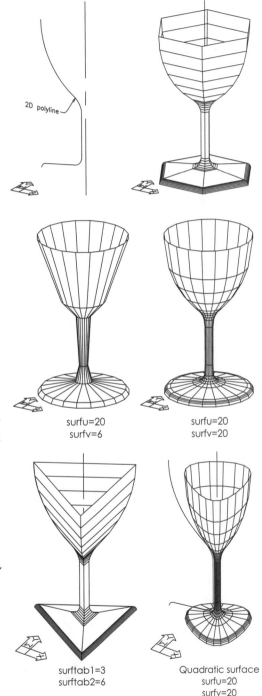

2D polyline

surfu=20
surfv=6

surfu=20
surfv=20

surftab1=3
surftab2=6

Quadratic surface
surfu=20
surfv=20

Exercise Two

Retrieve mfe09201.dwg from the CD-ROM that accompanies this book and open it. The surface model in this file was made with AutoCAD's 3DMESH command. It has eight vertices in the M direction and five in the N direction. The faces that appear to have only three sides (they are located on the corners of the model), were made by selecting the same point for two adjacent vertices, which makes one side of the face have a length of 0.

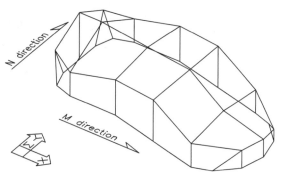

This is an open exercise in which you can modify the surface model in any way you want. You can move vertices with PEDIT, with STRETCH, or through the mesh's grips; and you can smooth the model using any of the three surface types. The model is complex enough to be interesting, but not so complex that it is difficult to work with. The figure on the right shows the model after it has been smoothed to a quadratic B-spline with **surfu** set to 32 and **surfv** set to 20.

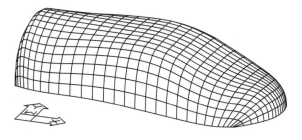

Building Solid Models

Getting Started in Solid Models

This chapter will start by giving you an overall picture of solid modeling processes. Then it will concentrate on some fundamental tools for creating 3D solid objects. Specifically, this chapter will

- demonstrate the general techniques of solid modeling by leading you through the construction of a simple solid model;
- introduce the ACIS Geometric Modeler that AutoCAD solid models are based on;
- list the uses and properties of regions, which are a 2D version of 3D solids, describe what their uses are, and how they are created;
- explain, and demonstrate through exercises, how to use the AutoCAD commands for making extruded and revolved 3D solids from 2D profiles.

Solid modeling is not at all like surface modeling. The object types are different, the commands for making the objects are different, and even the approach and strategy for making models are different. You will recall from Section Two of this book that most surface models are constructed by drawing wireframe objects to represent edges and boundaries on the model, then adding surfaces between those wireframe objects.

Solid models, on the other hand, start out as basic 3D geometric shapes, which can be joined or subtracted from one another to form complex models. Often, basic 3D geometric solids are referred to as *primitive* solids, and models made from combined primitives are referred to as *composite* solids.

AutoCAD solid models start as basic geometric shapes.

In general, you will probably find solid modeling to be easier and more intuitive than surface modeling, and if you are working with items that are typically made in a machine shop with tools such as lathes, milling machines, and drill presses, you will most likely model them as solids.

The commands for creating primitive solids can be conveniently divided into two categories. In one category, primitives are made from 2D profile objects. The commands in this category are EXTRUDE and REVOLVE, and we will concentrate on those two commands in this chap-

The basic geometric shapes are combined to make a complex solid model.

ter. In the other category, primitives are created directly in one of several basic geometric forms. The commands in this category are BOX, CONE, CYLINDER, SPHERE, TORUS, and WEDGE. We will discuss those commands in the next chapter. Then, you will know everything about creating primitives, and in Chapter Twelve we will discuss the ways in which primitives can be combined to form composite solid models.

Constructing a Simple 3D Solid Model

If you are not familiar with solid modeling, you should construct a simple 3D solid model by following the steps described in the next few pages. In building this model, you will be introduced to some of the fundamental concepts of solid modeling, as well as to some of the commonly used terms. It will give you an overall picture of how solid objects are created and

how they are combined to make a model with the geometry you want. We will use the command line to initiate all actions while building this model so you can concentrate on the actual commands rather than on menus and buttons.

This demonstration 3D solid model will not be one that you need to keep, and it does not matter which template or prototype drawing you start with. The standard AutoCAD new drawing named drawing.dwg will work fine. You will, however, probably find it helpful to have the UCS icon located at the UCS origin and to set the snap spacing to 1 unit.

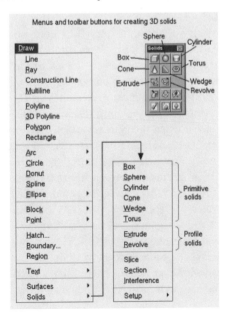

Extruded Solids

Start the model by drawing the object shown in the figure on the next page, using the given dimensions. Draw this object as a 2D polyline, and make certain that its lower-left corner is on the WCS origin. Set an SE isometric viewpoint, and zoom and pan as necessary to give yourself working room.

Turn the 2D polyline into a 3D solid by using the following command line input:

```
Command: EXTRUDE (Enter)
Current wire frame density:  ISOLINES=4
Select objects: Select the 2D polyline, and
    press Enter.
Specify height of extrusion or [Path]: 1
    (Enter)
Specify angle of taper for extrusion <0>:
    (Enter)
```

Your object should look similar to the one on the left side of the next figure. Despite the similarity in names, the EXTRUDE command makes an object that is completely different from wireframe objects with an extrusion thickness. If we had given the polyline an extrusion thickness of 1 unit, it would have been like a 1-unit-high wall. This extruded solid, however is a completely filled-in solid object. When HIDE is active, your model will look like the one on the right side of the figure. Notice that AutoCAD automatically adds facets to curved surfaces on a solid model during HIDE.

The object you created is often referred to as an extruded solid, due to the name of the command used to make it. Nevertheless, its AutoCAD database object type, which is a 3D solid, is no different from those made by the other seven commands for creating solids.

AutoCAD first issued a message about the **isolines** system variable. We will discuss that system variable in Chapter 14. Then you were asked to select the objects to be extruded. Almost any closed wireframe object can be used to make an extruded solid—circles, splines, and polylines in any of their various forms. Any width that a polyline might have is ignored. You may select more than one object, although this doesn't mean that you can make an extruded solid from a set of connected lines and arcs, even if they form a closed path when combined. Each object selected must be closed. Objects used for making extruded solids are automatically deleted when the system variable **delobj** is set to 1, which is its default setting. If you want to retain objects used to make extruded solids, set **delobj** to 0.

After you selected the object to be extruded, the EXTRUDE command asked you to enter an extrusion height or to specify that the extrusion is to be based on a path. You responded by entering 1. This caused the profile to be extruded 1 unit in the polyline's extrusion direction, which was the positive Z direction. We could have specified the extrusion height by pointing on the X-Y plane, and the resulting extrusion would still have been made in the polyline's extrusion direction.

When you choose the Path option, you will be prompted to select an object that will establish both the length and shape of the extruded solid. The profile object will be swept along the path as it forms the solid, even if the path is curved. This is a very powerful option—one that enables you to make unique, nonlinear 3D geometric shapes. We will discuss extrusions along a path at length later in this chapter.

Path

Profile object

Extruded solid

Straight extrusion   Tapered extrusion

The final prompt for the EXTRUDE command is for an extrusion taper angle, with a default angle of 0 degrees. A positive taper angle will cause the extrusion to taper inward (its cross-section area becomes smaller), while a negative taper angle causes the extruded solid to taper outward (its cross-section area becomes larger). Since we accepted the default taper angle of 0, the cross-section area of our solid remained the same through the extrusion length.

Primitives

We will make the second basic 3D geometric object for our model in the shape of a box. The command sequence to make this box is

```
Command: BOX (Enter)
Specify corner of box or [CEnter] <0,0,0>: (Enter)
Specify corner or [Cube/Length]: 1,3 (Enter)
Specify height: 2 (Enter)
```

The prompts and options for the BOX command are similar to drawing a 2D rectangle and then specifying a height for the box. We accepted the default location, which is at the UCS origin, for the first corner of the box. Then we placed the opposite bottom corner of the box at the coordinates of 1,3,0 and specified that the box was to be 2 units high. Your model should now look like the one shown in the figure on the right.

Even though the name of the command is BOX, the object you just created is more like a brick than an empty box—it is completely solid. In geometry books, this geometric shape is sometimes referred to as a *rectangular parallelepiped* and at other times as a *rectangular prism*; however, since both of those names are lengthy, we will follow Autodesk's lead and simply call them boxes.

We could have made this 3D solid by drawing a 2D polyline rectangle and extruding its units in the Z direction, but the BOX command is a shortcut method that creates a 3D solid without the need for a profile object. It is one of six commands for making basic, or primitive, 3D geometric shapes. The other five commands are CONE, CYLINDER, SPHERE, TORUS, and WEDGE.

You will notice that half of the box is inside the extruded solid. Soon we will join the two solids, but first we will make a cylinder-shaped primitive that will be the basis of a hole in the extruded solid. The command line sequence of prompts and options to make this cylinder is

```
Command: CYLINDER (Enter)
Current wire frame density:  ISOLINES=4
Specify center point for base of cylinder or [Elliptical] <0,0,0>: 3,1.5 (Enter)
Specify radius for base of cylinder or [Diameter]: .75 (Enter)
Specify height of cylineder or [Center of other end]: 1 (Enter)
```

Making a cylinder is similar to making a circle, then specifying a height. Our circle is centered in the arc portion of the extruded solid and has a radius of 0.75 units and a height of 1.0 units. We specified the height by entering a value, although we could have specified it by picking two points. Normally, the axis of the cylinder is in the Z axis direction, but if you select the "Center of other end" option, you can pick a point that establishes the end of the cylinder axis. The cylinder will start at the initial center point and end at the Center of other end pick point. Notice also that you can even make cylinders that have an elliptical cross-section.

Your three 3D solid objects should look similar to those on left side of the next figure. In wireframe form, the model looks reasonably finished—the extruded solid and the box appear to be united, and you can imagine that the cylinder is a hole. However, when you invoke the

HIDE command, as shown on the right side of the figure, there is no edge where the box intersects the extruded solid, and it becomes obvious that the cylinder is not a hole. We will have to join the box to the extruded solid, and we will have to subtract the cylinder's volume from the extruded solid.

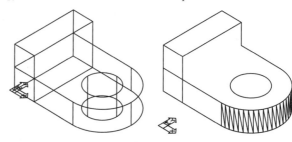

Boolean Operations

The three Boolean operations involve the interaction of two or more 3D solid objects. They are for shaping and transforming basic geometric shapes into complex solid models. Their name is based on the name of a mathematician (George Boole) who developed theories on logic and sets. AutoCAD has three commands for performing Boolean operations. In accordance with the arithmetic of sets, the Boolean operations differ from one another in how they handle common (or shared) volumes. AutoCAD's Boolean operation commands are

Command	Operation
UNION	Joins two or more 3D solids into one solid. Volume common to the solids is absorbed into the united solid.

SUBTRACT   Subtracts the volume of one set of solids from the volume of a second set of solids. The first set of solids is automatically deleted. If there is no common volume, the first set of solids is simply deleted.

INTERSECT   Creates a solid from the volume shared by a set of solids. Volume that is not common disappears, and if there is no common volume, all of the solids are deleted.

We will use two of these commands on our solid model—UNION and SUBTRACT. We will first subtract the cylinder's volume from the extruded solid's volume. The command line prompts and input to do this are

```
Command: SUBTRACT (Enter)
Select solids and regions to subtract from...
Select objects: (Select the extruded solid)
Select objects: (Enter)
Select solids and regions to subtract...
Select objects: (Select the cylinder)
Select objects: (Enter)
```

In wireframe form, as shown on the left side of the figure, nothing will appear to be different in the model, but in the hidden line mode, as shown on the right in the figure, you will see that the cylinder has gone away, and in its place is a hole in the extruded solid.

The cylinder was the same height as the extruded solid, but even if it had been taller, the result would have been the same. The object that is subtracted always disappears at the end of the operation. Notice that the command first asks for the solid to subtract from, and then asks for the solids to be subtracted from the first set. Any of the standard AutoCAD selection methods may be used, and there is no limit to the number of solids in each selection set. The reference to regions is a reminder that Boolean operations also apply to regions, which are a 2D relative to 3D solids (we will discuss regions later in this chapter).

Next, we will use the UNION command to join the box primitive and the extruded solid (we could have performed this operation before the subtract operation just as well). The command line sequence to join the two solids is

```
Command: UNION (Enter)
Select objects: (Select the box and the extruded solid.)
Select objects: (Enter)
```

That's all there is to it. The two solids are now one solid. In the wireframe viewing mode, the edges of the box that were inside and on the surface of the extruded solid will disappear, and a new edge will be created where the two solids intersected. Even if the two solids had not touched each other, they would have been combined into one solid, although the gap between them would still exist. You can join as many 3D solids as you like, using any of the standard AutoCAD selection methods in choosing them. In wireframe mode, your model should now look like the one on the left in the bottom figure on the previous page, and it should look like the one on the right when HIDE is active.

Modifications

While AutoCAD's set of tools for modifying 3D solids is not as complete as you would like, it does have the ability to round (fillet) and bevel (chamfer) sharp edges of 3D solids. These operations are done through the same AutoCAD commands—FILLET and CHAMFER—used for comparable operations on wireframe objects. AutoCAD also has a command, named SLICE, that cuts a 3D solid into two pieces.

We will discuss the commands for modifying 3D solids extensively in Chapter Thirteen. To give you an idea as to how the FILLET command works on 3D solids, though, we will round the sharp corner located at the intersection of the original box and extruded solid. The command line input to do this is

```
Command: FILLET (Enter)
Current settings: Mode = TRIM  Radius = 0.5000
Select first object or [Polyline/Radius/Trim]: (Pick the inside corner edge.)
Enter fillet radius <0.5000>: .25 (Enter)
Select an edge or [Chain/Radius]: (Enter)
```

Unlike fillets on wireframe objects, in which you must select two objects for each fillet, you select an edge between two surfaces for fillets on 3D solids. When you pick the edge of a 3D solid in response to the FILLET command's "Select first object" prompt, AutoCAD recognizes the object type and issues command line prompts appropriate for rounding edges of 3D solids. The first of these prompts allows you to change the current fillet radius. We entered a radius value of 0.25. The second of the special prompts allows you to select additional edges on the 3D solid. Since we wanted to fillet just the one edge, we pressed the Enter key in response to this prompt.

This ended the FILLET command, and AutoCAD rounded the initially specified inside corner.

In wireframe form, your completed model should now look like the one on the left side of the figure, and it should look like the one on the right when you invoke the HIDE command. We are finished with this model, and you do not need to save it. Before you abandon it, though, you may want to try SHADEMODE's hidden and shaded viewing modes on the model.

The ACIS Geometric Modeler

AutoCAD's solid modeler is based on the ACIS Geometric Modeler from Spatial Technology, Inc. This is a widely used program (often referred to as the ACIS kernel) that contains functions and tools for creating and modifying 3D objects. Organizations throughout the world involved with

3D modeling license the ACIS kernel, incorporate it into their programs, and add their own interface to it.

Autodesk uses the ACIS kernel for 3D modeling in the Mechanical Desktop as well as in AutoCAD. While the ACIS kernel is normally invisible to AutoCAD users, you will sometimes see references to it in error messages, in some AutoCAD documentation, and even in the names of some AutoCAD commands. The ACISIN command, for instance, permits you to import ACIS-based objects into AutoCAD, and the ACISOUT command saves 3D solids in a format usable by other programs that use the ACIS kernel.

Like all computer programs, the ACIS Geometric Modeler undergoes periodic revisions. AutoCAD 2000 uses ACIS Version 4.0. Early versions of AutoCAD Release 14, on the other hand, used ACIS 1.6, while later versions (beginning with Release 14.01) used ACIS 3.0. In most cases, the ACIS version is not important. You can though, control the ACIS version used by the ACISOUT command, by changing the default value, which is 40, of the **acisoutver** system variable. **Acisoutver** accepts values of 15, 16, 17, 18, 20, 21, 30, and 40.

Regions

When a 3D solid is exploded, its flat surfaces will turn into an AutoCAD database object called *regions*, while its nonplanar surfaces will turn into objects called *bodies*. Although they are a surface type of object (meaning that they can hide objects as well as reflect light in renderings and that they have no thickness), body database objects have no practical use. Moreover, the only way to create a body is to explode a 3D solid.

Regions, on the other hand, are an important object type. They are surface-type objects that respond to Boolean operations. You can also use the MASSPROP command on regions to find such things as their area, their geometric center, and moments of inertia. (We will discuss MASSPROP in Chapter Fourteen.) Moreover, regions can be used as profile objects with the EXTRUDE and REVOLVE commands to make 3D solids. Since regions can have interior holes (made by subtracting one region from another), they sometimes have an advantage over other profile objects.

The ability of regions to have interior holes, and edges of virtually any shape, also makes them useful for covering planar areas in surface modeling. For example, surfacing the front of the model shown in the figure below with polygon mesh objects is not only

The front of this surface model consists of four ruled surfaces.

The front of this surface model is one region.

The BOUNDARY command is useful for making a region from this interior area.

tedious, the resulting mesh lines tend to make the surface confusing. Covering this area with a region is much easier, and the surface is not cluttered.

Most of the time you will use the REGION command to make regions, but you can also make them with the BOUNDARY command. The BOUNDARY command is most useful when you want to make a region from an interior island, as shown in the lower-right figure on the previous page.

Exercise One

Draw the cross-section of a spur gear on the X-Y plane of the WCS, using the dimensions given in the figure on the right. The teeth on this gear, which have straight sides, are simplified since the exercise is in creating regions rather than in drawing gear teeth. Feel free to use involute teeth profiles and dimensions instead, if you have the knowledge and time to do so.

When you have finished your 2D drawing of the gear, invoke the REGION command and select all of the objects. AutoCAD will report that out of a total of sixty-eight objects it found two loops, and that it created two regions. The center hole and keyway are in one region, and the teeth profiles are in the other region. Your gear profile, however, will look the same as when it was composed of individual lines and arcs. Later in this chapter we will extrude these two regions to make 3D solids. These two regions are in the file mfe10101.dwg on the CD-ROM that accompanies this book.

Command: REGION

Purpose: Transforms existing objects into region database objects.

Initiate with:

- On the command line enter REGION.
- From the Draw pull-down menu, select Region.
- Select the Region button from the Draw toolbar.

Implementation:

A command line prompt asks you to select the objects that are to be transformed into regions. You may use any object selection method, and you may select as many objects as you wish. Press the Enter key to signal the end of the selection set.

A region can be created from most single planar closed objects—a circle, a 3D face, an ellipse, a closed spline, and a closed 2D polyline (including any member of the 2D polyline family, such as a polygon or a donut). Polyline width is ignored. Splines and 2D polylines qualify when their first and last vertices are in the same location, even if they were not finished with the Close option. Splines and 2D polylines that cross over themselves (self-intersect), or have two vertices in the same location, are not accepted as regions. Nonplanar splines are rejected, and all 3D polylines are rejected, even if they are planar. Polygon and polyface meshes are not accepted.

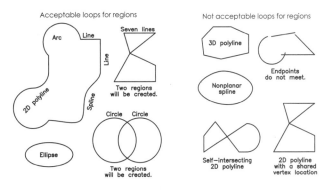

A region can also be created from a set of open wireframe objects that form a closed loop. The loop can be any combination of lines, arcs, 2D polylines, and splines. The objects must be end to end, with no gaps or non-coinciding endpoints, and they must all be in the same plane.

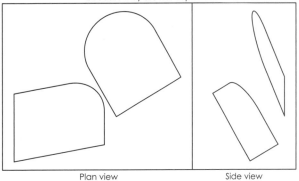

If both of these loops (each consisting of lines and an arc) are in the same selection set, no region will be created, because they are not coplanar.

Plan view   Side view

When you are creating a single region, whether it is based on a loop of open objects or on a single closed object, the orientation of the UCS with the plane of the object, or objects, is not important. Moreover, the orientation of multiple closed objects relative to each other and to the UCS is not important. However, multiple loops of open objects must be coplanar, although the orientation of their plane to the UCS is not important. Even if one out of several loops of open objects is not in the same plane as the other objects, no region will be created.

After you specify the objects that are to be transformed into a region, or regions, AutoCAD will report, on the command line, the number of loops it found in the selection set and the number of regions that were created. If some loops did not result in regions, AutoCAD will briefly explain why they were rejected.

The newly created region, or regions, will take on the current layer, color, and linetype properties. Thickness for region objects is always 0.

Notes:

- Regions can also be created by the BOUNDARY command. Unlike the REGION command, BOUNDARY can make regions from planar 3D polylines. BOUNDARY also retains the original objects, placing the region over them.

Related system variable:

- **delobj**

  When **delobj** is set to 0, the object, or objects, used to create a region are retained. When **delobj** is set to 1, they are deleted when the region is created.

Profile-Based 3D Solids

The eight commands for making 3D solids in basic shapes can be conveniently divided into two groups—those that make solids from profile objects and those that directly make solids having a fundamental geometric shape. The latter group of solids are generally referred to as primitives, although sometimes the word *primitive* is used for all of the basic 3D solids. The AutoCAD database object type, which is 3D solid, is the same regardless of the command used to make them. In the next chapter we will describe the commands for the six primitives and show how they can be used.

The two commands that base 3D solids on profile objects are EXTRUDE and REVOLVE. EXTRUDE makes a 3D solid by pushing the profile object linearly for a specific distance, or by pushing it along a path defined by a wireframe object. REVOLVE creates a 3D solid by revolving the profile object around an axis.

These two commands are even more fundamental than those that make the primitives because they can make any geometric shape that the commands for making primitives can. They can also make geometric shapes that the primitives cannot make. Any solid model that can be built with AutoCAD can be based on just these two commands. (Autodesk's other solid modeler—Mechanical Desktop—uses only profile-based solids and has no commands for making primitives.)

The EXTRUDE and REVOLVE commands have the same requirements for profile objects— each profile must be a single, closed, planar object. 2D polylines will be one of your most often used object types. Autodesk's documentation states that 2D polyline profiles cannot have more than five hundred vertices, but they can. This is a moot point, though, since even five hundred vertices in a profile will make a 3D solid that is unacceptably unwieldy.

Regions are especially useful as profile objects since they can have interior holes and can therefore create solids with interior holes. While it is not essential that the holes be present when the solid is first created, as they can be added later, it is convenient.

Profile object

Revolved solid

Extruded solid

Using this region as a profile...

can create this 3D solid.

Making Extruded 3D Solids

EXTRUDE is the most versatile of the commands for making 3D solids, and it will likely be the one you most often use. It can make solids having geometries that none of the other commands can make, and it can often make a geometric shape in one step that would require several steps if the commands for creating primitives were used.

The command gives you two distinct ways to extrude the profile—you can extrude it by specifying a height or by specifying a wireframe path for the extrusion to follow. Either way, you can extrude more than one profile with one call of the EXTRUDE command. Each extrusion, however, must have the same height or use the same path.

Extrusions based on height are so straightforward that little needs to be said about them. Notice, though, that the solid's extrusion direction is based on the profile object's extrusion direction. This is an object property representing the direction of the Z axis at the time the object was created. As a result, the extrusion will not necessarily be in the current Z direction. AutoCAD's LIST command will show you an object's extrusion direction.

Extrusions based on paths, on the other hand, can be extremely complicated and can produce unexpected results. It is a powerful option, though—one that enables you to create unique geometries. The following rules will help you control your extrusions by path:

- Keep path shapes as simple as possible. Even when you are making a complex shape, it is often better to create the shape in several steps rather than in one step that requires a complicated path. The Boolean operations can be used to combine and join the extruded segments.
- Start the path in a direction that is perpendicular to the profile.
- Position the path midway between the ends of the profile. This is not necessarily at the weighted geometric center (the centroid) of the profile.

Arcs and 2D polylines will be your most often used object types for planar paths. Splines can be tricky to use as path objects, since even a spline that appears to be relatively straight can contain small radius curves that would cause the surface of the solid to self-intersect. When this is the case, AutoCAD will display an error message and will not make the solid.

When you need a nonplanar path, 3D polylines are your only choice. Splines would be better, but AutoCAD will not accept nonplanar splines as paths.

Although circles can be used as paths, they must have a very large radius relative to the size of the profile. You may have more success with using a 2D polyline of two 180-degree arcs than using a circle. Furthermore, the REVOLVE command will probably create the solid shape you are after without the need for constructing a path.

Exercise Two

This will the first of several simple exercises in creating extruded 3D solids to give you a feel for the EXTRUDE command. In Chapter Twelve we will have more involved exercises as we create 3D models rather than individual components.

Open your drawing of the spur gear profile you made as an exercise in the REGION command. You can also use the file mfe10101.dwg on the CD-ROM that comes with this book. The spur gear profile consists of two regions—one for the gear teeth and one for the interior hole.

If you are using your drawing, create a layer named Sol01 and make it the current layer. If you are using the file from the CD-ROM, that layer already exists, and you need only to verify

that it is the current layer. Set an SE
isometric view point through one of Auto-
CAD's menus or toolbars, or by using the
VPOINT coordinates of 1,-1,1 and zoom
back a little to give yourself working room.

Then use the EXTRUDE command to
turn both regions into 3D solids. On the
command line, the prompts and input
will be

```
Command: EXTRUDE (Enter)
Current wire frame density: ISOLINES=4
Select objects: (Use any object selection method to select both regions.)
Specify height of extrusion or [Path]: 1 (Enter)
Specify angle of taper for extrusion <0>: (Enter)
```

This extrudes both of the regions 1 unit in
their extrusion direction, which was in the Z
direction. Your model should look like the one
in the next figure when HIDE is in effect. It
consists of two separate 3D solid objects. In
Chapter Twelve we will finish the model by
subtracting the solid that represents a hole
from the gear blank solid. On the CD-ROM,
this model is in file mfe10202.dwg.

Exercise Three

In this exercise, you will create a helix-shaped 3D solid that has a round cross-section. Start a
new drawing. We will not use this drawing after the exercise is finished, so its initial setup is not
important.

The first step is to draw the helix path for the extrusion. Load the spiral.lsp program that is
on the CD-ROM. (Probably the easiest way to do this is with the AutoCAD APPLOAD
command. This command displays a dialog box you can use to browse for and load the
AutoLISP program you want.)

Once spiral.lsp has been loaded use the following command line input to draw a helix.

```
Command: 3DSPIRAL (Enter)
Center point: 0,0,0 (Enter)
Number of rotations: 2 (Enter)
Starting Radius: 1.5 (Enter)
Horizontal growth per rotation: 0 (Enter)
Vertical growth per rotation: 1 (Enter)
Points per rotation <30>: 24 (Enter)
```

*MAKE SURE JOINTS
ARE CLOSED.

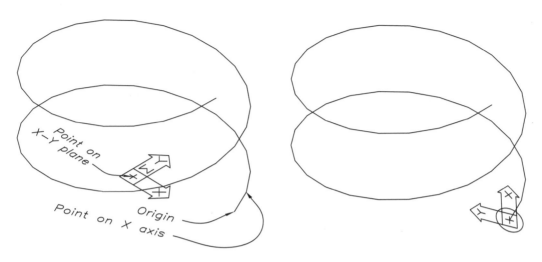

Switch the viewpoint to that of an SE isometric view. The VPOINT coordinates of 1,-1,1 will do this. Your next step is to set the UCS to be perpendicular to the first segment of the helix. This is not a straightforward step since 3DSPIRAL draws the first segment of the helix skewed to the principal planes. It does start on the X-Y plane, though. One of several ways to position and orient the UCS to be perpendicular to the first segment is to use the 3point option of the UCS command with the point selections shown in the upper-left figure. Then rotate the UCS minus 90 degrees about its Y axis.

When the UCS is positioned, draw a circle centered on the UCS origin and having a radius of 0.1875 units. This circle will be the profile for the 3D solid. Your circular profile and helix path should look like those in the upper-right figure.

Start the EXTRUDE command, pick the circle as the object that is to be extruded, and pick the 3D polyline for its path. The completed 3D solid is shown in the figure on the right. The solid in this figure may not look like the one on your computer screen because the system variable **dispsilh** has been set to a value of 1. This suppresses the display of facets on curved and rounded surfaces of 3D solids when the HIDE command is active, which can result in a less cluttered display of the solid. We will discuss the **dispsilh** system variable more extensively later in this section of the book. You should also invoke SHADE-MODE to see the effects of its viewing modes.

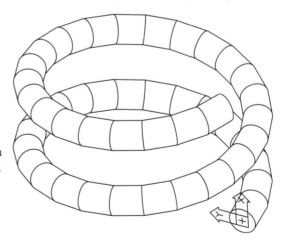

Notice that the 3D solid is composed of straight segments corresponding to the straight segments of the 3D polyline. A smooth helix curve made with the SPLINE command would be a much better path, but AutoCAD does not allow nonplanar splines, or even spline-fit 3D polylines, to be used as paths.

The profile and path for this exercise, as well as the completed 3D solid, is in file mfe10303.dwg on the CD-ROM that comes with this book.

Exercise Four

Start a new drawing. Create a layer, having a name such as WF01, for wireframe objects, and another, with a name such as CL (and a CENTERLINE line type), for center lines. From the WCS, rotate the UCS 90 degrees about the X axis and switch the viewpoint to a plan view of the new

UCS orientation. Make the CL layer current, and draw a straight line along the Y axis. This line will serve as a location reference in this exercise and as a rotation axis in a later exercise. Then change to the layer you are using for wireframe objects, and draw the profile shown in the figure above. Do not include the dimensions or the hatch lines. Turn the profile objects into a 2D polyline or a region.

Restore the WCS and change to an SE isometric viewpoint. You will use the profile you just drew to make one side of a pan-shaped solid model. You will also use the profile to make a second side of the model. Therefore, use the polar option of the ARRAY command (or the 3DARRAY command) to make a copy of the profile that is rotated 90 degrees about the center line from the original. Your two profiles should look similar to those in the lower-left figure.

Since you will use this profile in a future exercise to make a revolved solid, you should either make a copy of it or set the **delobj** system variable to 0 so it will not be deleted when it is used with the EXTRUDE command. Although you will be able to use the Height option of the

232

EXTRUDE command to make the solids, using a path for each extrusion will reduce the uncertainty as to which direction EXTRUDE will push the profile. Therefore, draw a 6-unit-long line along the X axis, and a 4-unit-long line along the Y axis. These lines will also be useful for making copies of the extruded solids.

Create a new layer, with a name such as SOL01, and make it the current layer. Start the EXTRUDE command, pick the profile that is in the WCS X-Z plane to be extruded, and pick the 4-unit-long line as its path. Start EXTRUDE again, this time picking the profile that is in the Y-Z plane to be extruded and the 6-unit-long line as its path. Your two extruded 3D solids should look similar to those in the lower-right figure on the previous page.

(# 10303.DWG)

Lastly, use the MIRROR command to make the opposite sides of the pan. Your model should look similar to the one in the figure above. The model is shown in this figure with HIDE active and with the **dispsilh** system variable set to 1. The model will have this same appearance when SHADEMODE's Hidden option is in effect. We will make the corners for this pan in an exercise with the REVOLVE command. The model, at this stage, is on the CD-ROM that comes with this book in file mfe10404.dwg.

Command: EXTRUDE

Purpose: This command creates a 3D solid by extruding a profile object. The direction and length of the extrusion can be in accordance with the profile object's extrusion direction or in accordance with the direction and length of a wireframe object serving as a path.

Initiate with:

• On the command line enter EXTRUDE.

• From the Draw pull-down menu, select Solids, then Extrude.

• Select the Extrude button from the Solids toolbar.

Options:

• Select Objects

You can extrude more than one profile object, and you can use any AutoCAD selection method in choosing them. Each profile must be a single closed planar object. Acceptable object types are circles, 2D polylines and any member of the 2D polyline family, splines, ellipses, regions, and 3D faces. Splines and 2D polylines are considered closed as long as their startpoints and endpoints are in the same location. They cannot, however, self-intersect or have more than one vertex on a single point. Splines must be planar. 3D polylines are not accepted as profile objects, even if they are planar and closed.

Thickness is ignored, as is 2D polyline width. Spline-fit 2D polylines are accepted as profiles, but they are a poor choice due to their large number of vertices. Traces and 2D solids (made with the SOLID command) may also be extruded. AutoCAD uses their outline for the extrusion boundary.

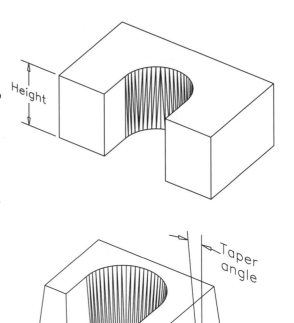

- Height of Extrusion

Once the profile objects have been selected, you are given two choices for an extrusion method—by height or by a path. When you select the height method, you will be asked to specify a height for the extruded solid. You can either enter a number or pick two points in specifying the height. When a positive number is entered for the height and when the height is specified by pointing, the extrusion will be in the profile object's positive extrusion direction, which is the direction of the Z axis at the time the object was created. If you enter a negative number, the extrusion will be in the profile object's negative extrusion direction.

- Extrusion Taper Angle

After you specify a height for the extrusion, you will be prompted to specify its taper angle. (This is sometimes, even by AutoCAD's on-screen messages, referred to as *draft angle*.) The angle's units (degrees, radians, and so forth) are determined by the **aunits** system variable. You can specify the angle by entering a number or by pointing. When a nonzero taper angle is entered, the sides of the extrusion will be sloped rather than vertical.

The extrusion slopes inward when a positive taper angle is specified. That is, the cross-section area of the solid becomes smaller along the length of the extrusion. If you specify an angle that is so large that the extrusion sides would intersect before the specified height is reached, AutoCAD will display an error message and no 3D solid will be created. When you specify a negative taper angle, the cross-section area of the solid will become larger along the length of the extrusion.

Positive taper angle   Negative taper angle

- Path

    When the Path option is selected, you will be prompted to select one object that will determine the extrusion's length, direction, and shape. You will not, however, be able to taper the extrusion. The path object may be either open or closed. Allowed object types are lines, arcs, circles, ellipses, 2D polylines and any member of the 2D polyline family, 3D polylines, and planar splines. Spline-fit 2D polylines can be used as paths, but spline-fit 3D polylines cannot. Nonplanar 3D polylines made of line segments can be used as paths. Nonplanar splines, however, are not accepted.

    The path cannot be parallel to the plane of the profile object, and it cannot contain curves having a radius less than the profile length. Profile length is the distance from the path to the furthest edge of the profile.

    On sharp corners and nontangent arc segment endpoints, the solid will be mitered.

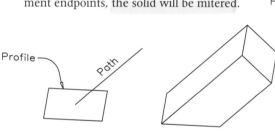

Unless the path is a spline, the extruded solid will start at the profile and its end plane will be perpendicular to the end of the path. This means that if the start of the path is not perpendicular to the profile, the cross-section area of the solid, perpendicular to the path, will be smaller than the profile's area.

However, if the path is a spline that is not perpendicular to the profile, AutoCAD will rotate the profile so that it is perpendicular to the start of the path. The end plane of the solid will be perpendicular to the end of the path, the same as with paths of other object types.

The object used for a path does not have to touch the profile. AutoCAD projects the path to the geometric center of the profile (although the location of the object used for the path does not change). If the path object is perpendicular to the profile, this projection is of no consequence. However, if the path object is not perpendicular to the profile, its length and the radius of any arcs on it will change according to the direction and distance of the projection.

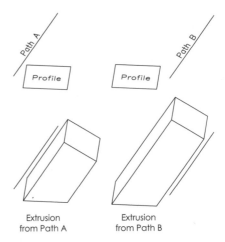

The figure on the right shows two extrusions from a profile that is the same, using path objects that have the same length and angle but different relative locations to the profile. The resulting extrusions have different lengths, and neither extrusion is equal to the path object's length.

If the path is closed and has sharp corners, such as a hexagon, AutoCAD will move the path so that its closest corner to the profile is centered on the profile, and it will rotate the profile to be in line with the mitered corner of the extruded 3D solid.

Notes:

- Extruded 3D solids assume the current layer, linetype, and color properties.
- Regions are an especially useful profile object since they allow you to make extruded solids with interior holes.

Related system variables:

- **delobj**

  When **delobj** is set to 0, profile objects are retained when 3D solids are created. When **delobj** is set to 1, its default setting, profile objects are deleted when 3D solids are created.

- **aunits**

  This system variable controls the units for angles. Its default setting of 0 sets angle units to decimal degrees.

Making Revolved Solids

AutoCAD's REVOLVE command transforms the path in space made by revolving a flat profile object about an axis into a 3D solid. Any real world object machined by turning processes, such as with a lathe, is a likely candidate for a revolved solid. Pipe elbows, rounded corners of almost any object, as well as countersunk and counterbored holes, can also be easily made with REVOLVE.

Using REVOLVE is a three-step operation. First you select the profile object, then you specify the axis of revolution, and lastly, you specify the angle through which the profile is to be revolved. One thing that might surprise you in selecting the profile is that AutoCAD allows you to select as many objects as you want, but it will use only one of them. Therefore, you should confine your profile selections to just one closed object.

Defining the axis of revolution is a straightforward and flexible step. You can define the axis by picking two points in space, by selecting an existing linelike object, or by using the UCS X or UCS Y axis. The axis has a positive direction, which is important if you do not intend to revolve the profile in a complete circle. See the description of the REVOLVE command for details about the axis orientation.

While the axis of revolution can touch the profile, no part of it is allowed to be inside the profile. The figure at the top of the page shows some examples of acceptable and unacceptable axes. You can revolve the profile about the UCS Y axis, but not about the X axis; and you can revolve it about the axes labeled A-A and B-B, but not about the axis labeled C-C.

You can also revolve the profile about the axis labeled D-D, although revolving it a full revolution will result in an object that would be virtually impossible to manufacture.

Select this profile.

Select this line for an axis, with a pick point on the lower half of the line.

Exercise Five

This exercise will demonstrate how one profile can create entirely different solid forms, depending upon the choice of an axis. Start a new drawing. Its setup is not important since we will do nothing with the exercise when it is finished. Rotate the UCS 90 degrees about the X axis and draw the profile shown in the figure on the bottom of the previous page, using the given dimensions. You do not need to include the dimensions or the hatch pattern. Either draw the profile as a 2D polyline, or turn it into one. (Turning it into a region will work just as well.)

When you have finished the profile, make a copy of it and switch your viewpoint to that of an SE isometric view. (Using VPOINT with the coordinates of 1,-1,1 is one way to do this.) Then, draw the center lines shown in the upper-left figure to serve as an axis of revolution for each profile. The length of the center lines is not important.

Then use the REVOLVE command twice to turn each profile into a revolved solid. Use the Object option in specifying an axis of revolution and revolve both profiles full circle. Your two solids should look similar to those in the upper-right figure when **dispsilh** has been set to 1 and HIDE is in effect. These two solids, along with copies of their profile, are in file mfe10503.dwg on the CD-ROM that comes with this book.

Exercise Six

Open the drawing you used for Exercise Four, or file mfe10404.dwg on the accompanying CD-ROM. This file contains four extruded 3D solids that you will temporarily want out of the way. Therefore, you should freeze or turn off the layer they are on and create a new layer, having a name such as Sol02, for the revolved solids you are about to make.

238

Start the REVOLVE command and pick the profile that is in the X-Z plane as the object to be revolved. For an axis of revolution, choose REVOLVE's Object option and pick the vertical center line. Your object selection pick point should be in the lower half of the center line, as shown in the bottom figure on the previous page. (Alternately, you could select the other profile and pick the axis on its upper half.)

When the REVOLVE command asks for the angle of revolution, enter 90. Your revolved 3D solid should look like the one shown in the upper-left figure.

Make three copies of this solid, using any suitable sequence of AutoCAD commands you are familiar with (or make copies of the profile to be used in making revolved solids), at the other corners of the model. Then your model should look like the one shown in the upper-right figure after you thaw, or turn on, the layer containing the 3D solids you made in Exercise Four.

The model is on the accompanying CD-ROM in the file mfe10603.dwg. We will add more features, including a bottom, to this model in the next chapter.

Command: REVOLVE

Purpose: This command creates a 3D solid by revolving a profile object about an axis.

Initiate with:

- On the command line enter REVOLVE.

- From the Draw pull-down menu, select Solids, then Revolve.

- Select the Revolve button from the Solids toolbar.

Options:

- Select Objects

    You can use any AutoCAD selection method in choosing profile objects. Although you can select any number of profile objects, AutoCAD will use only one of them. A profile must be a single closed planar object that is one of the following object types: circle, 2D polyline or any member of the 2D polyline family, spline, ellipse, region, or 3D face. Splines and 2D polylines are considered closed, as long as their startpoints and endpoints are in the same location. They cannot, however, self-intersect or have more than one vertex on a single point. Splines must be planar. 3D polylines are not accepted as profile objects, even if they are planar and closed.

Thickness is ignored, as is 2D polyline width. Spline-fit 2D polylines are accepted as profiles, but they are a poor choice due to their large number of vertices. Traces and 2D solids (made with the SOLID command) may also be revolved. AutoCAD uses their outline to make the revolved solid's surface.

- Axis of Revolution

  When you have specified the profile object that is to be revolved, AutoCAD gives you four options for specifying the axis of revolution. This axis has a positive and negative end, and the angular direction of revolution of the profile follows the right-hand rule. The axis must be located so that the profile object does not cross it.

  The command line menu to establish the axis of revolution is

  ```
  Specify start point for axis of revolution or
      define axis by [Object/X (axis)/Y (axis)]: (Specify a point or choose an option.)
  ```

- Start Point of Axis

  If you specify a point in response to the Axis of revolution menu, AutoCAD will accept it as the starting point of the axis and will prompt for its endpoint. The positive direction of the axis is from the first point to the second point.

Profile revolved 180°

- Object

  This option bases the axis on an existing line or a single segment 2D or 3D polyline. The positive direction of the axis is from the end closest to the pick point to the opposite end.

Profile revolved 90°

- X

  The X option causes the current UCS X axis to be the axis of revolution. The positive direction of the axis of revolution is the same as the positive direction of the X axis.

Profile revolved 90°

- Y

  The profile is revolved about the current UCS Y axis when this option is selected. The positive direction of the axis of revolution is in the positive direction of the Y axis.

Profile revolved 90°

- Angle of Revolution

  After each option for specifying the axis of revolution, you will receive a command line prompt to enter the angle through which the profile is to be revolved. You may specify any angle up to a full circle. The units for angles is determined by the value of AutoCAD's aunits system variable. Rotation angles follow the right-hand rule, which is that positive rotation is counterclockwise when the axis is viewed from its positive end.

Notes:

- The solid always begins on the profile object and rotates through the specified angle of revolution.

- While the axis of revolution can touch the profile, it cannot cross it.

Related system variables:

- **delobj**

  When **delobj** is set to 0, the profile object is retained when the revolved 3D solid is created. When **delobj** is set to 1, its default setting, the profile object is deleted.

- **aunits**

  This system variable controls the units for the angle of revolution. Its default setting of 0 sets angle units to decimal degrees.

Primitive Solid Objects

T his chapter concentrates on AutoCAD's 3D solid primitives—those basic geometric shapes that can be used as building blocks to create complex solid models. For each of the six commands—BOX, CONE, CYLINDER, SPHERE, TORUS, and WEDGE—this chapter will

- describe how the primitive can be used;
- explain how the command is implemented;
- introduce an AutoLISP program that enhances the SPHERE command;
- demonstrate the use of each command.

The word *primitive*, when used in conjunction with solid modeling, refers to fundamental geometric forms, rather than to crudeness or roughness. The primitive geometric shapes, along with the AutoCAD commands that make them, are

Geometric Shape	Command
Right prism	BOX
Right wedge	WEDGE
Cylinder	CYLINDER
Cone	CONE
Sphere	SPHERE
Torus	TORUS

Singly, the primitives are of little use, but they can make surprisingly complex solid models when they are combined and modified with the Boolean functions. While the EXTRUDE and REVOLVE commands can make the geometric shape of any of the primitives, the commands for making

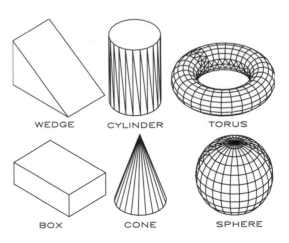

WEDGE   CYLINDER   TORUS

BOX   CONE   SPHERE

primitives directly do not require profile objects, and they usually involve less manipulation of the UCS. We will take a look at the six commands for making primitives to see what they can do and how they work.

The Box Primitive

Boxes (despite their name they are not hollow) will probably be the primitive you most often use since many of the objects you model will be comprised of boxlike shapes. The command is limited to drawing boxes that have their sides aligned with the principal coordinate system axes. If you need a box that is askew from the principal axes, you will have to either reposition the UCS before you make the box or rotate the box after it is made.

Menus and toolbar buttons for creating 3D solids

When the BOX command is initiated, you will be given the choice to base the box on a corner or on its center. The center option is useful when you want the box to be centered on a particular point in space, such as the center of gravity of an existing solid.

Most of the BOX command options involve picking a base corner for the box, drawing a rectangle to establish its length and width, and lastly, specifying a height. If you are making the box from a plan view, AutoCAD will drag a rubberband rectangle from the base corner to help you locate the other corner. From all other viewpoints, and when the Center option is used, AutoCAD simply drags a single rubberband line rather than a rectangle.

Exercise One

Open the file you used for Exercise Six in Chapter Ten. The same model is in the file mfe10603.dwg on the CD-ROM that accompanies this book. You will recall that the sides of this model were made by extruding a profile and that the corners were made by revolving the same profile 90 degrees. In this exercise we will make the bottom of the model.

Freeze the layer that the sides are on so that you gain a better view of the bottom part of the model. In the file on the CD-ROM, the layer to freeze is Sol01. Make certain that the layer you used for the corners is current, and invoke the BOX command.

When you are prompted to specify a corner for the box, use an object endpoint snap to pick the point labeled "First corner of box" in the previous figure. And, when you are prompted to specify the other corner of the box, use an object endpoint snap to pick the point labeled "Other corner of box" in the figure. Since these points have different elevations, AutoCAD will make the 3D solid without any additional prompts or input. When HIDE is in effect, and the system variable **dispsilh** is set to 1, your model should now look like the one in the figure on the right. On the CD-ROM this model is in file mfe11102.dwg.

Command: BOX

Purpose: BOX creates a 3D solid in the shape of a right prism.

Initiate with:

- On the command line enter BOX.

- From the Draw pull-down menu, select Solids, then Box.

- Select the Box button from the Solids toolbar.

Options:

When the BOX command is initiated, it displays the following command line menu:

`Specify corner of box or [CEnter] <0,0,0>: Enter C, specify a point, or press Enter.`

Entering the letter *C* will base the box on its center point, while specifying a point or pressing Enter will base the box on a corner.

- Corner of box

If you pressed the Enter key in response to the main menu, the first corner of the box will be on the UCS origin. If you specified a point, the first corner of the box will be on that point. In both cases, AutoCAD will display the following menu for establishing the other three key corners of the box.

`Specify corner or [Cube/Length]:`
`    Enter C or L, or specify a point.`

- ○ Other corner

Specifying a point will establish a second corner of the box. This point must

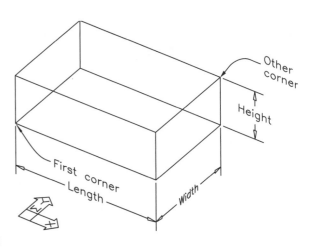

244

have different X and Y coordinates than the initial corner. If the point has a different Z coordinate than the initial corner point, AutoCAD will use the point's X coordinate for the length of the box, the point's Y coordinate for its width, and the Z coordinate for its height.

If the other corner has the same Z coordinate as the first corner, AutoCAD will use it to set the box's length and width and will prompt for the height of the box. Height is entered as a distance, rather than as a point. A positive distance value draws the box in the positive Z axis direction, while a negative value draws the box on the negative Z axis side of the X-Y plane.

° Cube

This option makes a box that has equal-length sides. You will be prompted to specify a length by entering a number or by pointing. Pointing or entering a positive number will cause the box to be positioned on the X-Y plane in the positive X and Y quadrant. Entering a negative number will cause the box to be located below the X-Y plane in the negative X and Y quadrant.

° Length

When this option is selected, AutoCAD will issue command line prompts for the box's length, width, and height. Length represents the X dimension of the box, width is its Y dimension, and height is its Z dimension. Entering negative dimension values will draw the box in the negative direction of the axis.

• Center of Box

Selecting the Center option from the main BOX menu will base the box on its geometric center rather than on a corner. AutoCAD will issue command line prompts for you to specify the box's center and to establish its dimensions.

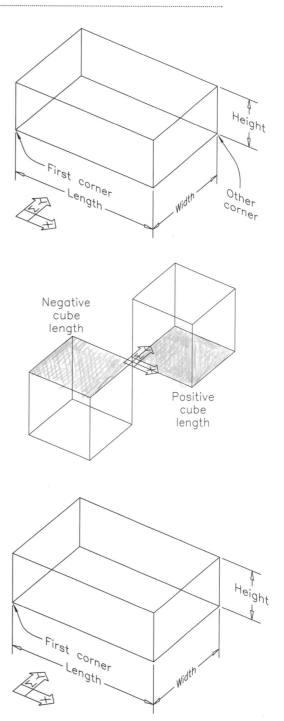

```
Specify center of box <0,0,0>: Specify a point or press Enter.
Specify corner or [Cube/Length]:  Enter C or L, or specify a point.
```

○ Corner of box

Specifying the location of a point will establish a corner edge of the box. The point must have X and Y coordinates that are different from those of the box center. If you specify a point that has a different Z coordinate than the center of the box, AutoCAD will use it to establish the length, width, and height of the box. The length, width, and height dimensions of the box will be twice the distances in the X, Y, and Z directions from the center of the box to the box corner.

If the specified point is at the same elevation as the box center point, AutoCAD will use it to set the length and width of the box and will prompt for a distance to set the box's overall height. The resulting height is the same regardless of whether negative or positive distance values are entered.

○ Cube

The length, width, and height of the box will be equal when this option is selected. AutoCAD will issue a command line prompt for the box's length. A negative length value produces the same results as a positive length value.

○ Length

This option is for specifying the dimensions of the box with distance values, rather than with point locations. AutoCAD will present command line prompts for you to enter the length, width, and height dimensions of the box. You can enter a

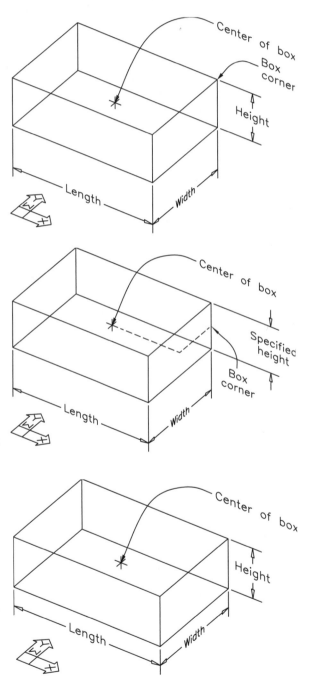

246

numerical value or select two points to specify a dimension. Negative values produce the same results as positive values.

Notes:

- The sides of the 3D solid box are always aligned with the current UCS X, Y, and Z axes.

The Wedge Primitive

Wedges are like boxes that have been sliced diagonally from opposite edges. Consequently, the prompts and input for the WEDGE command are very similar to those of the BOX command. The sides of wedge primitives are always in the shape of a right triangle, and the slope of the wedge is always in the Y axis direction. You can, however, control whether the horizontal side of the wedge is on its top or on its bottom side, and whether the wedge's sharp end points in the positive or negative Y direction by using positive and negative numbers when specifying the wedge's dimensions. Positive numbers for wedge length point the wedge in the positive Y direction, while negative numbers point the wedge in the negative Y direction. And, positive numbers for height input place the horizontal side of the wedge on the bottom, while negative numbers place it on the top.

Exercise Two

Start a new drawing. You will not want to retain the model you make during this exercise, so the drawing setup is not important. Use VPOINT to set a viewpoint rotated 305 degrees in the X-Y plane from the X axis, and 35 degrees from the X-Y plane.

Use the following command line input to create a wedge that is based on its center point, will fit in a 1-unit-sized cube, and is centered at the UCS origin:

```
Command: WEDGE (Enter)
Specify first corner of wedge or [CEnter] <0,0,0>: c (Enter)
Specify center of wedge\<0,0,0>: (Enter)
Specify opposite corner or [Cube/Length]: c (Enter)
Specify Length: 1 (Enter)
```

Your wedge should look similar to the one shown in the figure on the right. Notice that what AutoCAD calls the center of the wedge is on the center of its slope, rather than at its center of gravity (the centroid). The coordinates for the center of this wedge are 0,0,0, while the coordinates for its center of gravity are -0.1667,0.0000,-0.1667. (The MASSPROP command, which we will discuss in Chapter Fourteen, reports the location of a 3D solid's center of gravity.) On the CD-ROM that accompanies this book, this wedge is in file mfe11201.dwg.

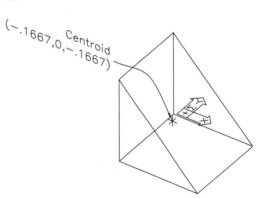

Command: WEDGE

Purpose: WEDGE creates a 3D solid in the shape of a right-angle wedge.

Initiate with:

- On the command line enter WEDGE.
- From the Draw pull-down menu, select Solids, then Wedge.
- Select the Wedge button from the Solids toolbar.

Options:

Wedges are similar to boxes that have been split diagonally from opposite edges. The flat side of the wedge is always parallel with the UCS X-Y plane. The WEDGE command begins by displaying the following command line menu:

```
Specify first corner of wedge or [CEnter]<0,0,0>: Enter C, specify a point, or
    press Enter.
```

Entering the letter *C* will base the wedge on a point that is midway between its length, width, and height, while specifying a point or pressing Enter will base it on one corner of its high side.

- Corner of wedge

  If you pressed the Enter key in response to the main menu, the first corner of the wedge will be on the UCS origin. If you specified a point, the first corner of the wedge will be on that point. In both cases, AutoCAD will display the following menu for establishing the other three key corners of the wedge.

  ```
  Specify corner or [Cube/Length]: Enter C or L, or specify a point.
  ```

  o Other corner

     Specifying a point will establish an opposite corner of the wedge. This point must have X and Y coordinates that are different from those of the initial corner. If the point has a different Z coordinate than the initial corner point, AutoCAD will use the point's X coordinate for the length of the wedge, the point's Y coordinate for its width, and the Z coordinate for its height.

     If the other corner has the same Z coordinate as the first corner, Auto-CAD will use it to set the wedge's length and width and will prompt for the length of the high side of the wedge. Height is entered as a distance, rather than as a point. A positive distance value draws the wedge in the positive Z axis direction, while a negative value draws it on the negative Z axis side of the X-Y plane.

248

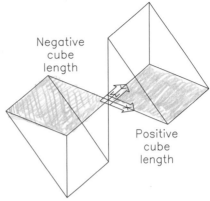

○ Cube

This option makes the wedge's length, width, and height equal. You will be prompted to specify the length by entering a number or by pointing. Pointing or entering a positive number will cause the wedge to be positioned on the X-Y plane, in the positive X and Y quadrant, and pointed in the positive X direction. Entering a negative number will cause the wedge to be located below the X-Y plane, in the negative X and Y quadrant, and pointed in the minus X direction.

○ Length

When this option is selected, AutoCAD will issue command line prompts for the length, width, and height of the wedge. Length represents the X dimension of the wedge, width is its Y dimension, and height is its Z dimension. Entering negative dimension values will draw the wedge in the negative direction of the axis.

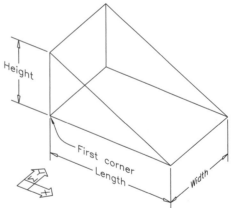

• Center of wedge

Selecting the Center option from the main WEDGE menu will base the wedge on a point midway between its length, width, and height, rather than on a corner. This point will be on the slanted surface of the wedge. AutoCAD will issue command line prompts for you to specify the center point of the wedge and to establish its dimensions.

```
Specify center of wedge <0,0,0>: Specify a point or press Enter.
Specify opposite corner or [Cube/Length]:  Enter C or L, or specify a point.
```

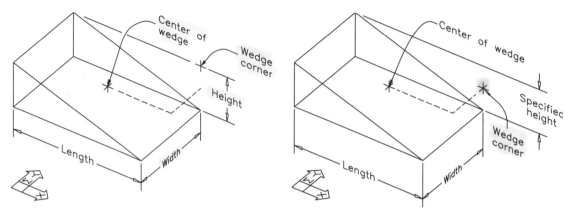

- ○ Corner of wedge

  Specifying the location of a point will establish a corner on the high side of the wedge. The point must have X and Y coordinates that are different from those of the wedge center. If you specify a point that has a different Z coordinate than the center of the wedge, AutoCAD will use it to establish the length, width, and height of the wedge. The length, width, and height dimensions of the wedge will be twice the distances in the X, Y, and Z directions from the center of the wedge to the selected corner.

  If the specified point is at the same elevation as the wedge center point, AutoCAD will use it to set the length and width of the wedge and will prompt for a distance to set its height. If a negative height value is entered, the flat side of the wedge will be on its top side, rather than on its bottom side.

- ○ Cube

  The length, width, and height of the wedge will be equal when this option is selected. AutoCAD will issue a command line prompt for the wedge's length. When a positive length is used the flat side of the wedge will be on the bottom. When a negative length is entered the flat side of the wedge will be on the top.

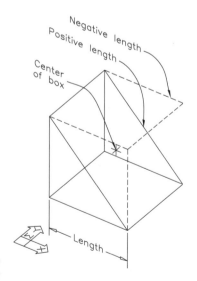

- ○ Length

  This option is for specifying the dimensions of the wedge with distance values, rather than with point locations. AutoCAD will present command line prompts for you to enter the length, width, and height dimensions of the wedge. You can enter a numerical value or select two points to specify a length. A negative length will point the sharp edge of the wedge in the minus X direction, and a negative height will place the flat side of the wedge on top. Negative width values have no effect.

Notes:

- The straight sides of the 3D solid wedge are always aligned with the current UCS X, Y, and Z axes, and the wedge always slopes in the Y direction. Whether it slopes in the positive or negative Y direction depends on input to the WEDGE command.

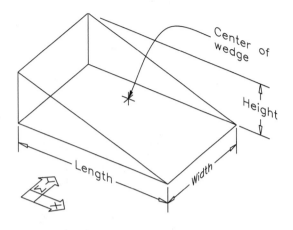

The Cylinder Primitive

Cylinders, which are made with the CYLINDER command, are likely to be your second most often used primitive because they can be used to make round holes. In fact, if you routinely make holes in certain specific sizes, such as 7/16 of an inch or 10 mm, you could benefit from a macro that would implement the CYLINDER command with preset cylinder diameters.

The default input of the CYLINDER command, which is to specify a height, points the axis of the cylinder in the Z axis direction. Positive height draws the cylinder in the positive Z direction, while entering a negative height draws it in the minus Z direction. You can also specify a point representing the center of the opposite end of the cylinder. Since this point sets both the orientation and length of the cylinder, you can use this option to make cylinders that point in any direction.

You will probably not use the option for drawing cylinders with an elliptical cross-section often, but it is there when you do need it. Establishing the base dimensions of the elliptical cross-section is similar to drawing a 2D ellipse, but it is not as flexible. Although you can base the ellipse on its endpoints, or on its center, an ellipse rotation angle option is not available, and AutoCAD does not drag an ellipse-shaped rubberband outline to help you draw the ellipse.

Exercise Three

Open the solid model you used in Exercise One to make a bottom for the 3D model of a thick-walled pan. On the CD-ROM that accompanies this book the model is in file mfe11202.dwg. In this exercise you will make some cylinders within the top flange of the part. In Chapter Twelve we will use the Boolean subtract operation to turn these cylinders into holes.

251

Move the UCS to the top of the flange. Then start the CYLINDER command to make one cylinder that has a radius of 0.25 units and a height of -0.25 units, located in the position shown in the figure on the previous page. The negative height value places the cylinder inside the flange.

Place cylinders in the same position in the other three corners of the flange by copying the original cylinder or by implementing the CYLINDER command three more times. If you want to, you may also place cylinders at other locations of your choice on the flange. When you finish, your 3D model should look similar to the one in

the figure on this page when HIDE is in effect and when the **dispsilh** system variable is set to 1.

The model looks complete, but we need to join its corners and sides to the bottom, and we need to turn the cylinders into holes. We will do that in the next chapter. On the CD-ROM, the model at this stage is in file mfe11302.dwg.

Command: CYLINDER

Purpose: CYLINDER creates a 3D solid in the shape of an extruded circle or an extruded ellipse.

Initiate with:

- On the command line enter CYLINDER.
- From the Draw pull-down menu, select Solids, then Cylinder.
- Select the Cylinder button from the Solids toolbar.

Options:

The CYLINDER command can make cylinders having either a circular or an elliptical-shaped cross-section. It starts with the following command line menu:

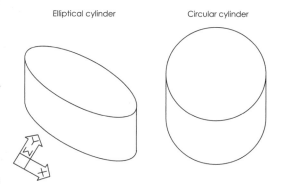

Elliptical cylinder   Circular cylinder

```
Specify center point for base of cylinder or [Elliptical] <0,0,0>: Enter an E,
    specify a point or press Enter.
```

Specifying a point will establish the base center of a cylinder with a circular cross-section, and pressing the Enter key will result in a cylinder with a circular cross-section that is based on the UCS origin.

- Center point

  Once the center point of a cylinder with a circular cross-section has been established (by picking a point or pressing the Enter key in response to the main CYLINDER menu), AutoCAD will anchor a rubberband line on the center point and issue the following prompt
  for you to specify the cylinder's cross-section size.

  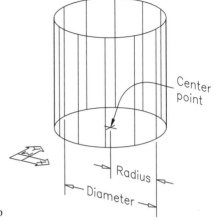

  Specify radius for base of cylinder or [Diameter]:
     Specify a radius distance or enter a D.

  Responding to this prompt with a distance, by either pointing or entering a value, will establish the radius of the cylinder. Responding by entering a *D* (or by entering the entire word *Diameter)* will bring up a prompt for you to specify the diameter of the cylinder. You can specify the cylinder's diameter by entering a value or by picking a point.

  After you specify the radius or diameter of the cylinder, AutoCAD will display the submenu:

  Specify height of cylinder or [Center of other
     end]: Specify a distance or enter a C.

  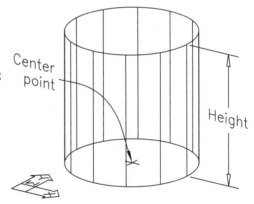

  ○ Height

    When you respond to the submenu by specifying a distance, whether by entering a number or by picking two points, AutoCAD uses that distance as the length of the cylinder and makes the cylinder with its axis pointed in the current Z axis direction. Entering a negative number will draw the cylinder in the minus Z axis direction.

  ○ Center of other end

    When you enter a *C* in response to the submenu, AutoCAD will issue the prompt:

    Specify center of other end of cylinder:
       Specify a point.

    The point you specify represents the opposite end of the cylinder's axis and will therefore set both the length and the orientation of the cylinder.

- Elliptical

  Choosing the Elliptical option from the main CYLINDER menu makes a column that has an elliptical cross-section. AutoCAD will display the menu:

  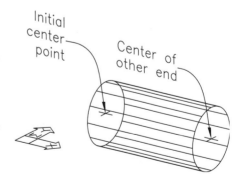

> Specify axis endpoint of ellipse for
> base of cylinder or/Center: *Specify*
> *a point or enter a C.*

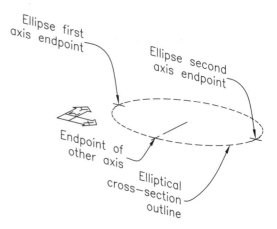

∘ Axis endpoint

When a point is specified, by entering its coordinates or by picking its location, AutoCAD will use it as one end of the elliptical cross-section axis and will ask for the opposite endpoint of this axis.

> Specify second axis endpoint of
> ellipse for base of cylinder: *Spec-*
> *ify a point.*

As soon as the second point is specified, AutoCAD will anchor a rubberband line midway between the two points and will ask for the distance to one end of the other axis of the ellipse:

> Specify length of other axis for base
> of cylinder: *Specify a distance.*

∘ Center

Entering the letter *C* will bring up a series of prompts for basing the elliptical cross-section of the cylinder on its center rather than on the endpoints of one axis:

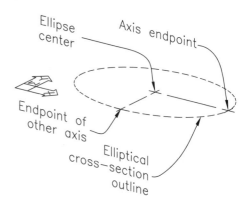

> Specify center point of ellipse for
> base of cylinder <0,0,0>: *Specify a*
> *point or press Enter.*

> Specify axis endpoint of ellipse for
> base of cylinder: *Specify a point.*

> Specify length of other axis for base
> of cylinder: *Specify a distance.*

After you define the position and size of the elliptical cross-section of the cylinder, AutoCAD will display the submenu

> Specify height of cylinder or [Center
> of other end]: *Specify a distance*
> *or enter a C.*

∘ Height

When you respond to this submenu by specifying a distance, whether by entering a number or by picking two points, Auto-

254

CAD uses that distance as the length of the elliptical cylinder and makes the cylinder with its axis pointed in the current Z axis direction. Entering a negative number will draw the cylinder in the minus Z axis direction.

○ Center of other end

When you enter a *C* in response to the submenu, AutoCAD will issue the prompt

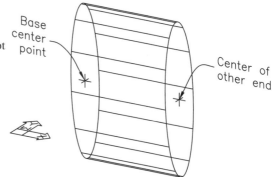

Base center point

Center of other end

Specify center of other end of
    cylinder: *Specify a point.*

The point you specify represents the opposite end of the elliptical cylinder's center axis and will therefore set both the length and the orientation of the cylinder.

Notes:

• In wireframe viewing modes, the number of lines on the surface along the length of the cylinder is controlled by the value of AutoCAD's **isolines** system variable.

The Cone Primitive

The only difference between cone primitives and cylinder primitives is that cones taper to a point rather than keeping the same cross-section size throughout their length. Therefore, it is no surprise that the options and prompts for the CONE command are very similar to those of the CYLINDER command.

After you specify the size of the cone base, which can be round or elliptical, the CONE command prompts for either the Apex or the Height of the cone. The Height option points the sharp tip of the cone in the Z direction, using the specified height as the base-to-tip length of the cone. The Apex option is equivalent to the Center of other end option for cylinders. With it you specify a point that serves as both direction and length to the tip of the cone. Cones always have sharp tips—there are no options for making truncated cones.

Exercise Four

Start a new drawing. Since we do not plan to use the model you will make in this exercise, the drawing's initial setup is not important. Set the view direction to that of an SE isometric view.

Use the following command line input to make a cone that is 3 units long, has an elliptical base, and is pointed 45 degrees in the X-Y plane from the X axis and 45 degrees from the X-Y plane:

```
Command: CONE (Enter)
Current wire frame density: ISOLINES=4
Specify center point for base of cone or [Elliptical] <0,0,0>: e (Enter)
Center/<Axis endpoint>: (pick any point on the XY plane)
Specify second axis endpoint of ellipse for base of cone: @2<0 (Enter)
Specify length of other axis for base of cone: @.75<90 (Enter)
```

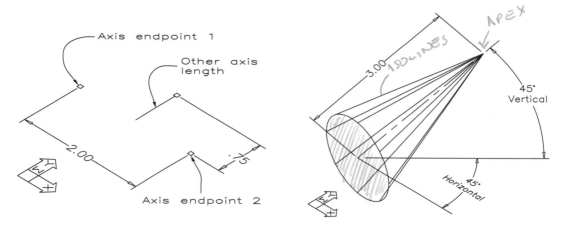

The preceding input, which is pictured in the upper-left figure, establishes the size and shape of the cone's base. The following input establishes the location of the cone's tip.

```
Specify height of cone or [Apex]: a (Enter)
Specify apex point: @3<45<45 (Enter)
```

Notice that we used relative spherical coordinates to set the apex point. Your cone should be similar to the one shown in the upper-right figure.

This figure shows the model in its wireframe mode when AutoCAD's **isolines** system variable has been set to a value of 8. This variable sets the number of lines along the length of the cone. A regen is required before changes to **isolines** take effect. On the CD-ROM, you will find this model in file mf311402.dwg.

Command: CONE

Purpose: CONE creates a 3D solid that tapers to a point from either a circular or elliptical base.

Initiate with:

- On the command line enter CONE.
- From the Draw pull-down menu, select Solids, then Cone.
- Select the Cone button from the Solids toolbar.

Options:

The cross-section perpendicular to the axis of cones can have either a circular or elliptical shape. CONE begins with the following command line menu:

```
Specify center point for base of cone or
   [Elliptical] <0,0,0>: Enter an E, specify
   a point, or press Enter.
```

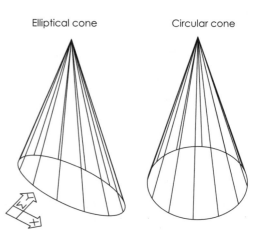

Elliptical cone   Circular cone

256

Specifying a point will establish the base of a cone having a circular cross-section, and pressing the Enter key will result in a cone having a circular cross-section that is based at the UCS origin.

- Center point

Once the base center point of a cone with a circular cross-section has been established (by picking a point or pressing the Enter key in response to the main CONE menu), AutoCAD will anchor a rubberband line on the center point and issue the following prompt for you to specify the size of the base.

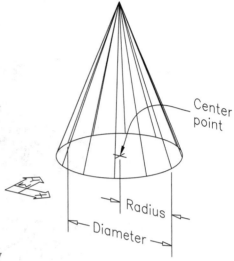

`Specify radius for base of  cone or [Diameter]:` *Specify a radius distance or enter a D.*

Responding to this prompt with a distance, by either pointing or entering a value, will establish the radius of the cone's base. Responding by entering a *D* (or by entering the entire word *Diameter*) will bring up a prompt for you to specify the diameter of the cone's base. You can specify the diameter by entering a value or by picking a point.

After you specify the size of the cone base, AutoCAD will display the submenu

`Specify height of cone or [Apex]:` *Specify a distance or enter an A.*

- Height

When you respond to the submenu by specifying a distance, whether by entering a number or by picking two points, AutoCAD uses that distance as the height of the cone in the current Z axis direction. Entering a negative number will point the cone in the minus Z axis direction.

- Apex

When you enter an *A*, or the word *apex*, in response to the submenu, AutoCAD will issue the prompt:

`Specify apex point:` *Specify a point.*

This point locates the cone's tip, and therefore sets both the length and the orientation of the cone.

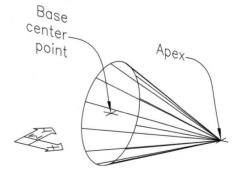

257

- Elliptical

  Choosing the Elliptical option from the main CONE menu makes a cone that has an elliptical cross-section. AutoCAD will display a menu for establishing the location and size of the base ellipse:

  ```
  <Specify axis endpoint of ellipse for base of cone or [Center]: Specify a point
      or enter a C.
  ```

  ○ Axis endpoint

  When a point is specified, by entering its coordinates or by picking its location, AutoCAD will use it as one end of the elliptical cross-section axis and will ask for the opposite endpoint of this axis.

  ```
  Specify second axis endpoint of ellipse
      for base of cone: Specify a point.
  ```

  As soon as the second point is specified, AutoCAD will anchor a rubberband line midway between the two points and will ask for the distance from this midpoint to one end of the other axis of the ellipse:

  ```
  Specify length of other axis for base
      of cone: Specify a distance.
  ```

  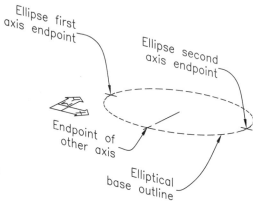

  ○ Center

  Entering the letter *C* will bring up a series of prompts for basing the elliptical base of the cone on its center rather than on the endpoints of one axis:

  ```
  Specify center point of ellipse for
      base of cone <0,0,0>: Specify a
      point or press Enter.
  Specify axis endpoint of ellipse for
      base of cone: Specify a point.
  Specify length of other axis for base
      of cone: Specify a distance.
  ```

  After you define the position and size of the elliptical cone base, AutoCAD will display the submenu:

  ```
  Specify height of cone or [Apex]:
      Specify a distance or enter an A.
  ```

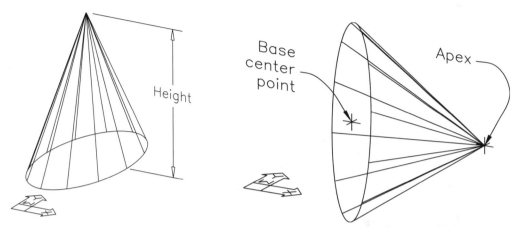

- ○ Height

  When you respond to this submenu by specifying a distance, either by entering a number or by picking two points, AutoCAD uses that distance as the cone's height in the current Z axis direction. Entering a negative number will draw the cone so that its tip is pointed in the minus Z axis direction.

- ○ Apex

  When you enter an *A*, or the word *Apex*, in response to the submenu, AutoCAD will issue the prompt:

  `Specify apex point:` *Specify a point.*

  The point you specify sets the location of the cone's tip and will therefore set both the length and the orientation of the cone.

Notes:

- In wireframe viewing modes, the number of lines on the cone's surface from its base to its apex is controlled by the value of AutoCAD's **isolines** system variable.

The Sphere Primitive

Making a sphere is the most straightforward operation of all of the primitives. The SPHERE command prompts you to specify a center point, then it prompts for the size of the sphere. The only option of the command is whether the size of the sphere is to be based on its diameter or its radius.

The SPHERE command always bases spheres on their center points. Often, though, you need to make a sphere that it is on, or touches, a particular surface or object. Sometimes, it would also be nice if you could make a sphere by specifying two points that establish both the size and location of the sphere—similar to the two-point option of the CIRCLE command. The AutoLISP program globexyz.lsp on the CD-ROM that comes with this book solves both of these problems.

One function in this program, SPHEREZ, makes a sphere that sits on top of (in the positive Z direction) a selected point. You merely specify a point and the radius of the sphere. The other function in this program, SPHERE_2P, allows you to make a sphere by specifying two points on its surface.

Exercise Five

Start a new drawing for this exercise. We will not do anything with the objects you create in this drawing, so its initial setup is not important. Set the view direction to that of an SE isometric view through the View pull-down menu, one of the two SE isometric tool bar buttons, or the VPOINT command. Then load the globexyz.lsp program. The APPLOAD command is a good way to do this.

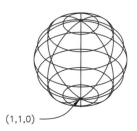

Make a 3D solid sphere that sits on the X-Y plane and has a radius of 1 unit by using the following command line input:

```
Command: SPHEREZ (Enter)
Bottom of sphere: 1,1 (Enter)
Radius of sphere: 1 (Enter)
```

The sphere will appear, sitting on the X-Y plane. Next, make a sphere by specifying two points:

```
Command: SPHERE_2PT
Specify a point on the sphere's surface: 3,3,0 (Enter)
Specify the opposite point: 3,3,-2 (Enter)
```

This sphere also has a radius of 1 unit and touches the X-Y plane, but it is below the plane, rather than above it. These two spheres are shown in the figure above. This figure shows the spheres when AutoCAD's **isolines** system variable has been given a value of 8 to make the round shape of the spheres more apparent.

Command: SPHERE

Purpose: SPHERE creates a 3D solid in the shape of a sphere.

Initiate with:

- On the command line enter SPHERE.

- From the Draw pull-down menu, select Solids, then Sphere.

- Select the sphere button from the Solids toolbar.

Implementation:

The SPHERE command first asks for the center of the sphere:

```
Specify center of sphere <0,0,0>: Specify a point or press Enter.
```

Then AutoCAD will anchor a rubberband line on the center point and prompt for the sphere's radius or diameter.

```
Specify radius of sphere or [Diameter]: Enter a D, or specify a distance.
```

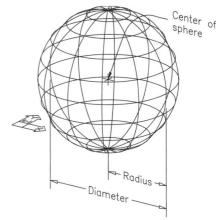

- Radius

  You can specify the radius of the sphere by entering a distance value or by picking a point.

- Diameter

  If you enter a *D* at the Diameter/Radius prompt, AutoCAD will leave the rubberband line anchored to the center of the sphere and will prompt for a diameter. If you pick a point for the diameter, the distance from the center of the sphere to the picked point represents the diameter rather than the radius of the sphere. You can also enter the diameter as a numerical value.

Notes:

- In their wireframe form, the number of latitude and longitude lines on spheres is controlled by AutoCAD's **isolines** system variable. If you have trouble visualizing spheres in their wireframe form, increase the value of **isolines** from its default of 4 to 12 or 16. A regen is required for the change to take effect. The **isolines** system variable is discussed at length in Chapter Fourteen.

The Torus Primitive

A torus is the geometric shape made when a circle is revolved about an axis located in the plane of the circle and (generally) outside the perimeter of the circle. A donut is an obvious example of a torus; an O-ring is another.

The command line prompts and input for the TORUS command reflect the geometric definition of a torus. First you specify the circle's distance from the axis (which AutoCAD calls the torus radius), then you specify the size of the circle (which is referred to as the tube by AutoCAD). The axis of the torus is always perpendicular to the current X-Y plane. You are allowed to have a tube radius larger than the torus radius, which makes a torus that does not have a hole. Despite the use of the word *tube*, these tori are not hollow.

The TORUS command also allows you to make objects in the shape of a football. You do this by entering a negative number in response to the torus radius (or diameter) prompt. When you do this, you must specify a tube radius that is larger than the absolute value of the torus radius.

Exercise Six

Start a new drawing for this exercise. Since we will not use the objects you make during this exercise, its initial setup is not important. Set the viewpoint to that of an SE isometric view. We will make three different tori. Use the following command line input to make the first one:

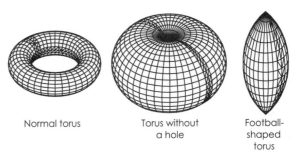

Normal torus   Torus without a hole   Football-shaped torus

```
Command: TORUS (Enter)

Current wire frame density: ISOLINES=4
Specify center of torus <0,0,0>: (Enter)
Specify radius of torus or [Diameter]: 1.0 (Enter)
Specify radius of tube or [Diameter]: 0.5 (Enter)
```

The resulting torus is shaped like a donut and centered on the UCS origin. Next, we will make a torus that does not have a center hole:

```
Command: TORUS (Enter)

Current wire frame density: ISOLINES=4
Specify center of torus <0,0,0>: 3,3,0 (Enter)
Specify radius of torus or [Diameter]: .75 (Enter)
Specify radius of tube or [Diameter]: 1.0 (Enter)
```

Lastly, we will make a football-shaped torus:

```
Command: TORUS (Enter)

Current wire frame density: ISOLINES=4
Specify center of torus <0,0,0>: 5,5,0 (Enter)
Specify radius of torus or [Diameter]: -2.0 (Enter)
Specify radius of tube or [Diameter]: 3.0 (Enter)
```

These three tori are shown when HIDE is in effect in the next figure.

Command: TORUS

Purpose: TORUS creates a 3D solid in the shape of a circular ring or in the shape of a football.

Initiate with:

- On the command line enter TORUS.
- From the Draw pull-down menu, select Solids, then Torus.
- Select the Torus button from the Solids toolbar.

Options:

A torus is the geometric shape defined by revolving a circle about an axis that is in the plane of the circle. Usually the axis is outside the perimeter of the circle, but it doesn't have to be. The axis and the circle of tori made by the TORUS command are always perpendicular to the current UCS X-Y plane.

Torus diameter < Tube diameter

The TORUS command first issues a command line prompt for you to specify the location of the axis:

Specify center of torus <0,0,0>: *Specify a point or press Enter.*

Then AutoCAD will prompt for the distance from the axis to the circle's center. You can express this distance as either a radius or a diameter:

Specify radius of torus or [Diameter]: *Specify a distance or enter a D.*

If you respond by entering a *D* (or the word *diameter*), AutoCAD will prompt for the diameter of the torus. Negative radius and diameter values are permitted—they create a football-shaped solid. Lastly, AutoCAD will prompt for the radius or the diameter of the circle that is to form the tube of the torus.

Specify radius of tube or [Diameter]: *Specify a*
    distance or enter a D.

If you enter the letter *D*, AutoCAD will prompt for the diameter of the tube.

The tube radius can be larger than the torus radius, which makes a torus without a center hole.

If a negative number was used to designate the radius or diameter of the torus, the tube must be larger than the absolute value of the torus. Thus, if you had entered a torus radius of -3, the tube radius must be larger than 3.

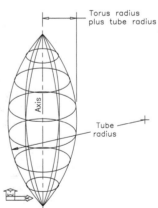

The radius of the thickest cross-section of a football-shaped torus (created by entering a negative torus radius or diameter) is equal to the torus radius plus the tube radius. For instance, if the torus radius is -3.0 and the tube radius is 4.0, the radius of the football will be 1.0 (-3.0 + 4.0). The radius of the arc-shaped profile of the football is equal to the tube radius.

Using Boolean Operations

The previous two chapters discussed the AutoCAD commands that create 3D solids. In this chapter, we will describe how individual 3D solid objects can be combined with one another to make complex 3D solid models. Specifically, this chapter will

- explain what Boolean operations are;
- describe how solids and regions can be joined with the Union Boolean operation;
- describe how one set of solids or regions can be subtracted from another set;
- describe how a new solid can be created from the intersecting volume of two or more solids, and a new region can be created from the intersecting area of two or more regions;
- lead you step by step through the construction of two 3D solid models.

Boolean Operations

By themselves, 3D solids made as primitives or as extruded or revolved profiles are seldom useful, and generally, you must combine two or more 3D solid objects to make the geometry you need for a complete model.

Boolean Logic Operator	AutoCAD Boolean Operator	AutoCAD Command
AND	Union	UNION
OR	Subtract	SUBTRACT
XOR	Intersection	INTERSECT

This is done through the Boolean operations. They are named after George Boole, the mathematician who developed theories on sets and logic that are used in computers and computer programs for switching and filtering data.

Most computer programs, including AutoLISP, have the three Boolean logical operators of AND, OR, and XOR. (In AutoLISP, a bit-wise form of these operators are in the BOOLE function.) AutoCAD has three operators, each implemented with its own command, for working with solids and regions that correspond to the logical operators for programming. The relationships between the logical operators, the Boolean operations in solid modeling, and the AutoCAD command for making them are shown in the table on the previous page.

You can perform Boolean operations on 3D solids and on regions. You cannot, however, mix the two object types. Despite their close relationship to set theory and programming, you do not need to know anything about those subjects to perform Boolean operations on 3D solids and regions. The three commands are easy to grasp and straightforward to use.

UNION joins two or more 3D solids or regions. The individual solids, or regions, become a new single object even if they do not touch one another. If they have some volume, or area, in common (that is, if one solid, or region, is partly inside another), the common volume, or area, is absorbed into the new object. If one object is completely inside another, it is simply absorbed by the new object.

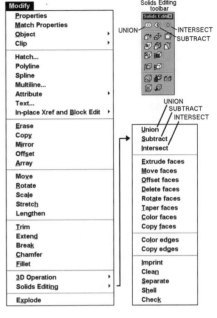

SUBTRACT removes the volume of one set of solids from another set, or the area of one set of regions from another. If they have no volume, or area, that is shared, the objects that are subtracted will disappear. When the objects that are being subtracted are partly inside those that are to be subtracted from, their entire volume, or area, is deleted along with the common volume, or area. If the objects being subtracted enclose those that are being subtracted from, all of the solids, or regions, will be deleted.

INTERSECT creates a new solid from the volume that two or more solids share, or a new region from the common area of two or more regions. If the objects have no volume or area in common, they are all deleted. If they have some volume (or area) in common, only that which is shared is retained—everything else disappears. If the solids or regions have the same shape and size and occupy the same space, they are all deleted.

These Boolean operations are summarized graphically in the diagram on the right. While this diagram uses just two solids to demonstrate each of the Boolean operations, they work equally well on any number of solids. The Boolean operations work in the same way on regions.

Often the solid that is obtained from a Boolean operation is referred to as a *composite solid*. While some solid modeling programs keep track of the primitives used to make up a composite

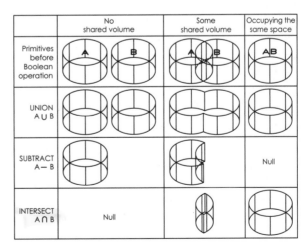

solid, and can even restore them to their original form if necessary, AutoCAD does not retain data of the original components of Boolean operations, and there is no way to restore them. Once a set of solids, or regions, has been modified by any of the Boolean operations, only the UNDO command can return them to their original state.

Because of this limitation, it is generally a good practice to postpone the Boolean operations as long as possible during the construction of a 3D solid model. This allows you to change individual components of the model before they are fused or subtracted from one another.

Joining Solids and Regions

Very little needs to be said about the UNION command, especially when 3D solids are involved. You do not even need to be particular about the selection set when specifying the solids that are to be joined, because AutoCAD will automatically filter out objects not subject to the UNION command. The solids can be anywhere in 3D space. The only requirement of the command is that at least two 3D solids must be selected.

When regions are involved, the command is more restrictive, since all of the regions must be in the same plane. The union operation will fail even if only one of several regions is not coplanar with the others. The current location of the UCS, however, has no bearing on the UNION command.

If the selected solids or regions are in a variety of layers, and you want the resulting solid or region to reside in a specific layer, you should make certain that the object you select first is in the layer you want. The layer that is current has no effect on the layer of the unioned objects.

The only aspect of the UNION command that might surprise you is that even solids and regions with a space between them can be unioned. AutoCAD does not, however, fill the space between them, and there will be no change in their appearance (unless their layer changes). Nevertheless, AutoCAD will treat them as one object, and you can move them or erase them by picking any one of them.

Premade sets of unioned cylinders

can be used with blanks of flanges

to make holes in the flanges.

One possible use for unioning non-connecting solids (or regions) is for making a modeling version of subassemblies. For example: if you regularly design pipe flanges that have different sets of hole sizes, shapes, and spacing, you could have several different sets of unioned cylinders (which may be unioned with other solids to make countersunk or counterbored holes) to be subtracted from the flanges. It is similar to using blocks in 2D drawings. Incidentally, while you can make blocks from solids, inserted blocks of those solids cannot be unioned. They can, however, be exploded (provided they have equal X and Y scales) and then unioned.

266

Exercise One

Open the file that holds the solid model you last used in Exercise Three of Chapter Eleven. On the CD-ROM that comes with this book, the model is in file mfe11302.dwg. The model has all of the components that we intend for it to have; we just need to use them.

You will recall that the corners of this model were made by revolving a profile, its sides were made by extruding the same profile, its bottom was made by the BOX command, and the cylinders in its flange were made by the CYLINDER command. We will first join the four corners, four sides, and one bottom into one object.

Start the UNION command and select everything except the cylinders. The seam on top of the flange separating the corners from the sides will disappear. Otherwise the model will look the same. If you miss selecting any of the eight objects, just repeat the UNION command to join the overlooked objects with those that are already joined.

That is all we will do with the UNION command on this model. You could use it to combine the cylinders so that they could be subtracted as a single object from the flange of the pan, but there is no advantage to doing so. On the CD-ROM the model at this stage is in file mfe12101.dwg. We will finish this model in Exercise Three of this chapter.

Command: UNION

Purpose: This command performs the Boolean Union operation on two or more 3D solids, or on two or more regions.

Initiate with:

- On the command line enter UNION.
- From the Modify pull-down menu, select Solids Editing, then Union.
- Select the Union button from the Solids Editing toolbar.

Implementation:

When the UNION command is invoked, it simply issues a command line prompt for you to select the solids and regions that are to be joined. You may use any AutoCAD selection method for choosing the objects, but you must select at least two solids or two regions. AutoCAD will filter out objects in the selection set that are not 3D solids or regions and will join the qualifying objects with no further prompts or options.

3D solid objects will be unioned regardless of where they are located. They will become a single 3D solid even if they do not touch, although the space between them will remain open. Regions are unioned only if they are coplanar—that is they must be in the same

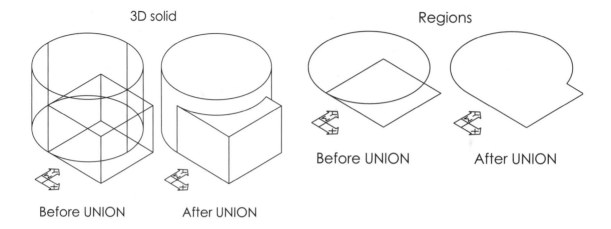

3D solid

Before UNION   After UNION

Regions

Before UNION   After UNION

plane. If any region in the selection set is not coplanar with the others, none of them will be unioned.

If both 3D solids and regions are included in the selection set, the 3D solids will be unioned to form one 3D solid, and the regions will be unioned to form a single region, provided they are coplanar.

The new composite 3D solid, or region, will take the layer of the first solid, or region, selected, rather than the layer that is current.

Subtracting Solids and Regions

Performing a Boolean subtract operation through the appropriately named SUBTRACT command is straightforward. First you are prompted from the command line to select a set of objects that are to have other objects subtracted from them. If more than one object is selected, AutoCAD automatically performs a union operation to consolidate them into a single object. Next, AutoCAD will issue a command line prompt for you to select the objects that are to be subtracted from the first set. The volume, or area, that is shared by both selection sets will be deleted as well as the volume, or area, that remains in the second selection set.

Exercise Two
Retrieve and open the file containing the 3D solid spur gear you created by extruding a region in Exercise Two of Chapter Ten. On the CD-ROM that comes with this book, the model is in file mfe10202.dwg.

You will recall that this model consists of two 3D solids—one is the main part of the gear, including the teeth, and the other is a solid that represents the center keyed hole of the gear. Use the following command line input to make a hole in the gear by subtracting the center solid from the gear blank.

```
Command: SUBTRACT (Enter)
Select solids and regions to subtract from...
Select objects: (Select the gear. Be certain that you do not include the center of
   the gear.)
1 found
Select objects: (Enter)
Select solids and regions to subtract...
Select objects: (Select the solid in the center of the gear.)
1 found
Select objects: (Enter)
```

In the wireframe viewing mode, the model will appear to be unchanged. If you invoke the HIDE command or use one of SHADEMODEs shaded modes, though, you can see that the gear does have a keyed hole in its center. We will not do anything further with this model. On the CD-ROM the completed solid model gear is in file mfe12201.dwg.

Exercise Three

Open the file you used in Exercise One of this chapter. In this exercise, we will finish the model by making the holes in the flange. On the CD-ROM, this model is in file mfe12101.dwg.

The hardest work in making the holes, that of making and positioning the cylinders for the holes, has been done. All we have to do now is to subtract the cylinders from the flange.

Start the SUBTRACT command and select anywhere on the pan to specify the object that is to be subtracted from. Then select the cylinders as the objects to subtract. You can use any object selection method in selecting them, including a crossing window. Your model should look similar to the one in the figure on the right when HIDE is active and the **dispsilh** system variable has been set to 1.

That completes our work on the 3D model, although you may want to experiment with it yourself by adding more features and performing Boolean operations. On the CD-ROM, the completed model is in file mfe12301.dwg.

Command: SUBTRACT

Purpose: This command performs the Boolean Subtract operation on two or more 3D solids or on two or more regions.

Initiate with:

- On the command line enter SUBTRACT.
- From the Modify pull-down menu, select Solids Editing, then Subtract.
- Select the Subtract button from the Solids Editing toolbar.

Implementation:

SUBTRACT issues two command line prompts for two sets of objects:

```
Select solids and regions to subtract from...
Select objects: (Use any object selection method.)
Select solids and regions to subtract...
Select objects: (Use any object selection method.)
```

The objects in the second selection set will be deleted, along with the volume, or area, that is common to the objects in both selection sets. You can include both 3D solids and regions in the selection sets, although there is no interaction between the two object types. Objects in either selection set that are not 3D solids or regions are ignored by the command.

3D solids

Before SUBTRACT   After SUBTRACT

If more than one solid or region is included in the first selection set, AutoCAD will automatically union them, then proceed with the subtraction operation. If you include an object in the second selection set that was part of the first selection set, AutoCAD will proceed with the subtraction as if the object had not been included in the second selection set. However, if you include an object in the first selection set that is also part of the second set, no subtract operation will be performed.

If the object, or objects, in the second selection set do not have any volume or area in common with those in the first set, they simply disappear without subtracting anything. If the objects in the second selection set completely enclose those in the first set, both sets of objects will disappear, and AutoCAD will report that a null solid, or region, was created and was deleted.

The layer of the resulting solid will be that of the objects in the first selection set. If more of the objects in the first selection set were in more than one layer, the resulting solid will take the layer of the object that was selected first.

Regions

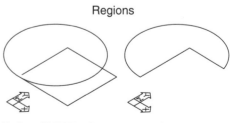

Before SUBTRACT   After SUBTRACT

Using Intersect

The Boolean intersection operation is performed by the INTERSECT command. It creates a new object from the volume, or area, shared by two or more 3D solids or regions. In some respects, intersection is the reverse of the union operation. When overlapping objects are unioned, everything that is not shared is retained, with the shared volume, or area, being absorbed into the new object. When overlapping objects are intersected, everything that is not shared is deleted, with only the common volume, or area, being retained.

Similar to the UNION command, INTERSECT simply prompts for the objects to be operated on, and it will filter out objects that are not 3D solids or coplanar regions. Although you will not use INTERSECT nearly as much as UNION and SUBTRACT, it is a more interesting operation to experiment with, and it can make shapes that cannot be made by the other two Boolean operations. Using INTERSECT is comparable to cutting a shape out of a block by cutting along an outline traced on the sides of the block, such as cutting the general shape of a duck decoy from a block of wood with a band-saw.

The INTERFERE command also performs an intersection-like operation on 3D solids and is a possible source of confusion. INTERFERE is not intended to be a command for modifying 3D solids—it is for checking for interference between two 3D solids in an assembly. Also, INTERFERE does not work on regions. We will discuss this command in Chapter Fourteen.

Exercise Four

We will use INTERSECT to make a pyramid-shaped 3D solid. Start a new drawing. Since we will do nothing with the model when it is completed, the initial drawing setup is not important. Rotate the UCS 90 degrees about the X axis, and draw a triangle on the WCS Z-X plane using the dimensions shown in the upper-left figure.

Turn the triangle into a 2D polyline or a region, and place a copy that is rotated 90 degrees from the original, as shown in the upper-right figure. If you return to the WCS, the ordinary ARRAY command can easily make the copy.

Next, use the EXTRUDE command to make two wedge-shaped 3D solids from the triangles, as shown in the lower-left figure. Extrude each triangle at least 2 units. You will probably have to extrude the triangle on the WCS Z-X plane in its negative extrusion direction, although this will depend on how the UCS was oriented when you drew its profile.

Lastly, invoke the INTERSECT command, and select both wedges. Your resulting 3D solid pyramid should look like the one in the lower-right figure when HIDE is active. That finishes the exercise. On the CD-ROM that accompanies this book, the pyramid is in file mfe12402.dwg.

Exercise Five

In the exercise we will create a 3D solid model from a 2D drawing. Since we will do nothing further with the model, your initial drawing setup is not important.

Make a 2D drawing on the WCS X-Y plane, using the dimensions given in the figure on the right. You do not need to include the dimensions or anything drawn in centerline or hidden line types. You should also leave out the horizontal line in the front view between the 0.25 radii. You need only the outline of each view and the circles in your drawing.

Turn the three view outlines and three circles into regions, and subtract the circle-

shaped regions from the outline they are in. Then, extrude the top view 2.5 units, the front view 1.5 units, and the side view 4.0 units. Do not taper the extrusions. Your three extrusions should be similar to those shown above.

Next, rotate the 3D solids representing the front and side views 90 degrees so that they are oriented as shown in the middle-right figure. The ROTATE3D command is a good way to rotate these solids.

Move the three 3D solids so that they occupy the same space, as shown in the bottom-right figure.

272

Lastly, invoke the INTERSECT command, and select all three solids. Your finished 3D model should look similar to the one in the figure on the right when HIDE is in effect. On the CD-ROM that comes with this book, this model is in file mfe12505.dwg.

Command:	INTERSECT
Purpose:	This command performs the Boolean Intersection operation on two or more 3D solids, or on two or more regions.

Initiate with:

- On the command line enter INTERSECT.—·
- From the Modify pull-down menu, select Solids Editing, then Intersect.
- Select the Intersect button from the Solids Editing toolbar.

Implementation:

The INTERSECT command issues a command line prompt for you to select objects. You can use any object selection method, but you must select at least two suitable objects. Objects other than 3D solids and coplanar regions are filtered out of the selection set. That is the extent of command usage; there are no other prompts, and there are no options.

A new 3D solid, or region, will be created from the overlapping volume, or area, of the selected objects. The resulting object will take the layer of the first object in the selection set. Unshared volume or area will disappear. If the objects do not share any volume, or area, they will be deleted, and AutoCAD will report that a null solid was created and then deleted.

3D solids

Before INTERSECT   After INTERSECT

Related command:

- The INTERFERE command is easily confused with INTERSECT because of their similar names and because they both create a 3D solid from the intersecting volume of two solids. INTERFERE, however, does not delete the original solids, and it operates on one pair of solids at a time. It is for checking for interference between two solids.

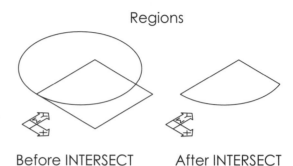

Regions

Before INTERSECT   After INTERSECT

Exercise Six

In this exercise, you will build a 3D model using a variety of the commands for creating and modifying the 3D solids we discussed in the last three chapters. In Section Four of this book you will make a 2D drawing from the model.

Start a new drawing and establish layers for wireframe objects, center lines, and 3D solid objects. Use your layer for wireframe objects to draw two circles centered at the WCS origin having the diameters given in the figure on the right. Turn the two circles into regions and subtract the inner one from the outer one to make a ring.

Rotate the UCS 90 degrees about the X axis, switch to your layer for center lines, and draw the center line that is also shown in the figure. This center line starts and ends with straight lines and has an arc in its middle. We will use this center line as an extrusion path—therefore, turn the two lines and the arc into a 2D polyline. Change to the layer you have reserved for 3D solids, and use the path option of the EXTRUSION command to make a curved tube from the ring.

Switch back to the WCS and to your wireframe layer, and draw a 1.5-by-1.5 square centered on the WCS origin and having corners rounded with a radius of 0.25, as shown in the figure on the right. Since we will use it to make an extruded 3D solid, turn it into a region. Also draw a circle having the same location and diam-

.125
30°
R1.125
.375
30°
Ø.875
Ø.750
WCS 0,0,0

4X
R.25
Ø.75
1.50
1.50

eter as the inside of the tube. Turn the circle into a region, and subtract it from the square-shaped region that has rounded corners. Then extrude the region 0.25 units in the Z direction. Do not taper the extrusion.

Move the UCS to the front side of the extruded base and rotate it 90 degrees about the X axis. Change back to your wireframe layer. Then draw a D-shaped profile (with the arc in the Z direction) as a 2D polyline, using the dimensions in the top-right figure. Since the dimensions are in increments of 1/16 of an inch, using AutoCAD's grid snap mode works well in drawing this polyline. Be certain you include a line segment along the bottom of the profile (on the edge of the base extrusion). Draw, also, a circle within the polyline using the dimensions given in the figure.

Extrude the D-shaped profile 0.375 units in its minus Z direction (toward the tube). Then union it with the tube extrusion and the base extrusion. Next, extrude the circle 0.50 units in its minus Z direction, and subtract the resulting 3D solid from the composite 3D solid. When the **dispsilh** system variable is set to 1, and HIDE is in effect, your model should now look similar to the one in the middle-right figure.

Restore the WCS, then rotate the UCS 90 degrees about the X axis. Draw the profile for a counterbored screw hole in the WCS Z-X plane off to the side and out of the way from the model. Use the dimensions given in the figure bottom-right for the profile. Then use the REVOLVE command to turn the profile into a 3D solid. The axis of revolution will be along the 0.25-long line on the profile. Your resulting 3D solid should look similar to the one in the figure.

Again restore the WCS, and move the revolved 3D solid into the base of the model as shown in the figure. Make three copies of the revolved 3D solid, positioned in the other

Profile

Revolved 3D solid

three corners of the base as shown in the figure on the right. Subtract the revolved 3D solids from the main composite model.

Position the UCS so that it is on the end of the extruded tube as shown in the middle-right figure. You can do this with the 3point option of the UCS command. Pick the end of the curved tube center line (or the center of the tube end) as the UCS origin, and use quadrant object snaps on the end of the tube to establish the X and Y axis directions. When the UCS is positioned, draw the profile shown to the right in the figure. Although the 3D solid is to be centered at the current UCS origin, we will draw its profile away from the main model since it is getting cluttered.

Turn the profile outline and the three circles into regions, and subtract the circles from the profile. Then extrude the profile 0.1875 units in its positive Z direction.

The 0.625-diameter hole in the 3D solid you just made is to be counterbored. Therefore, move the UCS origin to the end of this hole (a center object snap will position it), and draw a 0.75-diameter circle, as shown in the bottom-rightfigure.

Extrude the circle 0.0625 units in its minus Z direction. Make the counterbore by subtracting the extruded circle from the diamond-shaped solid. Restore the previous UCS (at the end of the curved tube), and move the diamond-shaped solid to the end of the tube so that their center points are in the same location.

The last step is to use the UNION command to join the two solids. Your model should be similar to the one shown in the figure on the top of the next page. On the CD-ROM that comes with this book, the model is in file mfe12609.dwg. We will add some fillets to this model in the next chapter.

Exercise Seven

You will build the model of a sheet-metal part in this exercise. We will use the EXTRUSION command to make the 3D solid object, and SUBTRACT and UNION for Boolean operations. In the next chapter, we will use the FILLET command to round many of the sharp corners this model will have.

Begin a new drawing and draw five lines on the WCS X-Y plane, using the orientation and the dimensions given in the middle-right figure. Then, draw an oval (or an obround, as it is called in the sheet-metal industry) as shown in the figure. Do not include the dimensions or the center lines.

Turn the outline and the oval into 2D polylines or regions and use EXTRUDE to make two 3D solids. The height of the solids should be 0.10 units, and the taper angle should be 0. Eventually, the extruded oval will be subtracted from the main 3D solid, but we will postpone the Boolean operations until all of the components of the model have been created. That will allow us to more easily recover from mistakes.

Orient the UCS as shown in the bottom-right figure. The viewpoint for this figure is 260 degrees in the X-Y plane from the X axis, and 20 degrees from the X-Y plane. The ZAxis option of the UCS command, followed by a rotation about the Z axis of 45 degrees, is a convenient way to position the UCS. Draw a rectangle according to the dimensions in the figure.

Turn the four lines into a 2D polyline or a region and extrude it to a height of 5.00 units, using no taper angle. Move and orient the UCS as shown in the figure on the top of the next page. One way to do this is to use the 3point option of the UCS command along with object endpoint snaps. Make certain that all three of the picked points are on the same side of the extruded 3D solid. The viewpoint for this figure is 335 degrees in the X-Y plane from the X axis,

and 35 degrees from the X-Y plane. Draw a
rectangle as a 2D polyline, along with two
circles, using the dimensions shown in the
figure, and extrude them to a height of
0.10 units, with no taper, into the
previously extruded 3D solid. Whether you
use a positive or negative extrusion direction will depend on which side of the previously extruded solid the profiles are on.

Next, position the UCS as shown in the
figure below. The ZAxis option of the UCS
command coupled with object endpoint
snaps is a convenient way to do this in one
step. Using the dimensions given in the figure, draw six lines. Turn them into a 2D
polyline or a region, and extrude it to a
height of 5.0 units, with 0 taper.

Leaving the UCS origin at its present
location, rotate the UCS minus 90 degrees
about the Y axis, and rotate it once more
-45 degrees about the X axis. This will position the UCS on the lower side of the 45-
degree slope on the most recently extruded
solid. Then draw three lines and one arc,
using the dimensions shown in the figure
on the right. The viewpoint for this figure is
210 degrees in the X-Y plane from the X
axis, and 45 degrees from the X-Y plane.
The solid to be made from the outline will
be subtracted from the main solid, and it
deliberately extends beyond the 45-degree

face on the solid to ensure that it will remove all of the material we want. Change the arc and the three lines into a 2D polyline or a region and extrude it to a height of 0.10 units, with no taper.

The last wireframe objects you need to draw are the two ovals and one square shown in the top figure. Position the UCS on the bottom side of the upper horizontal 3D solid face, and use the dimensions given to draw the objects. Turn the wireframe objects into 2D polylines or regions, and extrude them with no taper to a height of 0.10.

Change to a viewpoint that allows you to clearly see all of the 3D solids. The viewpoint for the middle figure is 280 degrees from the X axis in the X-Y plane and 50 degrees from the X-Y plane.

When you are satisfied that the 3D solids are as you want them to be, union the three solid objects that were extruded to a height of 5.0 units, and subtract all of the other solid objects from them. You can do this in one step with the SUBTRACT command by selecting the three 5.0-unit extruded objects as the solids to be subtracted from, and the remaining eight objects as the solids to be subtracted. Your model should look similar to the one in the bottom figure. In the next chapter we will finish this model by adding some fillets and chamfers to it. On the CD-ROM that comes with this book, the model at this stage is in file mfe12708.dwg.

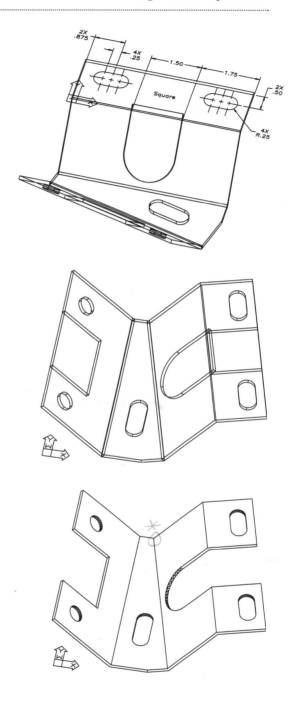

1. UCS. COROS/VIEW
2. ANGLES NOT CLEAR.

* NOTE: DISK VERSION
DOES NOT LINE
UP @ UNION

Modifying 3D Solids

U nlike the Boolean operations, the tools we will discuss in this chapter can modify single 3D solid objects. In this chapter, you will

- *learn how to round sharp edges and blend surfaces of 3D solids with the FILLET command;*
- *see how the CHAMFER command can be used to bevel sharp edges of 3D solids;*
- *find out how to cut a 3D solid into two separate pieces;*
- *edit 3D solids with AutoCAD 2000's SOLIDEDIT command.*

Using the Fillet Command

For 3D solids, a fillet is, basically, a rounded surface between adjacent faces that has an arc-shaped cross-section and is tangent to each face. Fillets can be on inside edges, between two surfaces, or on outside edges; they can bend around corners, and they will blend together at the intersection of three or more surfaces.

Sharp edges on 3D solids can be changed into fillets through AutoCAD's FILLET command. You will recall that this command starts by asking you to select the first object to be filleted. When you pick a 3D solid in response

No fillets   Fillets added

to this prompt, AutoCAD recognizes it and displays a special command line menu for 3D solids rather than prompting for a second wireframe object. Through this menu you can fillet any number of edges on the solid and you can specify various radii for the fillets. You can, however,

fillet the edges of only one 3D solid with each call to the
FILLET command—you cannot fillet two adjacent solids.

The fillets AutoCAD makes on 3D solids are sometimes
referred to as *rolling ball fillets* because the tangent points
of the fillet's arc (where it blends with the adjacent
surfaces) can be mapped by rolling a ball along the intersection of two surfaces. And, sometimes imagining a ball
rolling along the edge you want filleted can help you
determine if the edge will accept your fillet parameters. If the edge has curves that are smaller
than the radius of your fillet, or if one surface adjacent to the fillet isn't as wide as your fillet
radius, the fillet will fail.

Exercise One

In this exercise we will experiment with the FILLET command on a variety of 3D solids that
you will find in the file mf13103.dwg on the CD-ROM that accompanies this book. In this file
are filleted and unfilleted versions of three different 3D solids. You will add fillets to the
unfilleted version of each 3D solid and compare your results with the filleted version.

Find and zoom in close to the cube-shaped 3D solid. You will fillet three adjoining edges on
this cube, assigning a different radius to each fillet. On the command line, the prompts and your
input will be

```
Command: FILLET (Enter)
Current settings: Mode=TRIM Radius = 0.5000
Select first object or [Polyline/Radius/Trim]: (Pick a point on a vertical edge.)
Enter fillet radius <0.5000>: .25 (Enter)
Select an edge or [Chain/Radius]: R (Enter)
Enter fillet radius <0.2500>: .125 (Enter)
Select an edge or [Chain/Radius]: (Pick a point on an adjacent horizontal edge.)
Select an edge or [Chain/Radius]: R (Enter)
Enter fillet radius <0.1250>: .375 (Enter)
Select an edge or [Chain/Radius]: (Pick a point on the other adjacent horizontal
    edge.)
Select an edge or [Chain/Radius]: (Enter)
3 edge(s) selected for fillet.
```

The first radius you specified was for the edge you initially selected, while the other radius
inputs were for subsequent edge selections. The next figure shows the unfilleted and the filleted
versions of the cube.

Next, locate and zoom in close to the 90-degree
pipe bend that has a side outlet. Make three fillets
that have a radius of 0.06. Notice that the ends of
this bend are not identical—the bend's arc starts at
the flange on the left, while there is a short
straight segment between the arc's end and the
flange on the right. AutoCAD, nevertheless, fillets
both edges. AutoCAD also successfully fillets the
saddle-shaped edge between the bend and the
side outlet.

You may want to make copies of the unfilleted pipe bend so you can experiment with various fillet radii. You will find that because of the holes in the flange, you cannot have a fillet with a radius larger than 0.0938 on the pipe-to-flange edges.

Lastly, find the 3D solid that looks like two blocks and a wedge that are fused together, and zoom in close enough to work on it. Fillet the six edges that intersect, using a radius of 0.25. The result, which is shown on the right, is a complex blend among the six faces. You may want to make copies of the unfilleted version of this 3D solid, and try blending the surfaces using different fillet radii for different edges.

Exercise Two

You will add fillets to the pipe fitting you created in Exercise Six of Chapter Twelve. In this exercise, you will finish the model by using the FILLET command to round some of its sharp edges and corners. On the CD-ROM that accompanies this book, the model is in file mfe12609.dwg.

First, we will fillet the edges between the pipe and the square flange. The model has so many edges that it is difficult to find and select edges, so you should zoom in close to the lower part of the model as shown in the figure on the right. The viewpoint for this figure is 220 degrees from the X axis in the X-Y plane, and 20 degrees from the X-Y plane. Invoke the FILLET command, set the fillet radius to 0.06, and select the eight edges that are numbered in the figure. Notice that there are two edges on the vertical side of the side outlet, even though they appear to form a straight line. The edges numbered 4 through 8 are most conveniently selected by the Chain option of the FILLET command.

When HIDE is in effect, and the system variable **dispsilh** has been set to 1, the rounded edges you made should look similar to those in the bottom figure.

Pan to the upper flange area, start the FILLET command again, and use a radius of 0.06 to fillet the two edges marked 1 and 2 in the upper-left figure. Edge 1 is on the outside surface of the model, while edge 2 is on the inside.

When you switch to a viewpoint having the coordinates of 0,-1,0 (a front view), your two newest fillets should look similar to the ones in the upper-right figure when the wireframe viewing mode is in effect.

Those two fillets finish the construction of this model. Your model should look similar to the one in the figure on the right when it is viewed from a viewpoint that is rotated 230 degrees in the X-Y plane from the X axis and 30 degrees from the X-Y plane, with HIDE in effect and **dispsilh** set to 1. You will want to retain your model because we will make a 2D multiview drawing of it in Section Four of this book. On the accompanying CD-ROM, this model is in file mfe13205.dwg.

Command: FILLET

Purpose: On 3D solids, the FILLET command rounds sharp edges and corners and makes transition blends between two or more surfaces.

Initiate with:

- On the Command line enter FILLET.
- From the Modify pull-down menu, select Fillet.
- Select the Fillet button from the Modify toolbar.

Options:

When you select a 3D solid in response to the FILLET command's prompt to select the first object to be filleted, AutoCAD will issue a special set of prompts and options suitable for rounding sharp edges of 3D solids. Your pick point on the 3D solid can be on an edge or on an isoline. If it is on an edge, the edge will be highlighted.

Modify
toolbar

FILLET

FILLET

First, AutoCAD will issue a prompt for a fillet radius. You must specify a radius greater than 0. Then AutoCAD will display the following command line menu:

```
Select an edge or [Chain/Radius]: (Select an edge,
    enter C or R, or press Enter.)
```

When the Enter key is pressed, AutoCAD will report the number of edges that were selected, fillet them, and end the command.

• Select Edge

An edge must be selected by picking a point on it. AutoCAD will highlight the edge and redisplay the Select an edge [Chain/Radius] prompt. Once an edge has been selected, there is no way to deselect it.

• Chain

You can select several edges with one pick through this option. The edges, however, must be tangent to one another. The following submenu will be displayed:

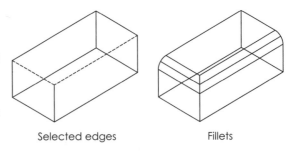

Selected edges   Fillets

```
Select an edge chain or [Edge/Radius]: (Select an edge, enter E or R, or press Enter.)
```

Pressing the Enter key will end the command and fillet all selected edges on the 3D solid.

○ Select edge chain

When you select an edge, it and all edges tangent to it will be highlighted for filleting, and the Chain option menu will be redisplayed. Only the selected edge will be highlighted if it is not tangent with its adjacent edges.

○ Edge

This option returns to the single edge mode.

○ Radius

When this option is selected, AutoCAD will prompt for a new radius value to be applied to subsequently selected edges. The radii of previously selected edges will not change.

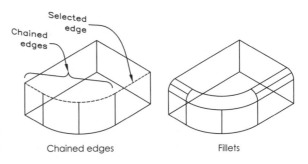

Selected edge

Chained edges

Chained edges   Fillets

- Radius

  This option of the main FILLET menu for 3D solids allows you to have fillets of various radii. AutoCAD will issue a command line prompt for a radius that will be applied to all subsequently selected edges. The radii of edges previously selected will not be affected by the new value.

Notes:

- You can fillet the edges of only one 3D solid with each implementation of the FILLET command. If, for instance, you want to round edges on two separate 3D solids, you must invoke the FILLET command twice.

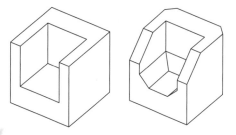

Fillets with different radii

Related system variable:

- **filletrad**

  The current radius value used for fillets is stored in this system variable.

Using the Chamfer Command

The CHAMFER command can turn the sharp edge of a 3D solid into a beveled surface. The command works equally well on inside and outside edges.

Unlike fillets, which require only one parameter (a radius), chamfers require two—a distance on one surface from the edge to the start of the chamfer, and a distance on the other surface from the edge to the start of the chamfer. These two distances can be different, and to keep track of them, AutoCAD refers to one of the surfaces adjacent to the edge that is to be filleted as the *base surface*. Consequently, the CHAMFER command requires that the base surface be identified, and it bevels only the edges of the base surface. To make the three sets of beveled edges on the model in the previous figure, the CHAMFER command was invoked three times.

Generally, you will be able to chamfer any edge you need to chamfer, although there are some restrictions when curved edges are involved. If a curved edge is tangent with its adjacent edge, neither edge can be chamfered alone. For example, edges B and C in the figure on the right are tangent, and therefore they cannot be chamfered by themselves, not even as a pair. On the other hand, edge A can be chamfered alone (as shown in the lower-right corner of the figure), since it is not tangent with either of its adjacent edges. Moreover, all three edges can be chamfered together, as shown in the upper-right corner of the figure.

As you would expect, you cannot have a chamfer distance that exceeds the face width. However, if only part of an adjoining face is too narrow, the chamfer will succeed. Thus, you can chamfer any of the three edges of the triangle-shaped faces on a wedge.

Exercise Three

This exercise will give you more experience in using the FILLET command on solids and will also demonstrate how the CHAMFER command can bevel corners, as we finish the sheet-metal part we built in Exercise Seven of Chapter Twelve. On the CD-ROM, this model is in file mfe12708.dwg.

First, we will round the edges of the fold lines of the part. There are four of them, and they are labeled in the figure below left. Start the FILLET command, and round the edge on the inside of each fold using a fillet radius of 0.10. Round the outside fold edges using a fillet radius of 0.20.

Next, pan to the side of the model that has the two round holes and zoom in so that you can easily pick points on the 0.10-long edges. Round the six corner edges in this area of the model using a fillet radius of 0.75 for the outside corners and 0.25 for the inside corners, as shown in the figure below right. The 0.75-radius fillets will completely round the ends of the two tabs containing the holes.

Now, pan to the other side of the model and zoom in to the horizontal flanges that contain an oval hole. You will need to be zoomed in very close to the model so that you can easily pick the 0.10-long edges. Start the CHAMFER command; pick an edge on the end of one of the two tabs and designate the end surface of the tab (its dimensions are 0.10 by 1.75) as the base surface. Set both chamfer distances to 0.25 and pick the 0.10 edges, as shown in the figure on the right, to be chamfered. Do the same with the other tab.

286

When you set the view direction to 280 degrees from the X axis in the X-Y plane and 50 degrees from the X-Y plane, and activate HIDE, your model should be similar to the one shown in the figure on the right. This finishes the model. On the CD-ROM the model is in file mfe13304.dwg.

Command:	CHAMFER
Purpose:	On 3D solids, the CHAMFER command bevels sharp edges.

Initiate with:

- On the Command line enter CHAMFER.
- From the Modify pull-down menu, select Chamfer.
- Select the Chamfer button from the Modify toolbar.

Implementation:

When a 3D solid is selected in response to the CHAMFER command's prompt for the first line to be chamfered, Auto-CAD switches to a set of command line prompts suitable for solid, rather than wireframe, objects. If you picked an edge as the first line to be chamfered, AutoCAD will highlight one of the two surfaces adjacent to that edge and issue the prompt

```
Base surface selection ...
Enter surface selection option [Next/OK (current)]<OK>: (Enter N or O, or press
    Enter.)
```

If the highlighted surface is the one you want as the base surface, choose the OK option. If you want the other surface adjacent to the selected edge to be the base surface, choose the Next option. AutoCAD will switch the highlights to the other surface and repeat the Next/OK prompt.

If an isoline or a mesh line was selected as the first line to be chamfered, AutoCAD will highlight its surface and will skip the Next/OK

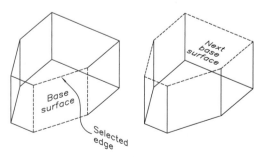

prompt. Isolines and mesh lines, which are present only on curved surfaces, will be discussed in Chapter Fourteen.

After you have identified the base surface, AutoCAD will prompt for the chamfer distances on the base surface and on the surfaces adjacent to the base surface:

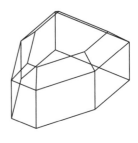

```
Specify base surface chamfer distance <current>:
    (Specify a distance or press Enter.)
Specify other surface chamfer distance <current>:
    (Specify a distance or press Enter.)
```

Press the Enter key to accept the current distance. Both chamfer distances must be greater than 0. Next AutoCAD will prompt for the edges that are to be chamfered:

```
Select an edge or [Loop]: (Enter L, select an edge, or press Enter.)
```

This prompt is repeated until you press the Enter key, which ends the command.

- Select edge

  Use this option to select individual edges of the base surface. AutoCAD will highlight the selected edges and chamfer them when the Enter key is pressed.

- Loop

  Use this option to chamfer all of the edges of the base surface with a single pick. AutoCAD will display the submenu

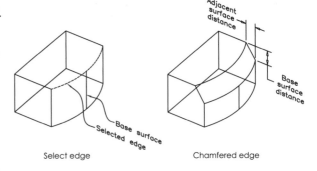

Select edge   Chamfered edge

```
Select an edge loop or [Edge]: (Enter E, select an edge, or press Enter.)
```

When an edge is selected, all edges of the base surface will be highlighted, and the Edge/Select edge loop menu will be repeated. Press the Enter key to chamfer all edges that are highlighted and end the CHAMFER command. The Edge option returns you to the Loop/Select edge menu.

Notes:

- You cannot set 3D solid chamfer sizes by distance and angle, as you can with wireframe objects.

- You can chamfer the edges of just one surface with the CHAMFER command. If you want to chamfer the edges of other surfaces on a 3D solid, you must invoke the CHAMFER command again.

Selected edge loop   Chamfered edges

288

Related system variables:

- **chamfera**

    This system variable holds the distance from the edge to the start of the chamfer for the base surface.

- **chamferb**

    This system variable holds the distance from the edge to the start of the chamfer for the surfaces adjacent to the base surface.

Slicing 3D Solids

You can divide a 3D solid into two pieces with the SLICE command. The command is aptly named since it uses a plane to slice through selected 3D solids. The slicing plane is infinitely large, so you cannot slice through just part of a solid. No volume is lost through the slice, and you can keep both portions of the solid, or just the portion on a selected side of the slicing plane. You can position the slicing plane in virtually any location and orientation you will ever need through the seven different options the command provides for defining the plane.

Most of the time, you will use SLICE as an editing command to reduce the length or height of some object. Occasionally, though, you will find it to be useful for creating a certain face or surface on a solid. We will use two brief exercises to demonstrate each of these two uses.

Exercise Four

Start a new drawing. You will not want to save the model you make, so the initial setup of the drawing is not important. Use the BOX command to create a 1-by-1-by-1 cube, and set an isometric-type view point. (VPOINT with the coordinates of 0.4,-0.6,0.6 will work well.)

Start the SLICE command, and select your cube as the 3D solid to be sliced. The command line prompts and your input for slicing the cube will be

```
Specify first point of slicing plane by [Object/Zaxis/View/XY/YZ/ZX/3points]
  <3points>: (Use an object mid-point snap to pick point 1.)
Specify second point on plane: (Use an object mid-point snap to pick point 2.)
Specify third point on plane: (Use an object mid-point snap to pick point 3.)
Specify point on the desired side of the plane or [keep Both sides]: (Use an object
  endpoint snap to pick point 4.)
```

Your sliced cube should look like the one on the right side of the figure. Cutting the corner of this cube off as you just did is almost trivially easy with SLICE, but it would take a great deal of work if you were to do it with the Boolean operations. Incidentally, the order in which you picked points 1, 2, and 3 is not important.

Point on desired side of plane

Exercise Five

In this exercise, you will use SLICE to shorten a 3D solid. Retrieve and open the file mfe13501.dwg from the CD-ROM that comes with this book. The model is of a specialized metric wrench.

We have decided that the wrench is too long, so you will use SLICE to make it 90 millimeters shorter. You will slice it once, retaining both pieces; then, you will slice it again 90 millimeters from the first slice, discarding the middle piece. Since the stem of the wrench is parallel to the X axis, you can use slicing planes that are parallel with the WCS Y-Z plane. The last step will be to move the two end pieces together and join them with the UNION command. These steps are illustrated in the figure on the right.

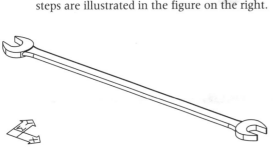

Command: SLICE

Purpose: This command uses an infinite-sized plane to slice through one or more selected 3D solids. You may discard the sliced solids on a selected side of the plane or keep all of the solids.

Initiate with:

• On the Command line enter SLICE.

• From the Draw pull-down menu, select Solids, then Slice.

• Select the Slice button from the Solids toolbar.

Options:

The SLICE command first asks you to select the objects that are to be sliced. You may use any object selection method to do this. AutoCAD will filter out objects that are not 3D solids. Then SLICE will display a command line menu offering seven different methods for defining the slicing plane:

```
Specify first point on slicing plane by [Object/Zaxis/View/XY/YZ/ZX/3points]
<3points>: (Specify a point, enter an option, or press Enter)
```

- 3points

  This option is initiated by specifying a point in response to the SLICE main menu or by pressing the Enter key. If you specified a point, it will serve as the first point of the plane, and AutoCAD will issue prompts for the second and third points. If you pressed the Enter key, Auto-CAD will issue prompts for three points:

```
Specify first point on plane:       Specify
    a point.
Specify second point on plane:      Specify a point.
Specify third point on plane:       Specify a point.
```

3points slicing plane   Result

A rubberband line, anchored at the first point, will assist you in locating the second and third points of the slicing plane.

- Object

  The plane of an existing object is used to define the slicing plane with this option. The object can be any member of the 2D polyline family, as well as an arc, circle, ellipse, or planar spline. Nonplanar splines, lines, and 3D polylines are not accepted. AutoCAD will issue the command line prompt

```
Select a circle, ellipse, arc, 2D-spline,
    2d-polyline: (Pick a point on one
    object.)
```

Object slicing plane   Result

- Zaxis

  This option uses two points in defining the slicing plane. The plane will be located on the first point and its orientation will be normal (perpendicular) to a line drawn from the first point to the second point. The option's prompts are

```
Specify a point on the section plane:
    (Specify a point.)
```
Zaxis slicing plane   Result
```
Point on Z-axis (normal) of the plane: (Specify a point.)
```

- View

  The view option asks you to specify a point. The slicing plane will be located at that point and it will be oriented so that it is perpendicular to the current viewing direction.

```
Specify a point on the current view
    plane <0,0,0>: (Specify a point or
    press Enter.)
```

If you press Enter, the slicing plane will
pass through the UCS origin.

- ### XY

This option orients the slicing plane so
that it is parallel with the UCS X-Y plane.
You will prompted to specify the plane's
elevation.

Selected point

View slicing plane   Result

```
Specify a point on the XY-plane
    <0,0,0>: (Specify a point or press
    Enter.)
```

This prompt is asking you to specify a
point in the Z direction for the X-Y slicing
plane rather than a point on the current
X-Y drawing plane. If you press Enter, the
slicing plane will be on the current X-Y
plane.

Selected point

XY slicing plane   Result

- ### YZ

The slicing plane will be parallel with the
UCS Y-Z plane when this option is
selected. A follow-up prompt will ask you
to specify the slicing plane's distance from
the current Y-Z plane.

```
Specify a point on the YZ-plane
    <0,0,0>: (Specify a point or press
    Enter.)
```

When Enter is pressed, the slicing plane
and the Y-Z plane will coincide.

Selected point

YZ slicing plane   Result

- ### ZX

This option orients the slicing plane parallel with the UCS Z-X plane. You will be
asked to set the plane's distance from the
UCS Z-X plane by specifying a point.

```
Specify a point on the ZX-plane
    <0,0,0>: (Specify a point or press
    Enter.)
```

If Enter is pressed, the slicing plane will be
on the Z-X plane.

Selected point

ZX slicing plane   Result

Once the slicing plane has been defined, AutoCAD will display a menu for you to specify which portion of the 3D solid is to be retained.

```
Both sides/<Specify a point on desired side of the plane or [keep Both sides]:
   (Specify a point or enter B.)
```

- Point on desired side of the plane

  This point, which must be on one side or the other of the slicing plane, shows AutoCAD which portion of the sliced solid you want to retain. The portion of the solid that is on the other side of the slicing plane will be deleted.

- keep Both sides

  When this option is selected, both portions of the sliced 3D solid will be retained as two separate 3D solids.

Notes:

- Since SLICE uses an infinitely large cutting plane, you cannot slice through only part of a 3D solid or have staggered sections through one.

- The SLICE command divides a 3D solid into just two objects, even if the sliced solid is split into more than two pieces. For instance, two separate pieces remain after the 3D solid shown in the next figure has been sliced. Even so, AutoCAD considers the two pieces to be one object.

Related command:

- SECTION

  This command uses the same options for defining a plane that the SLICE command does in making a region from the cross-section of a 3D solid. The selected 3D solid is not affected by the command.

Editing 3D Solids

AutoCAD 2000 contains a set of tools for editing 3D solids. Some of the operations you can perform with these tools are to

extend individual faces;

Before   After

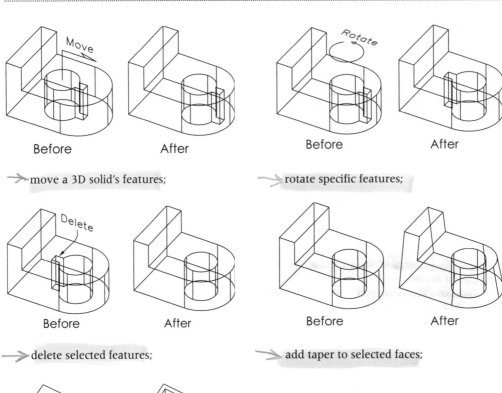

Before   After

move a 3D solid's features;

Before   After

rotate specific features;

Before   After

delete selected features;

Before   After

add taper to selected faces;

Before   After

hollow out a 3D solid.

All of the editing tools are accessed through one AutoCAD command—SOLIDEDIT. Within this command, the tools are separated into the categories of face, edge, and body; and options within these categories implement specific tools. You can select the options from the command line, from the Modify/Solids Editing pull-down menu, or from the Solids Editing toolbar.

Editing 3D Solid Faces

The tools that you are likely to use most frequently are those for editing faces. A face is a surface area that has either a sharp edge with adjacent faces or is tangent to adjacent faces. A slot, for example will have four faces—two for the straight sides and two for the rounded ends. Examples of typical editing operations on faces are shown in the figure below.

Notice in this figure that SOLIDEDIT's face options of Move, Offset, and Extrude can all be used to change the length of the boss and the thickness of the base. The Extrude option offers more flexibility, though, since you can taper the extrusion or use a path in making it. However, if you wanted to change the length or width of the part's base, you could only use the Move option because of the rounded corners. Extrude works only with planar faces, and offset will change the radius of the corners.

SOLIDEDIT's Move face option is useful for extending

Extrude, Offset, or Move this face to change the boss thickness.

Move this face to move the hole.

Rotate the interior faces to rotate the keyway.

Offset this face to change the hole diameter.

Move this face to change the slot length.

Move this face and the fillet to change the web thickness.

Extrude, Offset, or Move the bottom face to change the base thickness.

Delete and remake the fillets to change their radius.

Move this face and the fillets to change the base length.

or contracting features, such as the thickness of the web on the part in the figure, or the length of one of its slots. You would also use the Move option to reposition the holes or slots that are in the part. A limitation of the Move option is that faces cannot be moved to another face. Thus, in the figure below, you could not move the slot from one flange to the other.

You will use SOLIDEDIT's Offset face option to change the diameter of holes and cylinders, and to extend planar faces that are skewed to the coordinate system axes. Although the Offset option does change the radius of fillets, the tangent between the fillet and its adjacent surfaces is not maintained. Therefore, you must delete and remake fillets to change their radius.

You cannot move this slot to this plane.

Uses for the Copy option in SOLIDEDIT's face category are limited because it only copies faces. You cannot, for instance, copy a round hole; you can only copy the sides of the hole.

Probably the trickiest step in editing faces is that of selecting faces. You select faces by picking a point on an edge, an isoline, or on the surface of the face (even in wireframe views where the surface is invisible). Window and crossing selections are not allowed. When you pick a point on an edge, both faces adjacent to the edge will be selected. When you pick a point on a surface, the foreground face will be selected, and subsequent picks in the same point will step down through the layers of faces below. As a face is selected, AutoCAD will highlight its edges.

Often, you will end up having selected faces that you do want, so you must use the Remove option to remove the faces you do not want edited from the selection set. You can minimize the selection of unwanted faces by using multiple viewports, with each viewport showing the model from a different viewpoint to give you an unobstructed view of every face you extend to edit.

Editing 3D Solid Edges

Your options for editing edges are limited to making copies of them and adding color to them. With either option you can select as may edges as you want by picking points on them. Similar to AutoCAD's COPY command, you can use either base and destination points or relative displacements in positioning copied edges. The AutoCAD object types of copied edges will be lines, arcs, circles, or splines, depending on the shape of the edge.

Editing 3D Solid Bodies

The name of this category is potentially confusing since its options edit 3D solid objects, rather than body objects. (A body is an AutoCAD database object type that is a meshless 3D surface. Bodies cannot be created directly. They are created when a 3D solid is exploded. Planar faces on an exploded solid become regions, while nonplanar faces become bodies. Bodies are also created when nonplanar faces are copied with SOLIDEDIT's face Copy option.)

The Imprint option of this category creates an edge on the surface of a 3D solid. Usually, you will have the imprint either extend completely across a face or be closed (although it does not have to be either). As a result, the face will be divided into at least two faces, and you will probably then perform another editing operation—such as taper, extrude, offset, or move—on one, or both, of the faces.

The top frame of the imprint example in the figure on the right shows a 3D solid that has recesses with tapered internal sides on its top and bottom halves. The editing objective is to split the part with horizontal edges and then taper its external sides. Each of the eight external faces (four are rectangular and four are arc-shaped) will be divided by imprinting the intersecting region shown in the top frame onto the part. The second frame shows a hidden-line view of the part with the imprint. The region was deleted during the imprint operation. The third frame shows the part after each of the resulting sixteen faces have been tapered by the face Taper option of SOLIDEDIT. This frame also shows a hidden-line view of the part.

The Separate option turns separated components of a 3D solid into individual 3D solids. The components must have empty

Original 3D solid and region.

Region has been imprinted onto the solid.

Upper and lower faces have been tapered inward.

space between them. As soon as you select a 3D solid, AutoCAD will create a separate 3D solid from each separate component without any additional user input. The appearance of the solid objects will not change. This option does not decompose a 3D solid into its primitive, or more basic, components as the SOLSEP command of Autodesk's defunct AME (Advanced Modeling Extension) did.

Two components of one 3D solid

You can visualize the results of the Shell option by mentally removing the mass from your 3D solid to leave just the faces, deleting the faces you do not want, offsetting the remaining faces by a specified distance (the shell thickness), and lastly filling the space between the two sets of faces with mass. If you specify a positive shell thickness, the offset direction is toward the inside; if it is negative, the offset direction is toward the outside. The figure below shows a before and after example, in wireframe view, of a shell in which the top face of the 3D solid was removed and a positive shell thickness was used.

Faces and edges before Shell   Faces and edges after Shell

Command:	SOLIDEDIT
Purpose:	This command allows you to modify 3D solids by moving, rotating, extruding, offsetting, tapering, copying, and deleting specific faces. The command can also copy and create edges, and create shelled solids.

Initiate with:

- On the command line enter SOLIDEDIT.
- From the Modify pull-down menu, select Solids Editing, then a specific option.
- From the Solids Editing toolbar, select a specific option.

Options:

When you invoke SOLIDEDIT from the command line, a prompt listing three categories of editing options—face, edge, and body—is displayed. Upon selecting a category, a command line prompt for you to choose an option within that category will be displayed. Alternately, you can directly select a specific option within any category through the Solid Editing toolbar or pull-down menu.

Face Options

When you select this category of options from the command line, AutoCAD will display the following options:

```
Extrude/Move/Rotate/Offset/Taper/Delete/Copy/coLor/Undo/eXit
```

- eXit

This is the default option. It returns to the main SOLIDEDIT prompt.

- Undo

Reverses the last face editing operation.

- Extrude

This option uses the edges of a face as a profile that is extruded in the same way that Auto-CAD's EXTRUDE command extrudes a wireframe profile. A command line prompt will ask you to select the face that is be extruded. It must be flat. Then the following command line prompt is displayed:

```
Specify height of extrusion or [Path]: (Specify a distance or enter a P)
```

Positive extrusion distance values push the profile away from the existing solid, while negative values push the profile into the existing solid. After specifying a height, you will be prompted to specify a taper angle. If you choose the Path option, you will be prompted to select a path object. The requirements for a path object and the results of the path extrusion are the same as those of the EXTRUDE command.

Extruded face, using the Path option

- Move

Use this option to move one or more faces. After selecting the face, or faces, to be moved, prompts similar to those of the MOVE command will be displayed. As shown in the figure on the right, you cannot move faces from one face to another.

Moving faces

Before   After

- Rotate

You can rotate one or more faces about an axis with this option. After selecting one or more faces, the following prompt will be displayed for you to use in defining the rotation axis.

You cannot move these faces...

...from this face...

...to this face.

```
Specify an axis point or [Axis by object/View/Xaxis/Yaxis/Zaxis]<2points>:
  (Choose an option or specify a point.)
```

Axis point, 2points	Define the rotation axis by specifying two points that the axis is to pass through.
Axis by object	Define the axis by selecting an existing object. When a line, polyline, or spline is selected, the axis is through the object's start and end points. When a circle, ellipse, or arc is selected, the axis is in the center of the object and is perpendicular to its plane.
View	Aligns the axis with the line of sight of the current viewport. You will be prompted to select a point that the axis is to pass through.
Xaxis, Yaxis, Zaxis	The rotation axis will be parallel to the specified UCS axis. You will be prompted to select a point that the axis is to pass through.

Rotating faces, with 2point axis

Rotate faces with Zaxis option and reference angle

After specifying the rotation axis, you will be prompted to specify the rotation angle. You can enter an absolute angle, or define a reference angle by selecting three points, as shown in the figure above right.

• Offset

This option moves every point on a face in a direction that is perpendicular to the face. For flat faces, the result is as if the face was moved, but the radius of curved faces becomes larger or smaller as they are offset. After you select the faces that are to be offset, AutoCAD will prompt for the offset distance. Positive distance values offset faces away from the solid, while nega-

Offset faces

tive values offset faces into the solid. In the figure above, the faces of the slot have been offset away from the solid to make the slot smaller.

- **Taper**

  You can add a taper angle, which is often referred to as a draft angle, to individual faces with this option. After selecting the face, or faces, to be tapered, you will be asked to specify a base point for the taper and then to specify the direction of the taper. The face, or faces, will be rotated about an axis that is on the plane of the base point and is perpendicular to the direction from the base point to the second point. Lastly, you will be prompted to specify the taper angle. This angle is added to any taper that the face currently has.

  The figure on the right shows two examples of taper. In the first example, the selected base point is in the middle of an edge of the selected face, which causes the face to swivel. The second example shows how all four sides of the slot can be tapered.

Taper

Before   After

- **Delete**

  You will use this option to remove features from your 3D solids that you no longer want. AutoCAD will fill in the missing volume to match the adjacent faces. The selected faces must define a volume. In the figure on the right, for example, if only one face of the corner notch was selected, the delete operation would fail. Also, unless all four of the faces of the slot are selected, it could not be deleted.

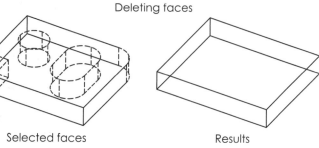

Deleting faces

Selected faces   Results

- **Copy**

  This option makes copies of one or more faces. After you specify the faces that are to be copied, AutoCAD issues prompts similar to those of the COPY command for you use in positioning the copy. Copies of planar faces are regions, while copies of nonplanar faces are bodies.

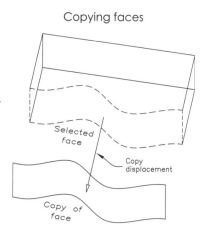

Copying faces

- coLor

   This option allows you to assign a specific color to a specific face. After you have selected the face, or faces, AutoCAD will display the Select Color dialog box for you to use in choosing one of the 255 AutoCAD colors.

Selecting Faces

After you have selected an option from the main prompt in the face category, you will be prompted to select one or more faces. All of the options issue the same command line prompts. The first prompt will be

`Select faces or [Undo/Remove]: (Select a face.)`

   You must select a face by picking a point on it—window and crossing selections are not allowed. The point you pick can be on an edge, an isoline, or on the surface of the face (even in wireframe views, in which the surface is transparent). The edges of the face you select will be highlighted, and AutoCAD will issue the prompt

`Select faces or [Undo/Remove/ALL]: (Enter an option, select a face, or press Enter.)`

   This prompt is repeated as each face is selected, until you press Enter to end the selection. When faces are behind other faces, a pick point on a surface will select the foreground face; and when you pick the same point again, the face behind the foreground face will be selected; and if you continue to pick the same point, the next face in the stack of faces will be selected. The figure below is an example showing the results of three picks in the same location.

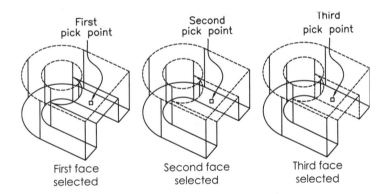

First pick point / Second pick point / Third pick point

First face selected / Second face selected / Third face selected

   The ALL option selects all of the faces on a 3D solid. The Remove option is for deselecting faces. It displays the prompt

`Remove faces or [Undo/Add/ALL]: (Enter an option, select a face, or press Enter.)`

   This prompt is repeated after each face is selected, until you press Enter to end the selection. Selecting faces to be removed from the selection set works the same as adding them. The ALL option deselects all faces, and the Add option returns to the Select faces prompt.

Edge Options

When you select Edge from the main SOLIDEDIT prompt, the following options will be offered:

    Copy/coLor/Undo/eXit

- eXit

  This, the default option, returns to the main SOLIDEDIT prompt.

- Undo

  Reverses the last edge editing operation.

- Copy

  This option makes copies of edges. After you select the edge, or edges, to copy, command line prompts that are similar to those of the COPY command are issued for you to use in specifying the displacement position of the copy. Each copied edge is a separate line, circle, arc, or spline, depending on the shape of the edge.

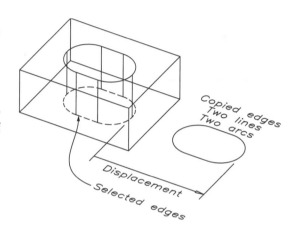

- coLor

  You can change the color of specific edges with this option. First you will be prompted to select one or more edges, and then Auto-CAD's Select Color dialog box will be displayed for you to use in choosing a color.

Selecting Edges

When you choose either the Copy or coLor option, the following prompt will be displayed:

    Select edges or [Undo/Remove]: (Enter an option, select an edge, or press Enter)

After an edge has been selected, this prompt is repeated. Press the Enter key to end the selection of edges. You must select an edge by picking a point on it—window and crossing selections are not allowed. Selected edges are highlighted. The Undo option cancels the last edge selection. The Remove option is for removing edges from the selection set. It displays the prompt:

    Remove edges or [Undo/Add]: (Enter an option, select an edge, or press Enter)

When you select an edge, by picking a point on it, this prompt will be repeated. The Undo option reselects the last edge that was removed. Press the Enter key to end the selection process, or choose the Add option to return to the Select edges prompt.

Body Options

When you choose Body from the main SOLIDEDIT prompt, a command line prompt listing the following options will be displayed:

    Imprint/seParate solids/Shell/cLean/Check/Undo/eXit

- eXit

  This option returns to the main SOLIDEDIT prompt.

302

- Undo

  Reverses the last body editing operation.

- Imprint

  You will use this option to divide a face into two or more faces. Often you will then perform another editing operation on those faces. You may for instance use Imprint to divide a face and then taper one of the resulting two faces, as shown in the figure on the right.

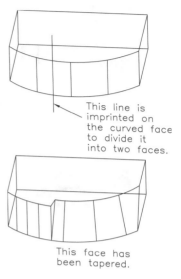

This line is imprinted on the curved face to divide it into two faces.

This face has been tapered.

  You will first be prompted to select a 3D solid. You must select it by picking a point on one of its edges or isoline. Then you will be asked to select the object that is to be used for the imprint. Valid objects for imprinting are lines, arcs, circles, splines, ellipses, 2D and 3D polylines, regions, bodies, and even 3D solids. You select the imprint object by picking a point on it. AutoCAD will ask if you want to delete the imprint object, and will then prompt for another imprint object. Press Enter to end the command. The imprint will be where each imprint object touches or intersects the selected 3D solid.

- seParate solids

  This option creates separate 3D solids from a 3D solid that has empty space between two or more individual components. As soon as you select a 3D solid, AutoCAD will create separate 3D solids from each of the individual components without further user input. This option does not decompose a 3D solid into its internal primitives.

- Shell

  Shell offsets the faces of a 3D solid and deletes the volume outside the faces to create a relatively thin-walled shell. You can also specify that some faces will be deleted to make openings in the model. An example is shown in the next figure, in which the original 3D solid is shown on the left and its shelled version is shown on the right.

  This option first prompts you to select the 3D solid that is to be shelled. Then, it will prompt you to select the faces that are to be removed. This selection process works in the same was as selecting and deselecting faces for the Face options of SOLIDEDIT. Lastly, you will be prompted to enter the shell offset distance. Positive values offset the faces inward, while negative values offset the faces outward.

Original 3D solid

After the Shell option of SOLIDEDIT. The top face was opened.

- cLean

  This is a utility option that removes imprints and any redundant edges and geometry that a 3D solid might have. You will be prompted to select the 3D solid that is to be cleaned.

- Check

  This option inspects a 3D solid for internal errors. You will be prompted to select one 3D solid. AutoCAD will then report whether the 3D solid is valid or not. When the system variable **solidcheck** is set to 1, AutoCAD automatically implements this option after every SOLIDEDIT operation.

Related system variable:

- **solidcheck**

  When **solidcheck** is set to its default value of 1, AutoCAD will automatically perform a validation check after each SOLIDEDIT operation. When **solidcheck** is set to 0, automatic solid validation will be turned off.

Visualizing and Using 3D Solid Models

*Y*ou now know how to use all of the tools AutoCAD provides for the construction and modification of 3D solids. In this chapter you will learn how you can control the appearance of 3D solids and how you can extract useful objects and information from them. This chapter will

- describe how to use the system variables that control the appearance of 3D solids, whether they are in their wireframe mode or hidden-line mode;
- explain how you can check for interference between two mating 3D solids in an assembly;
- show how to extract a region object from the cross-section of a 3D solid;
- describe the mass properties of regions and 3D solids.

Controlling the Appearance of Solid Models

You have undoubtedly noticed during your use of the HIDE command in the previous three chapters that, by default, 3D solids automatically assume a faceted appearance in their hidden-line mode. Also in the previous three chapters, we have occasionally used, with virtually no explanation, the **dispsilh** system variable to turn off the faceted appearance during HIDE.

Although we have not used, or even mentioned, the hidden-line mode of the SHADEMODE command, you will sometimes find that viewing mode useful, especially when you are setting viewpoints with 3DORBIT. Unlike the HIDE command, SHADEMODE's hidden line mode is perserved during zooms, pans, and 3DORBIT, and it never shows curved and rounded portions of a 3D solid as facets. Incidently, when SHADEMODE's 3D wireframe mode is in effect, the HIDE command uses the SHADEMODE version of hidden-line removal.

The **dispsilh** system variable is but one of four system variables that give you some control over the appearance of 3D solids, whether they are in their wireframe or hidden-line viewing mode. The others are **isolines**, **facetres**, and **facetratio**. We will discuss each of those system variables, describing what they do, and how you can use them.

You can set the value of **isolines**, **facetres**, and **dispsilh** through the Performance dialog box of the PREFERENCES command. **Facetratio**, however, can be set only through the SETVAR command or by accessing it directly from the command line.

The Isolines System Variable

Unlike the other three system variables affecting the appearance of 3D solids, **isolines** affects the appearance of solids only when they are in their wireframe viewing mode.

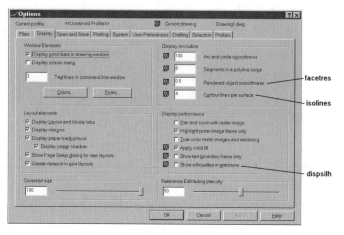

In their wireframe form, the edges of surfaces on 3D solids are indicated by lines or curves, depending upon the solid's shape. No lines are drawn across planar surfaces, but lines and curves are drawn across nonplanar surfaces. They are to help you identify and visualize the surfaces, and their quantity is controlled by the **isolines** system variable.

Isolines, which accepts an integer number from 0 to 2047, represents the number of lines per 360 degrees on a curved surface. For example, when **isolines** is set to 4, a hemisphere-shaped solid that is resting on the X-Y plane will have one horizontal isoline (through 90 degrees) and four vertical isolines (through 360 degrees).

The figure on the right shows the effect of three different **isolines** values on the wireframe appearance of a cylinder. Notice that when **isolines** is set to 0, no lines are drawn along the side surface of the cylinder.

Only nonplanar surfaces are affected by **isolines**, and the system variable has

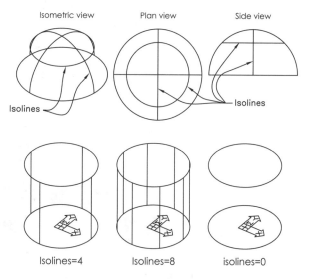

no effect on the density of mesh lines and facets when the HIDE command is in use. The current setting of **isolines** applies to all 3D solids—it is not possible for some 3D solids to have one **isolines** setting while others have another setting. A screen regeneration is required before any changes in **isolines** take effect.

Usually, you will keep **isolines** at its default setting of 4, but when a curved surface is difficult to visualize, you may want to increase its value. Increasing the **isolines** value can be especially useful when you are working with spherical surfaces. Conversely, you may occasionally want (at least temporarily) to decrease the value of **isolines** when you are working with a cluttered 3D solid.

The Dispsilh System Variable

Dispsilh, which stands for **disp**lay **silh**ouette, affects 3D solids in both their wireframe and hidden-line viewing modes. It is a toggle-type system variable that can have a value of either 0, which means it is turned off, or a value of 1, which means it is turned on.

When **dispsilh** is set to its default value of 0, nonplanar surfaces on 3D solids in their wireframe mode are delineated solely by their isolines, as shown on the left in the top figure. When HIDE is in use, curved surfaces on 3D solids are delineated by three- and four-sided facets, similar to those on polygon mesh surface models, as shown on the right in the top figure.

When **dispsilh** is set to 1, curves or lines delineate the profile, or silhouette, of non-planar 3D solid surfaces in the wireframe viewing mode. These are in addition to the isolines, and they are automatically adjusted to match the current view direction, as shown in the middle figure.

While these profile lines can help in visualizing a surface's shape in the wireframe viewing mode, **dispsilh**'s effect in the hidden-line viewing mode is even more pronounced. Only edges and the profiles of curved surfaces are shown. No facets are used to indicate curved surfaces when HIDE is in effect. This results in a clean, uncluttered appearance similar to that shown in the bottom figure. Also, **dispsilh** must be set to 1 to have SHADEMODE's hidden viewing mode display the profiles of curved and rounded surfaces.

The Facetres System Variable

The relative size of the facets that AutoCAD uses for curved and rounded surfaces on 3D solids when HIDE is in effect and **dispsilh** is set to 0 is controlled by the **facetres** system variable. **Facetres** accepts any number from 0.01 to 10.00, with 0.50 being its initial value. The larger the

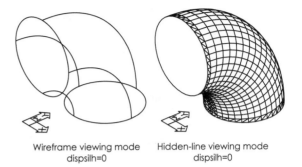

Wireframe viewing mode
dispsilh=0

Hidden-line viewing mode
dispsilh=0

Profile
Isoline
Profile
Isoline

Wireframe viewing mode
dispsilh=1

Wireframe viewing mode
dispsilh=1

Hidden-line viewing mode
dispsilh=1

number assigned to **facetres**, the smaller but more numerous are the facets.

Facetres also controls the apparent roundness of curved surfaces—such as the ends of cylinders, the edges of round holes, and the profile of spherical surfaces—during HIDE and RENDER, even when **dispsilh** is set to 1. AutoCAD approximates round edges and profiles of rounded surfaces with short straight lines during HIDE, and RENDER. When **facetres** has a low value, the lines are relatively long and are noticeable. When **facetres** has a high value, the lines are so short that they can scarcely be seen.

While the effects of **facetres** on the number and size of facets and on the length of lines approximating curved edges and profiles are relative to the magnitude of its value, you cannot directly control their number and size. In other words, doubling the value of **facetres** will increase the number of facets, but it will not necessarily double their number. Furthermore, the effect of **facetres** is different on the computer screen than it is for printed output. For a given **facetres** value, printed output of hidden-line views of 3D solids will have more facets than those of the same

Hidden-line viewing mode
dispsilh=0
facetres=low value

Hidden-line viewing mode
dispsilh=0
facetres=high value

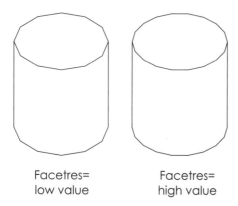

Facetres=
low value

Facetres=
high value

objects shown on the computer screen. Keep in mind, though, that **facetres** affects only the display and printed output of 3D solids, and it has no effect on wireframe view modes. Round 3D solids, for instance, are perfectly round even if they don't appear to be.

The Facetratio System Variable

Facetratio controls the number of facets on cylindrical and conic 3D solids during HIDE and SHADE operations when **dispsilh** is set to 0.

Facetratio can have a value of either 0—its default value—or 1. When the variable is set to 0, it is off and has no effect. 3D solid cylinders and cones will have facets on their round surfaces that extend for their entire length during hidden-line modes. Each facet, for instance, on the side of a cylinder will extend from one end to the other.

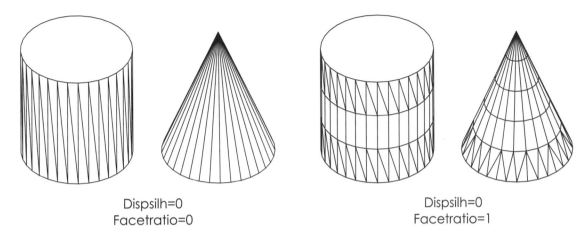

Dispsilh=0
Facetratio=0

Dispsilh=0
Facetratio=1

When **facetratio** is set to 1, facets are added to the side surfaces of cylinders and cones by dividing each lengthwise facet into two or more facets. Although this system variable can make renderings and hidden-line views more accurate, you will seldom have a need to change **facetratio** from its default of 0 to 1.

Checking for Interference

Although the INTERFERE command resembles the INTERSECT command in that it can create a 3D solid from the intersecting volume of two or more solids, it is an inspection tool rather than a modification tool. It is for determining whether mating solids have clearance or whether they have an interference fit with each other. Consequently, when overlapping volume is found, creating a new 3D solid from it is optional. Moreover, unlike the INTERSECT command, the original 3D objects are not deleted when INTERFERE creates a solid from their common volume.

When interference is found, AutoCAD will ask you whether you want to create a solid from the overlapping volume or whether you just want the interfering solid objects highlighted. Usually, you will want to have the interference volume turned into a 3D solid because AutoCAD highlights just the solids that share the same volume—the interference volume is not highlighted by itself. This new solid will not only allow you to see precisely where the interference is but to measure it as well. These solids should be in a separate layer and have a distinct color so that they will stand out and can be discarded when you are finished with them.

While INTERFERE allows you to select as many solids as you want to be checked for interference, pinning down interference locations can be difficult and confusing even when as few as three or four solids are checked at once. Generally, you will find it best to select one key solid and compare it with its mating solids one by one, rather than all at the same time.

Exercise One
Retrieve the file mfe14102.dwg from the CD-ROM that comes with this book and open it. Four separate 3D solids are in this file—a base part, a mating part, and two cylinders representing the bolts that will hold the two parts together. The upper-left figure on the next page shows an exploded view of this assembly.

The model in the drawing file will already have its four parts in position, as shown in the upper-right figure. We will use the INTERFERE command to ensure that the bolt holes are properly located and that the bolts will pass through the holes without any interference.

Switch to the drawing file's layer named Sol_interfere. In the event that we do find interference, we will create an interference solid in that layer. Start the INTERFERE command and check Bolt 1 in the previous figure with the base part and the mating part using the following command line input:

```
Command: INTERFERE (Enter)
Select first set of solids:
Select objects: (Use a crossing window to select the base part, the mating part, and
    Bolt 1)
Select objects: (Enter)
Select second set of solids:
Select objects: (Enter)
Comparing 3 solids with each other.
Solids do not interfere.
```

Those three parts check out, so we will next see if the other bolt has no interference with the base part and the mating part:

```
Command: INTERFERE (Enter)
Select first set of solids:
Select objects: (Use a crossing window to select the base part, the mating part, and
    Bolt 2)
Select objects: (Enter)
Select second set of solids:
Select objects: (Enter)
Comparing 3 solids with each other.
Interfering solids: 2
Interfering pairs: 1
Create interference solids? [Yes\No] <N>: Yes (Enter)
```

The figure on the right shows a close-up of the problem area, with the new solid moved up so that you can see the size and shape of the interfering volume. In your model, it will still be down in the mating part and Bolt 2. The hole in the mating part needs to be moved with the face Move option of SOLIDEDIT. Since you know how to do that, we will not describe the necessary steps.

Command:	INTERFERE
Purpose:	INTERFERE identifies 3D solids that overlap. The common volume can be made into a new 3D solid.

Initiate with:

- On the command line enter INTERFERE
- From the Draw pull-down menu, select Solids, then Interference.
- Select the Interfere button from the Solids toolbar.

Options:

The interfere command issues command line prompts for you to select two groups, or sets, of 3D solids:

```
Select first set of solids:
Select objects: (Use any object selection method to
  select one or more 3D solids.)
Select second set of solids:
Select objects: (Use any object selection method to select one or more 3D
  solids, or press Enter.)
```

AutoCAD will automatically filter out objects in the selection sets that are not 3D solids. Specifying a second set of solids is optional and can be bypassed by pressing the Enter key in response to its prompt. If you have only one set of solids, each solid is checked for interference with the other solids. If you have two sets of solids, each solid in the first set is checked for interference with each solid in the second set, but solids within the same selection set are not checked for interference with each other. If a solid in the first set is also included in the second set, its inclusion in the second set is ignored.

As soon as the solids have been selected, AutoCAD will report the number of solids that were compared, the number of interfering solids, and the number of interfering pairs. AutoCAD will also highlight all of the interfering solids and will ask if you want to create 3D solids from the volume they share.

```
Create interference solids? [Yes/No] <N>:
  (Enter Y or N, or press Enter.)
```

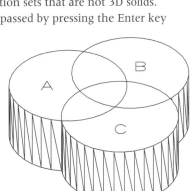

```
If A, B, and C are in the same selection set:
  A will be compared with B
  A will be compared with C
  B will be compared with C

If A and B are in one selection set, and C is
in the other selection set:
  A will be compared with C
  B will be compared with C
```

If you enter the letter *Y*, AutoCAD will create new 3D solids from each of the interfering volumes. The new solids will be in the current layer, rather than in the layer of the original 3D solids. If you enter the letter *N* or press the Enter key, AutoCAD will not create any new 3D solids, but will highlight the interfering solids. When there are more than two interfering 3D solids, AutoCAD will ask if you want the individual pairs of interfering solids highlighted:

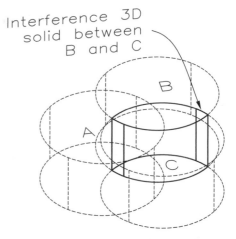

Interference 3D solid between B and C

```
Highlight pairs of interfering solids?
   [Yes/No] <N>: (Enter Y or N, or press Enter.)
```

If you press the Enter key or enter the letter *N*, the command will end. If you enter the letter *Y* (or the entire word *yes*), AutoCAD will highlight one pair of interfering solids. Each entire solid will be highlighted—not just the common volume. If there is more than one pair of interfering solids, AutoCAD will display the prompt

```
Enter an option [Next pair/eXit] <Next>: (Enter X or N, or press Enter.)
```

AutoCAD will highlight the next pair of interfering 3D solids when the letter *N* is entered or the Enter key is pressed. Entering an *X* will end the command.

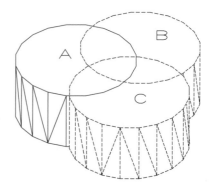

Notes:

- The INTERFERE command does not accept regions. It works only with 3D solid objects.

- If you want to check only two solids for interference, it makes no difference if they are both in the first selection set or if one is in the first selection set and the other is in the second selection set.

Related command:

- INTERSECT

  The Boolean intersect operation performed by INTERSECT also creates 3D solids from the common volume of two or more 3D solids. Unlike INTERFERE, however, the original solids are deleted, and the common volume is transformed into one 3D solid rather than into a 3D solid for each pair of intersecting solids.

Extracting Cross-Sections from 3D Solids

Cross-sections of 3D solids can be created through the SECTION command. This command uses the same options for defining the cross-section's plane that the SLICE command uses for defining a slicing plane. Unlike the SLICE command, though, SECTION does not alter the selected 3D solid. Instead, it creates a new object, a region, from the outline of the 3D solid as it passes through the section plane.

Generally, you will make cross-sections from 3D solids for one of two reasons. One reason is to better examine the solid's shape, to ensure that it has the form and dimensions you intended. The other is to use the cross-section for stress and deflection analysis. (We will say a little more about this later in the chapter as we discuss the mass properties of solids and regions.) You do not need to make cross-sections for use in 2D drawings, since AutoCAD has special commands for doing just that (we will describe them in Section Four of this book).

The SECTION command is straightforward to use. You simply select one or more 3D solids, then define the cross-section plane. The resulting region will take the properties of the current layer, and it will remain in the 3D solid. To examine the region, you can either move it out of the solid or freeze the solid's layer.

Exercise Two

We will extract a cross-section from the 3D solid we used in Exercise One. In Exercise One, the INTERFERE command told us that some of the 3D solids in this model share the same volume. We will now use the SECTION command to examine the problem area.

Open the file mfe14102.dwg from the CD-ROM that comes with this book. Use this version of the model, rather than the one you ended up with at the conclusion of Exercise One (which created a 3D solid from the interfering volume).

Use the 3point or Face option of the UCS command to position the UCS as shown in the figure on the right. The viewpoint for this figure is rotated 330 degrees in the X-Y plane from the X axis and minus 15 degrees from the X-Y plane. Notice in this figure that the angled arm on the 3D solid is 0.75 units thick. We will set the cross-section plane to be parallel with the UCS X-Y plane and in the middle of the angled arm (at an elevation of -0.375 units).

Switch to the drawing's layer that is named Section and use the following command line input to create the cross-sections:

```
Command: SECTION (Enter)
Select objects: (Use a crossing window to select
    all four 3D solids.)
Select objects: (Enter)
Specify first point on section plane by [Object/Zaxis/View-
    /XY/YZ/3points] <3points>: XY (Enter)
Specify a point on the XY-plane <0,0,0>: 0,0,-.375 (Enter)
```

Since the newly created region of the cross-section is within the 3D solids, you will probably not be able to see it. When you freeze the layers of the 3D solids, though, the four regions will appear as they do in the figure on the right. The region representing the model's cap is one region, even though it is in three pieces. You can clearly see that one of its holes is incorrectly positioned, and you can take measurements from the regions to find its correct location.

Command: **SECTION**

Purpose: The SECTION command creates a region from the cross-section of a 3D solid. Seven options exist for you to position the cross-section plane.

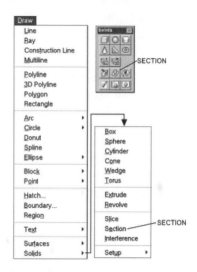

Initiate with:

- On the command line enter SECTION.
- From the Draw pull-down menu, select Solids, then Section.
- Select the Section button from the Solids toolbar.

Options:

The SECTION command issues a command line prompt for you to specify the 3D objects that are to be the basis for the cross-sections. If more than one solid is selected, a separate region will be created for each solid. Then AutoCAD will display a command line menu for you to choose a method for defining the cross-section plane:

```
Specify first point on section plane by [Object/Zaxis/View/ XY/YZ/ZX/3points]
    <3points>: (Specify a point, enter an option, or press Enter.)
```

- 3points

This option defines a section plane through the position of three points located on the plane. You can start the option by specifying a point from the main SLICE menu, by entering the number 3, or by pressing the Enter key. If you specified a point, it will serve as the first point of the plane, and prompts for the second and third points will be issued. If you entered the number 3 or pressed the Enter key in response to the main menu, AutoCAD will prompt for three points:

```
Specify first point on plane: (Specify a point.)
Specify second point on plane: (Specify a point.)
Specify third point on plane: (Specify a point.)
```

- Object

The plane of an existing object is used to define the cross-section plane when this option is selected. An arc, circle, ellipse, any member of the 2D polyline family, or a planar spline

3points section plane   Resulting region (shown hatched)

Object section plane

Resulting region (shown hatched)

314

may be used as the defining object. Nonplanar splines, lines, and 3D polylines cannot be used. The option displays the following command line prompt for an object:

```
Select a circle, ellipse, arc, 2D-spline, or 2D-polyline: (Pick a point on one
    object.)
```

- Zaxis

This option uses two points to define the cross-section plane. The plane will be located on the first point, and it will be normal (perpendicular) to a line drawn from the first point to the second point. The option's prompts are

```
Specify a point on the section plane: (Specify a point.)
Specify a point on the Z-axis (normal) of the plane: (Specify a point.)
```

Zaxis section plane   Resulting region   View section plane   Resulting region (shown hatched)
(shown hatched)

- View

The View option uses a cross-section plane that is perpendicular to the current viewing direction and positioned at a specified point. Its command line prompt is

```
Specify a point on the current view plane <0,0,0>: (Specify a point or press
    Enter.)
```

The cross-section will pass through the UCS origin if the Enter key is pressed.

- XY

This option orients the cross-section so that it is parallel with the UCS XY plane. A prompt will ask you to specify the elevation of the cross-section:

```
Specify a point on the XY-plane
    <0,0,0>: (Specify a point or
    press Enter.)
```

If you press Enter, the cross-section will be on the UCS XY plane.

XY section plane   Resulting region
(shown hatched)

- YZ

    The cross-section will be parallel with the UCS Y-Z plane when this option is selected. You will be prompted to specify a point that the cross-section will pass through.

    `Specify a point on the YZ-plane <0,0,0>: (Specify a point or press Enter.)`

    The cross-section will be on the UCS Y-Z plane if you press Enter.

| YZ section plane | Resulting region (shown hatched) | ZX section plane | Resulting region (shown hatched) |

- ZX

    This option orients the cross-section parallel with the UCS Z-X plane. You will be asked to specify a point for the cross-section to pass through.

    `Specify point on the ZX-plane <0,0,0>: (Specify a point or press Enter.)`

    If you press Enter, the cross-section will be on the UCS Z-X plane.

Notes:

- The resulting regions reside in the current layer, rather than in the layer of the 3D solids they are based on.
- If the resulting region from one 3D solid is in two or more pieces, AutoCAD nevertheless considers it to be one region.
- The solid, or solids, selected for making cross-sections are not affected by the SECTION command.

Related command:

- SLICE

    The SLICE command cuts 3D solids into two pieces. It has the same options for defining a slicing plane that SECTION does for defining a cross-section plane.

Analyzing 3D Solids and Regions

One of the advantages that solid models have over wireframe and surface models is that you can obtain data related to their geometric properties (such as surface area, volume, and center of gravity) and to their mass properties (such as weight and moments of inertia). The AREA command recognizes 3D solids and is able to report their surface area, while the MASSPROP command reports the other geometric and mass properties of 3D solids. AREA also recognizes regions, but it does not give any information beyond that supplied by the MASSPROP command.

Before we take a look at the mass property reports for solids and regions, we'll explain what some of the terms, symbols, and numbers in the reports mean and give you some idea of how they are obtained.

Mass Property Mathematics

While the properties for rectangular regions and box-shaped solids are relatively easy to compute, when you throw in some arcs, curves, spheres, and hemispheres, or have some holes in the object, the calculations can quickly get involved. For most objects, calculating mass property data—moments of inertia, centroids, and even area—requires complex mathematics.

The idea behind most of the mathematical techniques for computing property data is to divide the area (for regions), or the volume (for solids), into extremely small elements; calculate the property for each individual element; then total the results. If you have ever estimated the size of an irregularly shaped object, such as an area on a map, by counting dots or squares on an overlaid grid, you have used a form of this same principle. The figure on the right shows a plane area, such as a region, divided into these small elemental areas.

The mathematical convention is to use the symbols dx, dy, and dz for the length, width, and height of these elements. These symbols are used in Tables 14-1 and 14-2 of this chapter, which show the equations behind the mass property data. Another symbol used in these tables is the uppercase sigma character, Σ, which signifies the summation of the results from operations on individual elements. For example, the equation used to find the area of a region is

$$A = \Sigma\ dxdy$$

This equation says that the length, dx, of each element is to be multiplied by its width, dy, to find an element's area. (The multiplication sign is implied.) Then the areas of the individual elements are added together, as denoted by the Σ, to obtain the total area, A, of the region. While the equations shown in the table may appear at first to be abstract, they are much clearer and more concise than words and sentences in describing how a property is calculated.

For 3D objects, the elements are box-shaped, and the volume of a 3D object, such as a 3D solid, can be found by multiplying the length, width, and height of each elemental box, then adding all of the volumes together. Using equation notation, this operation can be written as

$$V = \Sigma \; dxdydz$$

In this equation, dx represents the length of each elemental box, dy is its width, and dz is its height. Sometimes in Table 14-2, the volume of an elemental box is shown as simply dv, which is a shorthand version of $dxdydz$. Also, the mass (which we will define when we describe the mass property reports for 3D solids later in this chapter) of an elemental box is shown as dm in Table 14-2.

Although the principles for using elemental areas and boxes are simple, laying out the elements and computing the sums is tricky. It is part of a complex subject—numerical mathematics—that goes far beyond the comprehension of most of us. Fortunately, we do not have to understand the details to use the results, although it is helpful to know what is behind the data, as we have just described and as shown in Tables 14-1 and 14-2.

Integral calculus can be used when the object's shape can be defined by an equation, and this is the basis of the formulas found in mathematic and engineering handbooks for calculating the properties of various common shapes. Even with handbooks, however, the hand calculations are laborious and error prone and can be applied only to objects having standard shapes. Before AutoCAD had such objects as regions and solids, AutoLISP programs were sometimes used to calculate centroids and moments of inertia, but the results were approximations with often dubious accuracy.

Even Autodesk's Advanced Modeling Extension (AME) for AutoCAD Releases 11 and 12 used methods in calculating mass property data that sometimes gave obviously incorrect answers. It was possible to perform hand calculations that were more accurate than AME. This is not the case with AutoCAD's solid modeler based upon the Spatial Technology Inc. ACIS kernel. The ACIS specification claims a maximum error of 1 percent for mass property data. Mass property data from regions and solids is not only easily and quickly obtained with AutoCAD, you can be confident of its accuracy.

As you would expect, since one is a 2D object while the other is a 3D object, AutoCAD reports different information for regions than it does for solids. Generally, the information for regions is easier to understand (and often more useful) than mass property data for solids. Therefore we'll discuss regions first.

Mass Property Reports for Regions

Since regions are planar objects, and since AutoCAD combines all of the regions selected into one report, their relationship to the coordinate system and to each other is important in both selecting objects for MASSPROP and in the extent of the information AutoCAD reports. First of all, AutoCAD will ignore all regions that are not in the same plane as the first region selected. Second, AutoCAD gives more information for regions that are on the X-Y plane (coplanar) than for regions that are off the X-Y plane (noncoplanar).

AutoCAD reports the area, perimeter, bounding box, centroid, moments of inertia, radius of gyration, and the principal moments of inertia for regions that are coplanar with the X-Y plane. Since the moments of inertia properties, as well as the radius of gyration, are always relative to an axis in the plane of the region, Auto-CAD does not report them when the region is off of, or tilted to, the X-Y plane. Consequently, AutoCAD reports only the area, perimeter, bounding box, and centroid of noncoplanar regions.

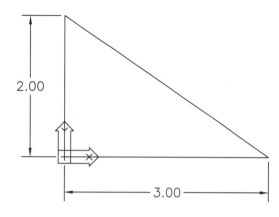

An example of AutoCAD's mass property report for a region is shown in Listing 1. The region of this report has the shape of a right triangle 3 units long and 2 units high, lying on the X-Y plane. The 3-unit side lies on the X-axis, and the 2-unit side is on the Y-axis. The following paragraphs describe the data in this mass property report.

Listing 1   Mass property report for a coplanar region

```
...............REGIONS................
Area:                      3.0000
Perimeter:                 8.6056
Bounding box:              X: 0.0000.....3.0000
                           Y: 0.0000.....2.0000
Centroid:                  X: 1.0000
                           Y: 0.6667
Moments of inertia:        X: 2.0000Y: 4.5000
Product of inertia:        XY: 1.5000
Radii of gyration:         X: 0.8165 Y: 1.2247
Principal moments and X-Y directions about centroid:
                           I: 0.4325 along [0.9056 -0.4242]
                           J: 1.7342 along [0.4242 0.9056]
```

Area

This is the size of the region's surface, expressed in units of square length.

Perimeter

Perimeter is the length of the region's boundary. If the region has one or more interior holes, the perimeter is the total length of both the inside and outside boundaries.

Bounding Box

AutoCAD displays the coordinates for the corners of the smallest rectangular-shaped box the region will fit in. The sides of this box are always parallel to the coordinate system axes. Conse-

Table 14-1   Region Properties—Basis Equations and Dimensions

Property	Basis Equation	Dimensions
Area	$A = \sum dxdy$	L^2
Centroid	$\bar{x} = \dfrac{\sum (dxdy)x}{A} \qquad \bar{y} = \dfrac{\sum (dxdy)y}{A}$	x,y
Area moments of inertia	$Ixx = \sum (dxdy)x^2$ $Iyy = \sum (dxdy)y^2$	L^4 L^4
Product of inertia	$Ixy = \sum (dxdy)xy$	L^4
Radius of gyration	$Kx = \sqrt{\dfrac{Ixx}{A}}$ $Ky = \sqrt{\dfrac{Iyy}{A}}$	L L
Angle (θ) of principal axis	$Tan(2\theta) = \dfrac{2Ixy}{Ixx\text{-}Iyy}$	Degrees
Principal moments of inertia	$I_{\substack{max \\ min}} = \left(\dfrac{Ixx + Iyy}{2}\right) \pm \sqrt{\left(\dfrac{Ixx + Iyy}{2}\right)^2 + \left(Ixy\right)^2}$	L^4

quently, a long thin region will have a smaller bounding box when its sides are parallel to the coordinate system axes than it will when it is askew of them. If the region is on the X-Y plane, only the X and Y coordinates of the bounding box are given. If the region is off of, or is tilted to, the X-Y plane, the bounding box will have a Z coordinate also.

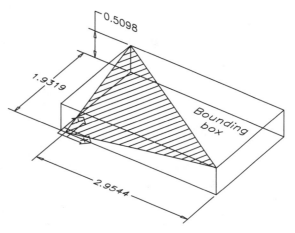

Bounding box for a noncoplanar region

Centroid

The centroid is a point representing the geometric center of the region. For most regions it is the point at which the region could be balanced on the point of a pin. However, some regions, such as those shaped like the letter *L*, will have their centroid outside the boundary of the region. If the region lays on the coordinate system X-Y plane, only the X and Y coordinates of the centroid will be given. If the region is not on the X-Y plane, or is tilted to it, the centroid point will have a Z coordinate as well as X and Y coordinates.

Moments of Inertia

Area moments of inertia are a more abstract property than area and centroids, and consequently they are not as easy to picture. Nevertheless, moments of inertia of areas are extremely important since they are used to calculate material-bending stresses and deformations (strains). Every region will have two moments of inertia—one relative to the X axis, and a second relative to the Y axis. Since this property involves no mass, and hence no inertial forces, some prefer to call it the *second moment of area,* rather than *moment of inertia.*

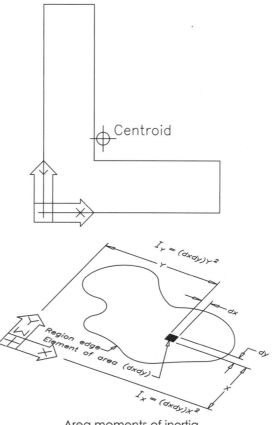

Area moments of inertia
for a single element

Product of Inertia

While area moment of inertia for an individual element is based upon the square of its distance from the X axis or the Y axis, product of inertia is based upon the product of the element's distance from the X axis and its distance from the Y axis. Consequently, a region has only one product of inertia, and its value may be either positive or negative, depending upon the location of the coordinate system. Product of inertia is used in computing the principal moments of inertia.

Radius of Gyration

An area's radius of gyration is the distance from the reference axis at which the entire area could be considered as being concentrated without changing its moment of inertia. The property has such a catchy name that it is hard to forget, even if you never have any reason to use it. Similar to moments of inertia, every plane area always has one radius of gyration relative to the X axis and another relative to the Y axis. Radius of gyration is useful in the design of support columns, since a column under a compression load tends to buckle in the direction of its least radius of gyration.

Principal Moments of Inertia and X-Y Directions about Centroid

When the origin of the coordinate system is anchored on the centroid of a plane area, the X and Y axes can be rotated around the Z axis to an angle such that the area's maximum moment of inertia is about one axis, while its minimum moment of inertia is about the other axis. These two moments of inertia are called the *principal moments of inertia*, and the axes about which they are taken are called the *principal axes of inertia*. Product of inertia for the plane always has a value of 0 relative to the principal axes of inertia.

Listing 2 AutoCAD Mass Property Report for a 3D Solid

```
                ..............      SOLIDS      ..............
                Mass:                           3.0000
                Volume:                         3.0000
                Bounding box:                   X: 0.0000.....3.0000
                                                Y: 0.0000.....2.0000
                                                Z: 0.0000.....1.0000
                Centroid:                       X: 1.0000
                                                Y: 0.6667
                                                Z: 0.5000
                Moments of inertia:             X: 3.0000
                                                Y: 5.5000
                                                Z: 6.5000
                Products of inertia:            XY: 1.5000
                                                YZ: 1.0000
                                                ZX: 1.5000
                Radii of gyration:              X: 1.0000
                                                Y: 1.3540Z: 1.4720
                Principal moments and X-Y-Z directions about centroid:
                            I: 0.6825 along [0.9056 -0.4242 0.0000]
                            J: 1.9842 along [0.4242 0.9056 0.0000]
                            K: 2.1667 along [0.0000 0.0000 1.0000]
```

Table 14-2 3D Solid Mass Properties—Basis Equations and Dimensions

Property	Basis Equation	Dimensions
Mass General: Element:	$M = \rho\, V$ $dm = \rho\,(dxdydz) = \rho\, dv$	M
Volume	$V = \sum (dxdydz) = \sum dv$	L^3
Density General: Element:	$\rho = \dfrac{M}{V}$ (Always equals 1 in AutoCAD) $\rho = \dfrac{dm}{dv}$	$\dfrac{M}{L^3}$
Centroid	$\bar{x} = \dfrac{\sum xdv}{V}$ $\qquad \bar{y} = \dfrac{\sum ydv}{V}$ $\qquad \bar{z} = \dfrac{\sum zdv}{V}$	x, y, z
Moments of Inertia	$I_{xx} = \sum (y^2 + z^2)\,dm \qquad I_{xx} = \rho \sum (y^2 + z^2)\,dv$ $I_{yy} = \rho \sum (x^2 + z^2)\,dv$ $I_{zz} = \rho \sum (x^2 + y^2)\,dv$	ML^2 ML^2 ML^2
Products of Inertia	$I_{xy} = I_{yx} = \sum xy\,dm \qquad I_{xy} = I_{yx} = \rho \sum xy\,dv$ $I_{xz} = I_{zx} = \rho \sum xz\,dv$ $I_{yz} = I_{zy} = \rho \sum yz\,dv$	ML^2 ML^2 ML^2
Radius of Gyration	$K_x = \sqrt{\dfrac{I_{xx}}{M}}$ $K_y = \sqrt{\dfrac{I_{yy}}{M}}$ $K_z = \sqrt{\dfrac{I_{zz}}{M}}$	L L L
Principal Moments of Inertia	$\begin{pmatrix} I_{xx} & I_{xy} & I_{xz} \\ I_{yx} & I_{yy} & I_{yz} \\ I_{zx} & I_{zy} & I_{zz} \end{pmatrix} \qquad \begin{pmatrix} I_1 & 0 & 0 \\ 0 & I_2 & 0 \\ 0 & 0 & I_3 \end{pmatrix}$ The moments and products of inertia are arranged in a matrix. Which is Diagonalized to find the principal moments of inertia.	ML^2

Principal moments of inertia as well as the orientation of the principal axes are based upon area moments of inertia and products of inertia, as shown in Table 14-1. In college classes covering engineering mechanics, a graphical technique called Mohr's circle is often used in finding the principal moments of inertia, as well as the orientation of the principal axes.

AutoCAD uses the letter *I* to indicate the principal moment of inertia about the principal axis corresponding to the X axis. Following this moment of inertia value are two numbers, enclosed within brackets, that are the coordinates of a point (relative to the current UCS) representing the end of a unit vector pointing in the direction of this principal axis. Thus, in Listing 1 the principal moment of inertia is 0.4325 about an axis pointed in the same direction as a line from 0,0 to 0.9056,-0.4242 (which is 25.1 degrees clockwise from the UCS X axis). AutoCAD uses the letter *J* for the other principal moment of inertia and indicates its axis direction also with a pair of point coordinates enclosed in brackets. As you would expect, these principal axes are always 90 degrees to one another.

If you were to rotate the UCS -25.1 degrees about the Z axis in the drawing for the region used for Listing 1, then move it to the region's centroid, the moments of inertia for the region would be 0.4325 units to the fourth power about the X axis, and 1.7342 units to the fourth power about the Y axis. Also, the product of inertia would be 0.

You will notice there is no mention of mass in Table 14-1. None of the properties for regions have mass—they are based solely upon length. Actually, this is to be expected since regions, by definition, are infinitely thin. They have no thickness, no volume, and no mass. The units of length in the mass property report for regions will be based upon the measurement unit you are working with. For instance, if millimeters have been used to draw the region, then area will be in square millimeters, moments of inertia will be in millimeters to the fourth power, and so forth.

Mass Property Reports for 3D Solids

Listing 2 shows the mass property report of a wedge-shaped 3D solid that was made by extruding the triangle-shaped region we used for illustrating AutoCAD's mass property report for a region to a height of 1 unit.

Unlike the mass property report for regions, AutoCAD does not report the surface area of 3D solids. You can find that property, however, by using the AREA command. The following paragraphs describe the data in the mass property report for solids.

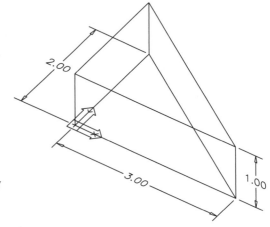

Mass

Although most of us generally use the words *mass* and *weight* interchangeably, there is a subtle difference between them. Mass is one of the three fundamental physical dimensions (length and time are the other two), while weight is an expression of force—it is mass multiplied by an acceleration-due-to-gravity factor. Mass is independent of gravity. Weight, on the other hand, is dependent upon the strength of a gravitational field. Consequently, you would weigh less on the moon than you do on Earth, but your mass would remain the same. Nevertheless, weight is usually the way in which we relate to mass, and it is also a convenient way to obtain an object's mass.

Since computer programs have no means to weigh 3D models, most solid modeling programs determine mass indirectly by multiplying the model's volume by a per-unit weight—the material's density. Density, which is designated by a lowercase Greek rho (r) in Table 14-2, is mass divided by volume. It is a material property.

AutoCAD, unfortunately, always uses a density of 1, and does not allow you to change it. Therefore, AutoCAD always reports the same value for mass as it does for volume. If you need to know the mass or weight of an AutoCAD 3D solid, you will have to do the calculation yourself.

Volume
Volume is the amount of space within the solid, expressed in units of length raised to the third power.

Bounding Box
These numbers are the diagonally opposite corner coordinates for the smallest box in which the solid would fit. The sides of the bounding box are always parallel to the coordinate system axes. Therefore, this box is not necessarily the smallest box into which the solid will fit.

Centroid
A solid's centroid is a 3D point representing its geometric center. If the solid's material's density is homogeneous (which is usually the case), the centroid will also be the solid's center of gravity—the point at which all of the solid's weight appears to be concentrated.

Moments of Inertia
The moment of inertia of a box element about an axis is defined as the element's mass multiplied by the square of its distance from the axis. Notice that unlike moments of inertia for a region, the calculation for solids really does involve mass.

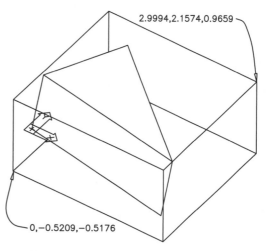

If a 3D solid is skewed to the principal planes, its bounding box will be larger than if it was aligned to the planes.

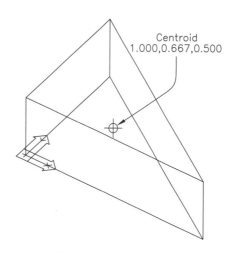

Since the mass of an object is equal to its density multiplied by its volume, an element's moment of inertia can also be found by multiplying its volume by the square of its distance from the axis and by its density. AutoCAD uses this approach, but it uses a density of 1. Thus, to obtain the correct moments of inertia of your solid, you'll have to multiply AutoCAD's values by the solid's material density. Mass moments of inertia are used principally in calculations of forces and motions of rotating objects.

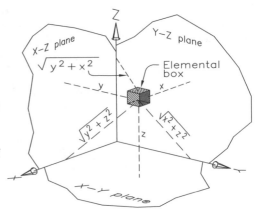

Products of Inertia

The product of inertia for an elemental box is defined with respect to two planes that are perpendicular to one another (orthogonal) as the product of the element's mass and the perpendicular distances from each of the planes to the element (see the figure shown in the section on moments of inertia). For example, the XY product of inertia is calculated by multiplying the elemental box's mass by its distance in the Y direction from the X axis and by its distance in the X direction from the Y axis. In other words, the box's mass is multiplied by its X and Y coordinates. While there are six products of inertia, only three of them are independent, as shown in Table 14-2.

Mass products of inertia can be calculated alternately by multiplying the element's volume, density, X coordinate, and Y coordinate together. AutoCAD uses this alternate calculation method, and as it does for moments of inertia, it uses a material density of 1. Therefore, you'll have to multiply the reported values by the solid's material density to obtain the true products of inertia.

Radii of Gyration

Radius of gyration is the distance from the axis of rotation at which the entire weight of a body may be assumed to be concentrated, without changing its moment of inertia. It is sometimes used in the design of rotating parts, such as flywheels and governors. Every solid has three radii of gyration—one for each axis of the coordinate system. Each is found by dividing the body's moment of inertia about the axis by its mass and taking the square root of the result. Since density was used in calculating both moments of inertia and mass, the radii of gyration reported by AutoCAD is correct.

Principal Moments and X-Y-Z Directions about Centroid

If the coordinate system origin is moved to the solid's centroid, it can be twisted to an orientation resulting in a maximum moment of inertia about one axis and a minimum moment of inertia about a second axis. The moment of inertia about the third axis will, of course, have a value somewhere between the maximum and minimum. These three moments of inertia are referred to as the principal moments of inertia, and the axes they are about are called the principal axes. The products of inertia will be 0 when the coordinate system is aligned with the principal axes.

326

The principal axes are important in the design of rotating equipment, since parts rotating about a principal axis will draw minimum power during speed changes. A rotating device, such as a shaft or propeller, is said to be *dynamically balanced* when its center of mass lies on the axis of rotation and it is rotating about a principal axis.

In AutoCAD's mass property report, the three principal moments of inertia are designated as I, J, and K, with the orientation of each corresponding principal axis shown within brackets. These numbers within brackets are the endpoint coordinates, relative to the current coordinate system, of a unit direction vector.

For example: if the UCS for the model used for the mass property report shown in Listing 2 is twisted so that the X axis is pointing in the same direction as a line from 0,0,0 to 0.9025, -0.4242,0; while the Y axis is pointing in the same direction as a line from 0,0,0 to 0.4242,0.9056,0; then the UCS origin is moved to the solid's centroid, and the mass moments of inertia will be 0.6825 about the X axis, 1.9842 about the Y axis, and 2.1667 about the Z axis. Also, all of the products of inertia will be 0. You will have to multiply AutoCAD's principal moments of inertia by density to obtain their correct values.

Command: MASSPROP

Purpose: MASSPROP reports the mass properties of 3D solids and the area properties of regions.

Initiate with:

- On the command line enter MASSPROP.

- From the Tools pull-down menu, select Inquiry, then Mass Properties.

- Select the Mass Properties button from the Inquiry flyout of the Standard toolbar.

Implementation:

The MASSPROP command will ask you to select the objects to be included in its mass properties report. You may select as many objects as you wish. AutoCAD will ignore objects that are not 3D solids.

When more than one 3D solid is selected, AutoCAD will issue a single report, as if the solids were a single, unified object. AutoCAD will also combine regions when more than one is selected, provided that they are not, AutoCAD will issue a report only for the first region selected. If a mixture of 3D solids and regions are selected, Auto-CAD will issue separate reports for each object type.

The properties on the right will appear in a text window.

| **Properties of 3D Solids** |
| Mass |
| Volume |
| Bounding box |
| Centroid |
| Moments of inertia |
| Products of inertia |
| Radii of gyration |
| Principal moments and |
| X-Y-Z direction about centroid |

| **Properties of Regions** |
| Area |
| Perimeter |
| Bounding box |
| Centroid |
| Moments of inertia |
| Products of inertia |
| Radii of gyration |
| Principal moments and |
| X-Y directions about centroid |

AutoCAD will ask if you want the data written to a file. The resulting file will be in ASCII text format, with a default filename the same as the current drawing file and with the file extension of .mpr.

Notes:

- If a region is not on the UCS X-Y plane, AutoCAD will report only its area, perimeter, bounding box, and centroid.

- AutoCAD always uses a density of 1 when it computes the mass of a 3D solid. Consequently, the reported values for mass and volume are always equal.

- The data for 3D solids is given in units of volume and mass, while the data for regions is in units of area.

- Mass property data is always relative to the current UCS origin.

Command: AREA

Purpose: AREA reports the surface area of 3D solids and the area and perimeter of regions.

Initiate with:

- On the command line enter AREA.

- From the Tools pull-down menu, select Inquiry, then Area.

- Select the Area button from the Inquiry flyout of the Standard toolbar.

Implementation:

Choose the AREA command's Object option and select a 3D solid in response to its prompt to select objects. You can select only one object (despite the prompt's plural use of the word *object*), and you must do so by picking a point on the object. AutoCAD will report the surface area of a 3D solid. It will also report the solid's perimeter, but since perimeter has no meaning for a 3D solid, the perimeter value will always be listed as 0.

The AREA command also recognizes regions and reports their area and perimeter length.

2D Output and Paper Space

Paper Space and Floating Viewports

T he role and use of paper space in transforming 3D models to 2D drawings will be described
in this chapter. When you have finished the chapter, you will

- *be familiar with the properties of paper space and of the floating viewports of paper space;*
- *know how to create floating viewports and how to set them up for making multiview orthographic 2D drawings;*
- *have learned the techniques for controlling the appearances of objects within floating viewports;*
- *be able to dimension, annotate, and plot 2D paper space drawings of 3D models.*

In the not too distant future, it will be common to send digital data from 3D computer models directly to the machine shop. Then, multiview 2D drawings, with their elaborate dimensions and symbols, will no longer be needed. Now, however, they are still a necessity.

Actually, some paper-based 2D form of mechanical part models will probably always be needed for reviews and documentation. Furthermore, at this time it is difficult to conceive of any technique that will transform 3D models of buildings and structures into real objects. Controlling the motions of milling machines and lathes is one thing; controlling the placement of two-by-fours and pouring concrete footings is altogether different.

Therefore, paper drawings, along with other media forms for 2D representations, are going to be around for many, many years; in this book section, we will explore the AutoCAD tools and techniques for converting 3D models to 2D drawings.

The Role of Paper Space

Up to this point, everything we have discussed in this book has pertained to model space—that fully 3D world where you can set viewpoints that look in any direction you choose, and where you can divide the AutoCAD graphics area into multiple tiled viewports to simultaneously view a

3D model from different view directions. While model space is well suited for creating 3D models, it is not suitable for making 2D drawings of those models. Among its problems:

- Only the contents of the current viewport can be printed. This makes the printing of multiview drawings that show aligned top, front, and side views of a 3D model virtually impossible.
- Prints having an accurate scale from any viewpoint other than plan views are difficult to set up.
- Drawing views having a scale different from that used for other views is not practical.
- Controlling which objects are to be shown and which are not to be shown (such as interior and back-face edges) is awkward, as is the practice of showing hidden edges with dashed lines.

These problems are largely solved through paper space. Paper space is a 2D world that acts as a screen placed over model space. You can make multiple viewports in this screen that look into model space, and you can establish different view directions in different viewports, just as you can in model space. Unlike model space, though, paper space allows you to simultaneously print all viewports—not just the current one.

Paper space's purpose is to make 2D drawings from 3D models. It is a space comparable to a sheet of paper attached to a drafting board. If you intend for a drawing to be on

Model space tiled viewports

paper that is 22 inches by 17 inches, for instance, you will set the extents of your paper space drawing to those dimensions. And, if you intend for the printed text height of the notes to be 0.125 inches, that is the paper space text height you will use.

Drawing scale is handled by adjusting the apparent size of the model in the paper space viewports. Moreover, since you can accurately scale the apparent size of the model viewport by viewport, you can have some views that have a different scale than the others. This enables you to conveniently have enlarged views showing details of your model.

Floating Viewports

The key feature of paper space is its *floating viewports*. They are similar to the *tiled viewports* of model space in that multiple viewports can coexist; that each viewport can have a different 3D view direction; and that each viewport can have different snap, grid, and UCS icon settings. Unlike tiled viewports, though, the floating viewports of paper space:

- Do not need to be side by side or fill the entire graphics area. There can be gaps between the viewports, and the viewports can overlap and even be on top of each other.
- Can be erased, moved, stretched, copied and scaled.
- Reside in a layer. Their borders take the color of the layer. If you turn off or freeze the view-

Paper space floating viewports

- port's layer, its borders will disappear while its contents remain visible.
- Allow you to control which objects are visible in a viewport. This is done by freezing layers on a viewport-by-viewport basis.
- Can precisely set the scale of the 3D model. Moreover, the scale can vary between viewports.
- Permit hidden-line removal during plotting to be controlled on a viewport-by-viewport basis.
- Can have a border having any shape that can be drawn as a spline or a 2D polyline.

The Properties of Paper Space

Despite the word *space* in its name, it is helpful to consider paper space more as an operational mode than as a location. In fact, even Autodesk uses the terms *drawing mode* and *model mode,* rather than paper space and model space in its Mechanical Desktop parametric 3D modeling program. Moreover, AutoCAD 2000 often uses the word *layout* when referring to paper space.

Controlling whether model space or paper space is active is done by the **tilemode** system variable. AutoCAD operates in model space when **tilemode** is set to 1, and it operates in paper space when **tilemode** is set to 0. The system variable's name is a reference to the tiled viewports used in model space—when **tilemode** is on (that is, when it is set to 1), tiled viewports are used; when **tilemode** is off (set to 0), floating viewports are used.

In AutoCAD 2000 you will seldom set **tilemode** directly. Instead, you will simply click one of the tabs that are located below the AutoCAD graphics window. Tabs with names such as Layout1 open paper space, while the tab labeled Model opens model space. You can also open model space from paper space with the MODEL command of AutoCAD 2000. This command, which can only be invoked from the command line, simply sets **tilemode** to 0.

As we will describe shortly, AutoCAD 2000 allows you to have multiple paper space layouts so that you can make multiple 2D drawings of one 3D model. For example, one layout could be for a multi-view orthographic drawing and another layout could be for an isometric drawing.

You can freely switch between the paper space and model space modes. Thus, you can return to model space if you discover

Click the Model tab to activate model space.　Click the Layout tab to activate paper space.　Click this button to enter a floating viewport.

your 3D model needs more work. When you are finished, you can switch back to paper space, with your paper space objects and environment as it was when you were last there, and the changes you made to your model will be shown in the floating viewports. You can even change view directions and zoom levels in model space without affecting the view directions and zoom levels in the paper space floating viewports. If you change the size or location of your model in model space, though, it may affect the contents of the paper space floating viewports.

You can also go into model space through the paper space floating viewports. We will describe how this is done later in this chapter. Changes in view direction and zoom levels will affect the appearance and contents of floating viewports when you enter model space through floating viewports.

As shown in the second figure of this chapter, the UCS icon has a different form in paper space— it is shaped like a 30- to 60-degree drafting triangle. The icon has a small *x* on the short side of the triangle to indicate the direction of the X axis. Other than its different form, though, the icon

Accessing model space through floating viewports

behaves the same as the model space UCS icon. The UCS command also works the same in paper space as it does in model space, although you are not likely to ever move the UCS X-Y plane away from the WCS X-Y plane or tilt it so that it is not parallel with the WCS X-Y plane.

The UCS icon will be displayed only in the main paper space viewport, which is always viewport 1 (the value in the system variable **cvport**). Individual floating viewports will not contain a UCS icon. An exception occurs when you enter model space through a floating viewport. Then, each floating viewport will have the model space version of the UCS icon, and the paper space UCS icon will not be displayed.

Paper space is intended to be strictly a 2D world. While you can draw 3D objects in paper space, you cannot easily work with them because only views that look straight down on the WCS X-Y plane are allowed. You cannot use the VPOINT, 3DORBIT, or DVIEW commands in paper space. Again, exceptions occur when you enter model space through a floating viewport.

Paper space and model space share the same layers, text styles, and dimension styles. Nevertheless, they are two distinct spaces, and from paper space AutoCAD only partially recognizes the model space objects that are within floating viewports. Although object snaps on model space objects work from paper space, you cannot erase, move, stretch, or copy model space objects from paper space. There is also no straightforward way to transfer objects from one space to another, but it can be done.

One way to change the space of objects is to use the AutoLISP program ps2ms.lsp on the CD-ROM that comes with this book. This program moves one object at a time from paper space to model space, or from model space to paper space. Thus, if you inadvertently write some text within model space when it should be in paper space, you can load ps2ms.lsp, enter PS2MS on the command line, and pick a point on the text. It will be moved to paper space at the same coordinates it had in model space. This program works by changing the object's database group code 67. An object's 67 group code will be 0 when it is in model space and 1 when it is in paper space. Another way to move objects from one space to another is to save them as a WBLOCK, switch to the other space, and insert the block.

Layouts

Paper space is more closely related to plotting in AutoCAD 2000 than in previous releases, and this relationship is maintained through specific, named combinations of plotting and paper space parameters that are called *layouts*. At a minimum, a layout will designate the printing device and its settings, including the paper size and orientation. Typically, though, a layout will also include floating viewport configurations and a title block. You can have several layouts in a drawing file, which enables you to have layouts for different paper sizes, view arrangements, and even printers. By default, AutoCAD drawing files start with two identical paper space layouts that have one floating viewport and page settings based on the current printer.

The names of layouts appear on tabs on the lower edge of AutoCAD's graphics window. The names of the default paper space layouts are Layout1 and Layout2. To activate any layout, simply click its tab. There is also a tab labeled Model that activates model space. With the exception of the model layout, you can change layout names, delete layouts, change the order of layout tabs, copy layouts, and import and export layouts.

Creating and Managing Layouts

The basic command for establishing and working with paper space layouts is LAYOUT. It displays the following options on the command line:

`Copy/Delete/New/Template/Rename/Save/Set/?`

The question mark option displays a list of all existing layouts, and Set activates a specified layout. You must enter the layout name on the command line. The SAve option exports a layout as a drawing template (DWT) file so that it can be used in other drawings, while the Template option imports an existing template or drawing (DWG) file. Only layout geometry and page settings are exported or imported. Importing a template is especially useful for adding borders and a title block to a layout. When you import a template or drawing file, AutoCAD automatically creates a new layout, rather than inserting the geometry in the current layout. AutoCAD has a collection of premade templates in both inch and metric formats that are located in the Template folder. The New option creates a basic layout that uses the default printer and has no floating viewport. You will use this option when you want to start from scratch in creating a new layout.

Most of the LAYOUT command's options are also available from the shortcut menu displayed when you right-click a layout tab, and you will probably use the shortcut menu more often than the LAYOUT command. Normally the layout tabs are arranged from left to right in the order that they were created, but you can rearrange them with the Move option of the shortcut menu. You can select several layouts at once by holding the shift key down as you pick their tabs. Then you can use the shortcut menu to move or delete the selected layouts. The shortcut menu also has an option that will select all of the layouts except Model.

Setting Page Parameters

Once a layout has been created, you will use the PAGESETUP command to establish page and printing parameters for it. By default, this command is automatically invoked when you activate a new layout. It displays a dialog box titled Page Setup that is similar to the one used by the PLOT command. You are probably familiar with this dialog box from your work in 2D, so

we will just describe its options that are particularly applicable to paper space layouts.

The options in the cluster labeled "Paper size and paper units" are based on the plotting device you selected from the Plot Device tab of the dialog box. The paper size of the layout is controlled by your selection of a paper size from the dropdown list box labeled "Paper size." Only those paper sizes than can be handled by the selected plotting device are available. Since virtually all plotting devices reserve a paper margin for handling the paper, the printable area is always less than the paper size. The inches and mm buttons toggle the paper size dimensions between inches and millimeters.

In the cluster of buttons labeled "Plot area," you will usually select Layout as the area to plot. The "Plot scale" options pertain to paper space, rather than model space objects. Drawing scale is controlled within floating viewports, using methods we will describe later in this chapter. Therefore, except in special situations (such as when plotting a C-sized drawing on A-sized paper), you will always use a plot scale of 1-to-1.

The "Page setup name" list box in the upper-right corner of the dialog box is for exporting and importing the page settings of a layout. To export the current settings, click the Add button and enter a name for the setup in the dropdown edit box. The page setup will be saved when you choose the OK button of the dialog box. To import a saved page setup into the current drawing, invoke PSETUPIN from the command line. (No tool bar buttons or menu options are available for this command.) A dialog box titled Select File will be displayed for you to use in locating and specifying the drawing file that contains the page setup you want. Then a dialog box titled Import user defined page setup(s) will be displayed that lists the name of all saved page setups in the selected drawing file. Select the one you want, and click the OK button of the dialog box. Nothing will appear to happen, but when you start the PAGESETUP command, the specified page setup will be listed in the "Page setup name" list box. If you select it, all of the layout parameters will assume the values of the imported page setup.

Using the Layout Wizard

Probably the easiest way to create and set up a paper space layout is with the LAYOUTWIZARD command. The Layout Wizard leads you through a series of dialog box–based steps to establish layout parameters. These steps are

- Assign a name to the layout.
- Select a printer from a list of those currently configured for your computer.
- Choose the paper size from a list of sizes available for the selected printer, and specify whether the units used in constructing the model represent inches or millimeters.
- Specify whether the orientation of the paper is to be portrait or landscape.
- Select a drawing border and title block for the layout. Twenty-five choices in both metric and inch formats are offered, and they can be inserted as a block or as an Xref. You can also choose to not have a border or title block inserted.
- Define the floating viewports that the layout is to have. You are given the options of having no viewports, a single viewport, a rectangular array of viewports, or a 3D engineering set of viewports. If you select Array, you will be prompted to specify the number of rows and columns for the array, and for the gap between the viewports. The 3D engineering set of viewports consists of four viewports, arranged in two rows and two columns, showing top, front, side, and isometric views of the model. You can also specify a scale to be used for displaying the model within the viewports. Scaled to Fit is the default scale.

- Specify the location of the floating viewport, or viewports. The wizard dialog box will temporally be dismissed to give you full access to the AutoCAD graphics area. The paper extents and margins, as well as the drawing border and title block will be displayed, and you will be prompted to specify the opposite corners of a rectangle that the viewports are to fit in.

Controlling the Display of Layout Elements

By default, AutoCAD displays a sheet of paper, as well as its margins, on a gray background for each layout. Also, one floating viewport is automatically created and the Plot Setup dialog box is displayed for every new layout. You can change these defaults, though, through the Display tab of the Options dialog box that is opened when the OPTIONS command is invoked. Choose the check boxes in the "Layout elements" cluster to specify the elements you want. When you are working with 3D models, you will most likely turn the "Create viewport in new layout" option off, and leave the others in their default settings. You can also use this dialog box to change the color used for the paper, or for the paper space screen if paper display has been turned off.

All layout elements are displayed.

Creating Floating Viewports

No layout elements are displayed.

In AutoCAD 2000 you can use either the MVIEW or VPORTS command to make viewports. MVIEW always uses command line prompts and input, while VPORTS generally uses a dialog box. However, if you start VPORTS in paper space from the command line and precede its name with a hyphen, command line prompts and options identical to those of MVIEW are displayed. In addition to making rectangular viewports, these commands can make viewports in any shape that can be drawn as a polyline, circle, spline, ellipse, or region. Furthermore, viewports based on regions can even have internal islands. In making drawings of 3D models, though, you will seldom need viewports in any shape other than rectangular.

Making rectangular floating viewports is a straightforward process. You can simply pick a point and drag the rubberband rectangle anchored at that point to set the viewport's opposite diagonal corner. Your model, as it appeared in the last current model space tiled viewport, will be displayed in the new floating viewport. The initial size and location of the floating viewport is not especially important, since you can stretch and scale the viewport to change its size and you can move it to another position. These operations do not change the floating viewport contents. If you change the size of a viewport, the relative size of the model within it stays the same; if you move a viewport, its contents move with it.

You can also copy floating viewports, with the contents of the original viewport remaining within the copies. If you want to get rid of a viewport, you simply erase it. You cannot rotate rectangular floating viewports so that their edges are oblique to the WCS X and Y axes. You can, though, freely rotate nonrectangular viewports. Only their borders will rotate; not their contents. You can also mirror viewports, and you can even make polar array copies of floating viewports. The contents of the viewports will not, however, be affected by either operation.

By default AutoCAD scales the image of the model as necessary to fit within a new viewport. You can, though, set a specific scale in viewports as they are created by assigning a positive value to the **psvpscale** system variable. For instance: If you intend for all of the viewports of a layout to have a scale relative to paper space of one-half, you can set **psvpscale** to 0.5. Once you have the scale of a viewport set, you can maintain that scale with the Lock option of the MVIEW and VPORTS commands. The ZOOM command is disabled in viewports that are locked, which prevents you from inadvertently changing the scale of the viewport. The PAN, DVIEW, and VPOINT commands are also disabled in locked viewports. 3DORBIT, though, is not disabled.

Floating viewports are special AutoCAD entities that reside in layers just as other entities do. Their borders take the color of their layer, but they are always drawn in a continuous linetype, even if a noncontinuous linetype has been assigned to their layer. Grips are located at their vertexes, and object snaps work on viewport vertexes, the midpoints of straight edges, and the center point of arc and circular edges. If you freeze or turn off the layer that a viewport resides in, the borders of the viewport will disappear, but its contents remaining visible. Since you will often do this to get rid of floating viewport borders, it is a good practice to place viewports in their own unique layer.

Although there is no limit to the maximum number of floating viewports you can create, there is a maximum number that can be active. If more than the allowed number of active viewports are created, no objects will be displayed in the extra viewports. You should not confuse the terms *active viewport* and *current viewport.* An active viewport is one that is visible and contains an image, while the current viewport is the one that contains the crosshair screen cursor. Many active viewports can exist simultaneously, but only one can be the current viewport.

The maximum number of active viewports is determined by the value in the **maxactvp** system variable, and in turn, the maximum value you can assign to **maxactvp** depends upon your computer system. However, even modest computer systems support up to 48 active viewports, so you are not likely to ever be concerned about exceeding the maximum allowed number of floating viewports. Furthermore, the contents of inactive floating viewports will be plotted even though you cannot see their contents, and the MVIEW and VPORTS commands allow you to switch active viewports by turning some off and others on.

The MVIEW and VPORTS commands also allows you to specify which floating viewports are to have hidden lines removed during plotting. In fact, this is the only way to have hidden lines removed during plotting—the Hide Lines option of the PLOT command has no effect on objects within paper space floating viewports.

Exercise One

We will start a paper space drawing of the surface model of the automobile oil pan we last worked on in Chapter Eight. Retrieve the file mfe08108.dwg from the CD-ROM that comes with this book and open it. The model is shown in the figure on the right, as it is seen in model space with hidden lines removed from a viewpoint that looks upward toward the bottom of the oil plan.

As is often the case with surface models, this model has no thickness. But, since our drawing is intended for making a die to be used for manufacturing the oil plan, rather than the oil pan itself, a single surface is what we want. There is no need to simulate the material thickness. Our 2D paper space drawing of the oil pan die will have three views: one each for showing its top, front, and right sides. In this exercise we will simply create three floating viewports for those views.

Open the Options dialog box and select the Display tab. Clear the check box labeled Create Viewport in New Layouts, and click the OK button to exit the dialog box. Then, select the tab labeled Layout1 that is located below the graphics area. This will activate paper space. A dialog box titled Page Setup - Layout1 should automatically appear. If it does not, enter PAGESETUP on the command line. In this dialog box, select the Plot Device tab, and from the drop-down list box of plotters that are configured for you computer, select one that can handle D-sized paper (34-by-22-inch). Return to the Layout Settings tab of the dialog box. Select an ANSI-D size paper from the list box labeled Paper Size, and then click the OK button of the dialog box. AutoCAD will display a 34-by-22-inch sheet of paper over a gray background and will indicate the printer margins with dashed lines.

Switch to the layer named Vports, and make three floating viewports. Two of the viewports are to be 12 by 6 inches in size and one is to be 6 by 6 inches, and they are to be located as shown in the figure below. You will do this with the either the MVIEW or VPORTS command, using any of several different approaches. (1) You can simultaneously make the two large viewports with the 2 option of MVIEW or VPORTS to make two horizontal viewports that fit in a square that is approximately 12 inches by 12 inches, and move the two viewports apart. Then make the third, smaller, viewport. (2) You can make just one 12-by-6-inch viewport, and copy it for the second viewport. And make the third viewport. (3) You can invoke MVIEW or VPORTS three times, drawing a single viewport each time.

Do not be concerned if your viewports are of a different size, shape, or location since it is virtually a given that viewports will need to be moved and resized after the viewpoints and model scales have been fixed. Their initial size, location, and contents are not critical.

That completes this exercise, so you should save your drawing file. In Exercise Two of this chapter, we will set the view direction in each viewport, adjust the scale of the model, and align the views.

Command: MVIEW

Purpose: MVIEW creates the floating viewports of paper space. It can also turn floating viewports on and off and remove hidden lines in selected viewports during plotting.

Initiate with:

• On the command line enter MVIEW.

Options:

This command has options for creating floating viewports, for turning existing floating viewports on and off, and for removing hidden lines in selected viewports during plotting. From the command line, it displays the following menu for selecting an option:

```
Specify corner of viewport or
    [ON/OFF/Fit/Hideplot/Lock/Object/Polygon/Restore/2/3/4]/<Fit>: (Enter an
    option, specify a point, or press Enter.)
```

- Corner of viewport

  When you specify a point, AutoCAD will use it as one corner of a new floating viewport and will issue a command line prompt for the opposite diagonal corner of the viewport. A rubberband rectangle anchored at the first point will help you judge the size and location of the viewport.

Other corner

First point

- ON — TURNS ON VIEWPORT

  This option turns on previously turned off viewports. Their model space contents will again be visible. A follow-up prompt will ask you to select the objects (the floating viewports) that are to be turned on.

- OFF — OFF VIEWPORT

  The OFF option turns off active viewports. Their model space contents will no longer be visible. AutoCAD will issue a command line prompt for you to select the objects (the floating viewports) that are to be turned off.

- Fit

  One floating viewport with its edges corresponding to the paper's print margins is created by this option. If paper display has been turned off, the viewport will fill the current graphics area. No additional input is called for. This is the default MVIEW option.

Hidden line removal OFF

Hidden line removal ON

- Hideplot — NO PLOT OF HIDDEN LINES

  This option controls the plotting of hidden lines in selected viewports. It does not control the display of hidden lines on the computer screen. The option uses the following command line prompts:

```
Hidden line removal for plotting [ON/OFF]: (Enter ON or OFF)
Select objects: (Select one or more floating viewports.)
```

340

Entering ON turns on hidden-line removal during plotting in the selected viewports—hidden lines *will not* be plotted. Entering OFF turns off hidden-line removal during plotting—hidden lines *will* be plotted.

- Lock — PRESERVES SCALE

Locking the view of a viewport preserves its scale, or zoom level, relative to paper space. When the ZOOM command is invoked within a locked viewport, the cursor automatically returns to paper space so that the zoom occurs in paper space rather than model space. The following command line prompt will be displayed for you to select the viewports that are to be locked, or unlocked:

```
Viewport View Locking [ON/OFF]: (Enter ON or OFF.)
Select objects: (Select one or more floating viewports.)
```

- Object — DEFINE VP. WITH OBJECT

This option uses an existing closed wireframe object to define a new floating viewport. The object can be a spline, 3D or 2D polyline, circle, ellipse, or region. Even splines and polylines that cross over themseleves are acceptable objects. You will be prompted to select one object:

```
Select object to clip viewport: (Select a closed wireframe object.)
```

- Polygonal

You can create a viewport that can have arcs and straight segments as in a 2D polyline with this option. Command line prompts similar to those of the PLINE command will be issued.

- Restore

When this option is selected, the number of viewports, their arrangement, and the view directions within them will correspond to an existing configuration of tiled viewports. AutoCAD will first display a menu for you to use in specifying a particular viewport configuration:

```
Enter viewport configuration name or [?] <*Active>:
(Enter a ?, a viewport configuration name, or press Enter.)
```

The tiled viewport configuration that is currently in use in model space will be used when the *ACTIVE* option is selected. When a question mark is entered, AutoCAD will display a list of all tiled viewport configurations that have been saved through the VPORTS command. Entering the name of a saved viewport configuration will base the number, arrangement, and view directions of the floating viewports on that configuration.

Tiled viewport configuration

Other corner

First point

Resulting floating viewports

Next AutoCAD will prompt for the rectangle that the floating viewports are to fit within:

```
Specify first corner or [Fit] <Fit>: (Press Enter, enter F, or specify a point.)
```

The Fit option will fit the floating viewports within the margins of the paper, or within the edges of the graphics area if the paper is not displayed. If you specify a point, AutoCAD will use it as one corner of a rectangle and will prompt for its opposite diagonal corner. Floating viewports corresponding to the tiled viewports will be fit within this rectangle. If the rectangle used to define the boundaries of the floating viewports has different proportions than those of the tiled viewport configuration, AutoCAD will adjust the proportions of the individual floating viewports to fit the specified area.

- 2

This option creates two floating viewports. It will issue the following command line prompts for you to specify the orientation, size, and location of the two viewports:

```
Enter viewport arrangement [Horizontal/Ver-
    tical] <Vertical>: (Enter H or V, or
    press Enter.)
Specify first corner or [Fit] <Fit>: (Press
    Enter, enter F, or specify a point.)
```

If you specify a point, AutoCAD will use it for one corner of the two viewports and will prompt for the opposite diagonal corner. Both viewports will fit within the specified rectangle. The Fit option fits the two viewports within the drawing margins, or within the extents of the graphics area if paper display has been turned off.

2/Horizontal   2/Vertical

3/Horizontal   3/Vertical   3/Above

- 3

Three viewports within a specified area are created by this option. AutoCAD

3/Below   3/Left   3/Right

will display command line menus and prompts for you to specify the arrangement of the viewports and their size, orientation, and location:

```
Enter viewport arrangement
[Horizontal/Vertical/Above/Below/Left/Right] <Right>:
(Enter an option or press Enter.)
Specify first corner or [Fit] <Fit>: (Press Enter, enter F, or specify a point.)
```

The Fit option will fit the three viewports within the paper margins, or within the current view if paper display is turned off. When you specify a point, AutoCAD will use it as one corner of a rectangle that the three viewports will fit in and will prompt for the other corner of the rectangle.

4

- 4

  This option creates four equal-sized viewports, arranged in quadrants within a specified rectangular area. Command line prompts will ask you to specify the size and location of the rectangle that the viewports are to fit within.

  `Specify first corner or [Fit] <Fit>:` *(Press Enter, enter F, or specify a point.)*

  Choose the Fit option to have the four viewports fit within a rectangle corresponding to the current paper margins, or to the current extents of the graphics area if paper display is turned off. If you specify a point, it will serve as one corner of the rectangle, and AutoCAD will ask you to specify its opposite diagonal corner.

Notes:

- AutoCAD displays absolute coordinates on the status line when you are dragging the rubberband rectangle to establish the opposite diagonal corner of a viewport. This may make it difficult for you to judge the size of the viewport. You can, though, enter relative coordinates on the command line in establishing the opposite corner of a viewport.

- The LIST command will report if hidden-line removal during plotting has been turned on for a particular viewport, and if view scale locking is in effect.

- If **psvpscale** is set to 0, AutoCAD does a zoom-all on the view within floating viewports when they are created. Otherwise, the zoom level (or scale) of the viewport is equal to the value in **psvpscale**.

- All of the options for creating multiple viewports place the viewports so that their sides exactly touch. There are no gaps between the viewports, but you can easily move them apart after they have been created.

- In AutoCAD 2000, the VPORTS command can also be used to create floating viewports. The command line version of VPORTS, which is invoked by preceeding the command's name with a dash, has prompts and options that are identical to those of MVIEW. The dialog box version graphically offers the MVIEW options of single, 2, 3, and 4.

Related system variables:

- **cvport** CURRENT VIEWPORT

  The number of the current viewport is stored in this system variable. The main paper space viewport is always viewport 1.

- **maxactvp** # VIEWPORTS

  This system variable controls the maximum allowed number of active viewports. Since the main paper space viewport is considered to be a viewport, the number of floating viewports is 1 less that the value in **maxactvp**

- **psvpscale** — SCALE ON PAPER SPACE

  When this system variable is set to its default value of 0, AutoCAD performs a zoom-all in new viewports. If you assign a positive value to **psvpscale**, that value will be used as a zoom scale factor relative to paper space in new viewports.

- **tilemode**

  When **tilemode** is set to 1, only tiled viewports can be created. When tilemode is set to 0, only floating viewports can be created.

Command: VPORTS

Purpose: VPORTS creates both model space tiled viewports and paper space floating viewports.

Initiate with:

- On the command line enter VPORTS
- From the View pull-down menu, select Viewports, then an option of your choice.
- Select an option from the Viewports toolbar.

Options:

When this command is started by entering -VPORTS on the command line, the same options offered by MVIEW are displayed on the command line. Otherwise VPORTS displays the New Viewports tab of the Viewports dialog box. The available viewport arrangements displayed in the Standard Viewports list box are the same as those for MVIEW and the command line version of VPORTS. When you select one, its viewport arrangement and the viewpoint within each viewport is displayed in the Preview window. If you select 3D from the Setup list box, you can set the viewpoint in each viewport to one

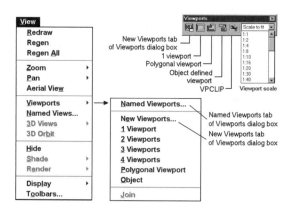

of the six orthographic views or to one of the four isometric views that look down on the X-Y plane. These viewpoints are pre-set in each viewport by AutoCAD, but you can change the viewpoint in any viewport with the Change View To list box. You can also specify a gap between the viewports by entering or selecting a number in the Viewport Spacing edit box.

When you select the OK button of the Viewports dialog box, AutoCAD will issue a command line prompt for you to draw a rec-

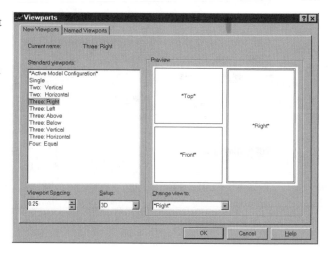

344

tangle that the viewports are to fit in, or to specify that the viewports are to fit within the paper margins or within the view border if paper display is disabled.

You can also access the Named Viewports tab of the Viewports dialog box. This tab will list any named and saved tiled viewport configurations available for defining floating viewports. You cannot, however, name and save floating viewport configurations.

Command: VPCLIP

Purpose: VPCLIP changes the shape and size of an existing floating viewport. The new boundary can be defined by an existing wireframe object or by a user-drawn polyline-type window.

Initiate with:

- On the command line enter VPCLIP.
- Select Clip Existing Viewport from the Viewports toolbar.

Options:

From the command line, VPCLIP will first ask you to select a viewport. Then it will issue the prompt

```
Select clipping object or [Polygonal/Delete] <Polygonal>: (Select an object,
    press Enter, or enter an option)
```

- Object

An existing object will be used to define the new viewport boundary. Valid objects are closed polylines and splines, circles, ellipses, and regions. You will be prompted to select one object.

- Polygonal

When you select this option, you will draw a polyline-type object to serve as the new viewport boundary. Prompts similar to those for 2D polylines will be displayed on the command lines as you draw the line and arc segments of the boundary.

- Delete

This option will only be displayed if the viewport has already been clipped. It restores the original viewport boundary.

Notes:

- You can also start VPCLIP by selecting a floating viewport boundary, pressing the return button of your pointing device, and selecting Viewport Clip from the shortcut menu.

- Despite the name of this command, the view within the viewport, depending upon the size and shape of the new boundary, will not necessarily be clipped.

Before VPCLIP   After VPCLIP

Viewport   Object for   Viewport
edge   clip boundary   edge

- The scale of the model within the viewport will not change when its boundary is changed.
- The LIST command will report that clipping is on for viewports that have been clipped.

Setting Up Multiview 2D Drawings

When you are making a 2D multiview drawing of a 3D model you will need to

- make one floating viewport for each view;
- set a view direction within each viewport that corresponds to the desired orthographic view;
- set the scale of the model in each viewport;
- align the views with each other.

AutoCAD has some special commands, which we will describe in the next chapter, for completing these steps when you are working with solid models. These commands work well and make the process of transforming 3D solid models into 2D drawings almost automatic (except for the dimensions).

When you are working with wireframe and surface models, though, you will have to manually make the floating viewports, set the viewpoints within them, set their scale, and align the views. These last three steps are done through the familiar AutoCAD commands of PLAN, DVIEW, VPOINT, ZOOM, and MOVE. AutoCAD 2000, though, does have some shortcuts. Its **psvpscale** system variable allows you to set the scale of viewports as they are created, and you can set their view directions as they are created through the New Viewports dialog box of VPORTS.

To set view directions and scale within floating viewports, you will use the MSPACE command or double-click within a viewport to access model space through a floating viewport. Once you are within a viewport, you can switch to another one by moving the cursor to the new viewport and pressing the pick button on your pointing device, just as you do with tiled viewports. You can also change viewports by simultaneously pressing the Ctrl and R keys. When you are finished working in model space, either use the PSPACE command or double-click outside a floating viewport to return to paper space.

Once a floating viewport has been created, you will need to set a view direction within that viewport corresponding to the view that the viewport represents. If the viewport represents the top view, for instance, you would use the VPOINT coordinates of 0,0,1 or else use the PLAN command. If the viewport represents the front view, you would use the VPOINT coordinates of 0,-1,0.

An auxiliary view of a surface that is not aligned with any of the principal planes will require a viewing direction that looks straight down on the surface. After you have set the view direction, you can use the Twist option of the DVIEW command to rotate the image in the auxiliary viewport so that it matches the inclined plane.

Top view

Auxiliary view

Front view

Use DVIEW to twist the image within the viewport.

Use a construction line to align the views.

Once you have set the view direction in each floating viewport, you will set each viewport's scale relative to paper space. This is done by using an XP scale factor with the ZOOM options of Scale, Center, and Left. (The AutoCAD 2000 command line menu for ZOOM doesn't list the Left option, but it still accepts it.) A scale factor of 1XP zooms the view so that it is the same as paper space dimensions, while a scale factor of 0.5XP scales the view so that it is one-half paper space sizes, and 2.0XP scales the view to twice paper space sizes. Since you will always treat paper space as a one-to-one space, the ZOOM XP scale factor of a viewport is also the scale at which its image will be printed. The LIST command will show a floating viewport's scale relative to paper space. Once you have set the scale of a viewport, you may want to use the Lock option of MVIEW and VPORTS to ensure that it is not inadvertently changed.

After you have set the view direction and the scale of each viewport for your multiview drawing, you will need to align the views so that corresponding points in the top and front view

match vertically, corresponding points in the front and side views match horizontally, and so forth. One method for doing this involves moving viewports. After selecting the viewport that will be moved, use an object snap on an object within the viewport as the base point and use a point filter, a snap to grid, an object snap on the corresponding point in another viewport, or typed-in coordinates as the destination point. Also, the MVSETUP command has an option for aligning orthographic viewports that works well. Aligning auxiliary views with orthographic views may require that you draw a temporary construction line or rotate the paper space UCS. When the views are aligned, the floating viewport borders are likely to not be aligned, but that is of no consequence since you will almost always hide the viewport borders before printing the drawing.

Views not aligned   Views aligned

Exercise Two

In Exercise One of this chapter, you created three floating viewports to serve as the basis of a 2D multiview drawing of an automobile oil pan. In this exercise you will set the appropriate view direction within each viewport, set their scale, and align the views.

Open the file you saved at the conclusion of Exercise One. Then use the MSPACE command, its status line button equivalent, or double-click in a floating viewport to go into model space. In the top viewport, use VPOINT to set the view direction coordinates of 0,0,1 (or simply invoke the PLAN command). In the viewport below the top one, use VPOINT with the view direction coordinates of 0,-1,0. We will refer to this as the front view, even though the name has more to do with the view direction than to the orientation of the oil pan. In the small viewport to the right, use VPOINT with the view direction coordinates of 1,0,0. This will be the right-side view. Your paper space drawing should now look similar to the one in the figure on the right.

Now that the view directions have been established, you will set the scale in each viewport. We will use a half-size drawing scale, so you will set each viewport's zoom level to one-half of the paper space sizes. With MSPACE still in effect, go into each viewport, invoke ZOOM, and enter a zoom scale of 0.5XP. Use the Lock option of MVIEW or VPORTS to fix the scale of the three viewports.

That finishes our work in model space. Use the PSPACE command, its status line button equivalent, or double-click outside a floating viewport to return to paper space. Before we align the views with each other, you should enlarge any floating viewport in which the model is partly hidden. You can do this with the STRETCH command or by pulling the grips on the viewport borders. Stretching a viewport does not affect the zoom level or view direction of the viewport's contents.

To align the views, turn on AutoCAD's grid snap mode and set a snap spacing of 0.5. Then move the viewports one at a time, using an object snap on the model to set the base point (such as an endpoint near one end of the oil pan's flange), and use a grid snap point in paper space as the destination point.

Our last step in this exercise will be to add a border and title block. Start the INSERT command and click the button labeled Browse. Find and open the folder named Template, and select the file named ANSI D title block.dwg. AutoCAD will return to the Insert dialog box. Specify 0,0,0 as the insert point for the block, 1.0 as its scale, and 0 as its rotation angle. Then, select the OK button to insert the title block. You may need to explode the block and then stretch or move some of its objects so that they will fit within the margins of your paper.

That finishes this exercise. When you freeze or turn off the layer that your floating viewports are in, your paper space drawing should look similar to the one shown in the figure at the bottom of the previous page. Save your drawing so that you can add dimensions to it in other exercises in this chapter.

Command: MSPACE

Purpose: MSPACE switches from the main paper space viewport to the last current float-
            ing viewport.

Initiate with:

- On the command line enter MSPACE.

- On the status bar, click the PAPER button.

    This command enters model space from the main paper space viewport through a floating
    viewport. The paper space UCS icon will disappear, the PAPER button on the status bar
    will be replaced by the MODEL button, and model space UCS icons will appear in
    all of the active floating viewports (provided the UCS icon is turned on). The screen
    crosshair cursor will be in the last current floating viewport.

Notes:

- In AutoCAD 2000 you can also enter a floating viewport by double-clicking inside its borders.

- If you need a close look at your model, you should zoom in while you are in paper space and then use MSPACE. Model space zooms will change the scale of the model

Before MSPACE

After MSPACE

relative to paper space and may also upset view alignments. Moreover, if the viewport is small, you may not get the model space magnification you want.

Command: PSPACE

Purpose: PSPACE switches from the current floating viewport to the main paper space
            viewport.

Initiate with:

- On the command line enter PSPACE.
- On the status bar, click the MODEL button.

PSPACE returns to paper space from the current model space floating viewport. The model space UCS icons will disappear from the floating viewports, the paper space UCS icon will reappear, and the MODEL button on the status bar will be replaced by the PAPER button.

Before PSPACE   After PSPACE

Note:

- In AutoCAD 2000 you can also return to paper space by double-clicking outside a floating viewport border.

Command: MVSETUP

Purpose: MVSETUP is a utility command for creating, scaling, and aligning space viewports and for inserting premade drawing borders and title blocks.

Initiate with:

- On the command line enter MVSETUP.

Options:

If **tilemode** has been set to 0, MVSETUP will display the following command line options:

`Align/Create/Scale viewports/Options/Title block/Undo:`

If **tilemode** has not been set to 0, MVSETUP will ask if you want to enable paper space. A negative answer will bring up a series of prompts for establishing the parameters of a drawing in model space—these parameters are not suitable for creating a drawing of a 3D model. If you give a positive answer, AutoCAD will set **tilemode** to 0 and display the menu shown previously.

- Align

This option is for aligning the contents of one viewport with those of another. AutoCAD will ask you to specify a base point in one viewport, and a point in another viewport corresponding to the base point. AutoCAD then pans the image in the second viewport until the two points are aligned. A menu is displayed offering options for aligning the viewports vertically, horizontally, or at a specified angle, plus an option for rotating the image in a viewport by a specified angle. If viewport scale locking is on, this option will not work properly.

- Create

Floating viewports are created through this option. Create also allows you to delete an existing viewport. Secondary menus are displayed for creating either one viewport, a rectangular array of viewports, or an arrangement of viewports called Standard Engineering in which four viewports are created. These four viewports show the top, front, and right side of the model, plus an SE isometric view of it. None of the other options for creating viewports set view directions.

350

- Scale viewports

  You can set the scale of the model as it appears in selected floating viewports with this option. It does this by asking you to specify a number for the paper space units and then a number for the model space units. The resulting scale is the paper space units divided by the model space units. If, for example, you specified 1.0 for the paper space units and 2.0 for the model space units, the resulting scale will be one-half.

MVIEW's Standard Engineering
viewport layout

- Options

  Preferences for the title block and for paper space units are set through this option. You can specify a layer for the title block, whether the paper space limits are to be adjusted to match the title block size, and whether the title block is to be inserted as an externally referenced object. Paper space units may be feet, inches, meters, or millimeters.

- Title block

  This option inserts a border and title block at the paper space origin. Five premade borders and title blocks for ISO (metric) sizes are offered, as are six for ANSI (inch) sizes and two for general inch sizes. You can add others to this list if you wish.

Notes:

- MVSETUP, which is based on an AutoLISP program named mvsetup.lsp, is intended to serve as a front end for the MVIEW and VPORTS commands. However, you will probably find that it is more convenient to use the MVIEW and VPORTS commands directly. With the exception of the Standard Engineering option for creating viewports, you must still use VPOINT to set view directions in each floating viewport. Its options for aligning viewports vertically and horizontally can be useful, though.

- When you select one of the command's twelve title blocks, it looks for a matching drawing and inserts it if one is found. If a drawing is not found, MVSETUP uses data in a file named mvsetup.dfs to draw the border and title block. For example: if you select an ISO A2 title block, MVSETUP looks for a file named iso_a2.dwg and inserts it if it is found. If it cannot find iso_a2.dwg, it uses data in mvsetup.dfs to draw the border and title block. It will be a set of individual entities rather than a block.

  The data in mvsetup.dfs draws the title blocks exactly according to the ANSI 14.1 specification. (ANSI is an acronym for American National Standards Institute.)

  AutoCAD 2000 includes title block drawings for German (DIN) and Japanese (JIS) standards, as well as for American (ANSI) and international (ISO) standards. You can directly insert any of these drawings as a block in paper space—you do not need to use MVSETUP. If you used the default directory names when you installed AutoCAD, these title blocks will be in the AutoCAD2000\Template folder. This directory also contains DWT files of the title blocks that can be inserted in a layour as a template.

Controlling of Appearance of Objects in Viewports

Object Visibility Control

Since the view direction in each floating viewport of a multiview paper space drawing is generally aimed toward the same location in 3D space, all of the objects in that location will be seen in all of the viewports. Indeed, looking at the same 3D model from different viewpoints is one of the advantages of paper space viewports and drawings because any changes that are made in the model are instantly reflected in all of the viewports. You do not have to go from view to view making changes manually as you do in pure 2D drawings.

Sometimes though, it is desirable for an object to be visible in one viewport but not in another. For instance, if you were working on a model that has separate but mating parts, you would likely find it useful to be able to look at the individual parts by themselves, but without moving them. AutoCAD allows you to do this through an object's layer—you can freeze selected layers within selected viewports. Therefore, you can have the different parts reside in different layers, and freeze certain layers in certain viewports.

Controlling object visibility is particularly important when you are adding dimensions to a 3D model. If all of the dimensions are in the same layer, all of them will appear in every viewport. They may be seen backward or even on edge, but they will be seen. Consequently, when you add dimensions to a 3D model, you use as many layers for the dimensions as you have viewports, and the layer for dimensions in a specific viewport will be frozen in all of the other viewports.

All objects are visible. / Only objects in layer Sol01 are visible. / Only objects in layer Sol02 are visible.

The AutoCAD command that selectively freezes layers on a viewport-by-viewport basis is VPLAYER, which stands for *Viewport LAYER*. Freezing layers with VPLAYER is subtly different from freezing them globally with the LAYER command, and a layer must be both thawed and on globally before it can be frozen in specific viewports by VPLAYER. Moreover, VPLAYER only works with the floating viewports of paper space. The command is disabled in model space.

You can also use the Layer Properties Manager dialog box of the LAYER command to selectively freeze layers in floating viewports. You can click the icon in the column labeled Active VP Freeze to selectively freeze or thaw a layer, and you can click the icon in the column labeled New VP Freeze to have the layer frozen or thawed in floating viewports that are to be created. Check boxes corresponding to these two options are in the Details area of the dialog box. In this dialog box, AutoCAD inappropriately refers to the current viewport as the active viewport.

Command: VPLAYER

Purpose: VPLAYER prevents objects from being displayed in specified viewports by freezing their layers in those viewports. They will continue to appear in viewports in which their layer is not frozen.

Initiate with:

* On the command line enter VPLAYER.

Options:

The VPLAYER command displays the following menu on the command line:

```
Enter and option [?/Freeze/Thaw/Reset/Newfrz/Vpvisdflt]:
   (Enter an option or press Enter.)
```

This menu is redisplayed after each option is completed. Press Enter to end the command and trigger the changes.

* ?

The question mark option will report the names of the layers that are frozen in a selected floating viewport. A follow-up prompt will ask you to select one viewport.

* Freeze

This option freezes specific layers in specific viewports. It will display the follow-up prompts:

```
Enter layer name(s) to freeze: (Enter a list of layer names.)
Enter an option [All/Select/Current] <Current>: (Enter an option or press Enter.)
```

You can specify as many layers to be frozen as you like by separating their names with commas and by using the standard wild card characters of ? and *.

The All option in the second prompt will freeze the specified layer, or layers, in all viewports, including the main paper space viewport. If PSPACE is in effect, the Current option will freeze the specified layer, or layers, in the main paper space viewport. If MSPACE is in effect, the Current option will freeze the specified layer, or layers, in the current floating viewport (the one that has the screen cursor). The Select option will bring up a prompt asking you to select specific viewports in which the specified layer, or layers, are to be frozen. If MSPACE is active, AutoCAD will temporarily switch to PSPACE to enable you to select the viewports.

* Thaw

This option thaws one or more layers in specified viewports. Layers frozen globally through the LAYER command cannot be thawed by this option. Its follow-up prompts are

```
Enter layer name(s) to thaw: (Enter a list of layer names.)
Enter an option [All/Select/Current] <Current>: (Enter an option or press Enter.)
```

Your input for these prompts is the same as those for the Freeze option.

- Reset

  You can reset specified layers in specified viewports to the default frozen or thawed condition established by VPLAYER's Vpvisdflt option. It uses the follow-up prompts of

  ```
  Enter layer name(s) to reset: (Enter a list of layer names.)
  Enter an option [All/Select/Current] <Current>: (Enter an option or press
      Enter.)
  ```

  Your input for these prompts is the same as those for the Freeze option.

- Newfrz (New Freeze)

  New layers can be created through this option. The layers, however, will be automatically frozen in all viewports—those that currently exist and those that will be created in the future—with the exception of the main paper space viewport. Its follow-up prompt is

  ```
  Enter name(s) of new layers frozen in all viewports: (Enter a list of layer
      names.)
  ```

  You can enter several names by separating them with commas.

- Vpvisdflt (Viewport Visibility Default)

  Whether specified layers are to be frozen or thawed by default in subsequently created viewports is controlled by this option. It uses the following command line prompts:

  ```
  Enter layer name(s) to change viewport visibility:
      (Enter a list of layer names.)
  Enter a viewport visibility option of [Frozen/Thawed] <Thawed>:
      (Enter F or T, or press Enter.)
  ```

  You can name as many layers as you like by separating their names with a comma and by using the wild card characters of ? and *. If you choose the Frozen option of the second prompt, the specified layers will automatically be frozen in subsequently created viewports. The Thawed option of the second prompt will cause the specified layers to be thawed in subsequently created viewports. It can override the effects of the Newfrz option of VPLAYER.

Linetype Scale

A potentially undesirable side effect of having viewports with different zoom levels, and hence different scales, is that noncontinuous linetypes—such as center, dashed, and hidden—will have different appearances in different viewports. The lengths of their line segments will be longer in some viewports than in others, including the main paper space viewport (unless the scale of a viewport is 1XP). This is illustrated by the upper-left figure on the next page, in which the lengths of the center linetype segments are different in the half-scale views, the one-fourth scale view, and the main paper space viewport.

To prevent that from happening, you can set the value of the system variable **psltscale** —LINE SCALE (which stands for *Paper Space LineType SCALE*) to 1. Then, in each floating viewport, the current global linetype scale will be multiplied by the viewport's scale relative to paper space. The

psltscale=0

psltscale=1

line segment length of noncontinuous linetypes will therefore be the same throughout the drawing, as shown in the upper-right figure. The initial setting of **psltscale** in AutoCAD's template drawings is 1.

PAPERSPACE LT SCALE

Dimensioning, Annotating, and Plotting Paper Space Drawings

Dimensioning 3D models for paper space drawings should always be done in model space. There the dimensions are close to the objects of the 3D model and are more readily changed if the objects are changed. AutoCAD also has full recognition of the objects so dimensioning proceeds in a manner similar to that used for pure 2D drawings. Although dimensions can be done from paper space, AutoCAD's incomplete recognition of objects in the model causes problems—

lines can be dimensioned only by picking their endpoints; since arcs and circles are not recognized, radius and diameter dimensions cannot be added directly. Moreover, since the dimensions and the model are in different spaces, associative dimensions are not connected to the feature they represent.

The sizes of dimension features—arrowheads, text, and so forth—must be adjusted in viewports that do not have a one-to-one scale with paper space. Otherwise, they will have different sizes in different viewports, and they will be too large in some viewports and too small in others.

When this box is checked, dimscale is set to 0.

355

Therefore, if you want dimension text to be printed at a height of 0.125 inches, the actual height of the text will have to be 0.25 inches in viewports that are half-scale, and will have to be 0.0625 inches in viewports that have a two-to-one scale with paper space.

While you can manually change the sizes of dimension features to adjust for a viewport's scale, a much better way is to use the **dimscale** system variable. AutoCAD will multiply the size of dimension features by the value in **dimscale**. Thus, if **dimscale** has an assigned value of 2.0, dimension text will be twice its specified height; if it has an assigned value of 0.5, dimension text will be one-half its specified height.

An even better way to manage the size of dimension features is to set **dimscale** to a value of 0. Then AutoCAD will automatically multiply the size of dimension features by the scale factor of the current floating viewport. You can set **dimscale** to 0 directly or by select-

ing the "Scale dimensions to layout (paper space)" check box in the Fit tab of the DDIM command's dialog box.

The figure above shows an example of the effects of **dimscale**. The paper space drawing has three floating viewports (their borders are turned off). Two of the viewports show the model at one-half scale and the other viewport shows the model at one-fourth scale. Nevertheless, the size of the dimension features are the same in all three viewports.

If you were to turn on **tilemode** and look at this dimensioned model from an isometric-type viewpoint, you would see that there are two sizes of dimension features—one twice as large as the paper space size and the other half as large.

356

If you do add dimensions from paper space rather than model space, you should have the **dimscale** system variable set to 1.0, and instead adjust the value of the **dimlfac** system variable to fit the scale of the viewport used for the dimension. While **dimlfac** has no effect on the size of dimension features, such as text height, it does multiply measured dimension lengths by the value it contains. For example, if **dimlfac** is set to a value of 2.0, a line that is 2.50 inches long would be given a dimension length of 5.00 inches; if **dimlfac** was set to 0.5, that same line would be given a dimension length of 1.25 inches. Since model space objects in a floating viewport that has a scale relative to paper space that is not one-to-one are not their true size, you must use **dimlfac** to correct their dimension lengths.

AutoCAD will set a value of **dimlfac** appropriate for the viewport you are going to dimension for you, if you use AutoCAD's dimension mode. This must be done from the command line as follows:

```
Command: DIM (Enter)
Dim: dimlfac (Enter)
Enter new value for dimension variable or Viewport <1.0000>: V (Enter)
Select viewport to set scale: (Pick the edge of a floating viewport.)
DIMLFAC set to -4.0000
```

The actual value of DIMLFAC will vary according to the scale of the viewport you selected, although it will always be a negative number to signify it is based on a floating viewport. You must then use object snaps on the model space objects to create dimensions for it. No good way exists for radius, diameter, and angular dimensions on model space objects from paper space.

Even on 3D models, dimensioning is a 2D operation that occurs on the current UCS X-Y plane, with horizontal dimensions being parallel to the X axis and vertical dimensions being parallel to the Y axis. AutoCAD projects objects that are being dimensioned onto the X-Y plane. Therefore objects that are askew of the X-Y plane will be foreshortened, and their dimensioned length will not be correct. This is illustrated in the figure below. The UCS X-Y plane is not parallel with the sides of the 1-by-1-by-1 cube on the left, and as a result, the horizontal dimension for it is incorrect. The UCS X-Y plane, however, is parallel with one side of the left-hand cube, so both its horizontal and vertical dimensions are correct. Notice in both cases how the dimensions have been projected onto the X-Y plane, regardless of the selected object's location.

Dimensioning 3D models presents a few unique problems, especially when you work with surface models. Their surface mesh lines tend to make the drawing cluttered and confusing, and no satisfactory method exists for removing them. Surfaces also are likely to hide the extension lines of dimensions, so you must make certain that the UCS X-Y plane is in front of the model when you add dimensions. Furthermore, hidden edges that you would like to have shown in dashed linetypes are either completely hidden (when hidden line removal is on) or completely visible (when hidden line removal is off). There is no in between. Even the selection of objects to be dimensioned can be uncertain in orthographic views, because objects will be stacked on top of each other.

Furthermore, the spline curves that commonly occur on surface models cannot be dimensioned completely. This is not due to a shortcoming of AutoCAD—rather it is a characteristic of splines. Even planar splines have curves with continually changing radii, which means that radius dimensions do not apply, and the radius and diameter dimensions used for arcs and circles simply have no meaning in nonplanar splines. In earlier times, plaster or wood models were used as masters for objects having spline curves and surfaces. Both machining and inspection were based on the physical model. Now, organizations working with such objects often use a computer model as the master for manufacturing and inspection. Their 2D drawings, which merely show the object's general shape and size, are used to document part numbers, specify materials, and provide other necessary information for manufacturing.

You will always locate a drawing's title block, borders, general notes, and other annotation in paper space using a one-to-one scale. Occasionally, you will also need to draw some objects in paper space, perhaps to make an end line or a break line for a partial view or a broken view. When your drawing is dimensioned, viewports are in their correct locations, and (if needed) hidden-line removal during plotting has been specified in selected viewports, you will turn off or freeze the layer you have used for the floating viewports. This will cause the viewport borders to disappear, while their contents will remain visible.

Plots will be made using a one-to-one scale. You do not need to specify in the Plot Settings tab of the Plot dialog box that hidden objects are to be removed (in fact, that parameter has no effect in paper space floating viewports). If you are using a pen plotter, you will probably want to eliminate the plotting of overlapping lines. To do this, select the Plotting tab from the Options dialog box, and click the Add or Configure Plotters button. From the list of currently configured plotters, select the plotter you are using. Then select Pen Configuration from the outline-like list of parameters, and in the Pen Optimization Level drop-down list box select Adds elimination of overlapping diagonal vectors.

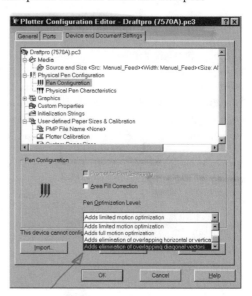

Exercise Three

Our last exercise in this chapter will finish the paper space drawing of a die for manufacturing an automobile oil pan. In Exercise Two, you set up the orthographic views for the drawing and inserted a D-sized border and title block. In this exercise you will add dimensions and general notes and will fill in the title block.

Open your drawing file of the oil pan. If the floating viewport borders are not visible, then the layer they are in is either frozen or turned off. Since you will need to work with the viewports, they must be thawed and turned on. Increase the size of the three viewports so that there will be space in them for the dimensions you are going to add. You can do this without affecting the viewport's contents through the STRETCH command or through the viewport's grips.

This particular 3D surface model is well defined by its wireframe objects, and the surfaces only add clutter to the 2D drawing. Therefore, you should freeze all of the layers that the surfaces are in.

Create three new layers that have names such as Dim-top, Dim-front, and Dim-side to be used for the dimensions. Use the Freeze option of VPLAYER to have only one of these new layers appear in each floating viewport. For example: Dim-top should be thawed only in the viewport showing the top view, and the layers Dim-front and Dim-side should be frozen in the top view.

Set the dimension style parameters to conform to your methods and work standards for making 2D drawings. The only parameter that will be different from those of a D-sized 2D drawing will be that **dimscale** will be set to 0 (by either setting it directly, or by checking the "Scale dimension to layout (paperspace)" check box in the Fit dialog box of the DDIM command).

Now, you are ready to add the dimensions. The general steps you will take in doing this are

1. Choose a particular view to work in, such as the top view, and zoom in until you can see the 3D objects clearly. Zooms and pans should be done only in paper space, since zooms and pans within a model space viewport will affect the view alignment and scale of the orthographic views. You may want to turn on scale locking in all of the floating viewports to ensure that you do not inadvertently change their scale.

2. Use MSPACE, or one of its equivalents, to go into model space. Make the viewport you have chosen to work in be the current viewport.

3. Adjust the UCS so that its X-Y plane is perpendicular to the viewport's line of sight. The View option of the UCS command is often a convenient way to do this.

4. Switch to the layer you intend to use for the dimensions in the chosen viewport. Then dimension the view's objects as you would in any 2D drawing.

5. When you have finished dimensioning objects in that viewport, use PSPACE or any of its equivalents to return to paper space. Zoom back so that you can see your entire drawing.

6. Repeat steps 1 through 5 until the model is completely dimensioned.

Often the viewports will need to be repositioned to increase or decrease the gap between them or to move them away from the drawing's borders. You can freely move the viewports, but you must take care that their alignment is preserved. When the dimensions and viewport positions are as you want them, you can freeze or turn off the layer that the viewports are in.

When you have finished with the dimensions, add the drawing's general notes to the main paper space viewport and fill in the title block as you would with a pure 2D drawing. Since the drawing will be plotted using a one-to-one scale, the height of this text will be its true height.

Our version of the finished 2D drawing is shown in the next figure. Your choices for dimension arrangement and for annotation, though, may be different. Notice that we did not dimension the spline curves on the model. We also cleaned up the views by selectively freezing some wireframe layers, and we added some lines and arcs to delineate the edges of fillets and rounds on the model. This version of the model and drawing is in file mfe15301.dwg on the CD-ROM that accompanies this book.

2D Drawings from 3D Solid Models

This chapter will explain how 3D solid models can be transformed into 2D multiview drawings. The commands and techniques described in this chapter pertain only to solid models. You will learn how to

- make 2D isometric-type drawings of 3D solid models with the SOLPROF command;
- use the SOLVIEW command to set up the views for multiview 2D drawings based on a 3D solid model;
- use SOLDRAW to draw 2D objects in the views set up by SOLVIEW that are suitable for dimensions;
- dimension and annotate multiview drawings.

Although you can use the techniques described in Chapter Fifteen to make 2D drawings directly from 3D solid models, there are problems with this approach.

- While you can set the system variable **dispsilh** to a value of 1 to eliminate facets on 3D solids and thereby obtain a clean, uncluttered look when HIDE is on, you cannot show hidden edges.
- When **dispsilh** is set to 1, visible tangential edges—the boundary along the tangent between two curved surfaces or between a curved surface and a plane—will always be shown. Thus, all fillets will have lines where they blend with their adjacent surfaces. Sometimes you will want these tangential lines to be shown, but not always.
- Section views can be made only indirectly.
- The model itself can hide extension lines and other parts of dimensions. Although you can prevent this by making certain that the UCS X-Y plane is in front of the model before you add dimensions, this is an additional step, as well as one more thing to remember.
- Two or more edges will almost always be on top of one another in orthographic views, which can make the process of selecting objects to be dimensioned uncertain. Also, if you are using a pen plotter, you must change the plotting optimization parameters to prevent overlapping lines from being retraced.

A better way to make a 2D drawing from a 3D solid is to project the solid's edges and profile onto a plane where they are drawn as 2D objects. The problems of dimensioning 3D objects are eliminated, hidden edges can be shown as dashed lines, and section views are conveniently made.

This is the approach taken by three commands for making 2D drawings from 3D solid models—SOLPROF, SOLVIEW, and SOLDRAW. These commands are in an external program named solids.arc, which is automatically loaded whenever any of the three commands are called. They work only on 3D solid objects—not on wireframe or surface models.

SOLVIEW and SOLDRAW are for making multiview, orthographic 2D drawings from 3D solid models. These two commands must be used in tandem. SOLVIEW is used first to set up drawing views, and SOLDRAW is used to create 2D objects that are suitable for dimensioning in those views. The third command, SOLPROF, is for making general-purpose isometric-type drawings from 3D solids.

Menus and toolbar buttons for creating 2D drawings from 3D solids

Making 2D Isometric-Type Drawings from 3D Solids

SOLPROF projects the edges and profiles of selected 3D solids onto a plane that is perpendicular to the viewing direction. While it can be used to make any of the six principal orthographic views, SOLPROF is especially useful for making 2D isometric-type drawings that can be used in presentations, assembly drawings, and for catalog illustrations. The results can be virtually identical to those drawn within AutoCAD's isometric snap mode.

You don't, however, have to manipulate isoplanes or use ellipses for making arcs and circles as you draw objects. In fact, even if your objective is to make just an isometric 2D drawing, you may find it easier to make it as a 3D solid and convert it to 2D with SOLPROF.

SOLPROF is especially useful for making drawings that have *isometric projection views*. These are a special form of axonometric views in which the viewing plane is tilted to have equal angles (hence the name, isometric) with the three cardinal planes. Since lines in the cardinal directions are all inclined relative to the line of sight, they are not seen in their true length—they are foreshortened 81.65 percent. Also, horizontal angles are shown sloped 30 degrees.

To make isometric projection views in AutoCAD, first pick the corner of the 3D model you want the view to look

This isometric drawing of an instrument knob is easier to make as a 3D solid that is converted to 2D than as a 2D drawing from AutoCAD's isometric snap mode.

362

toward, and use the X, Y, Z coordinates of +/-1,+/-1,+/-1 with the VPOINT command. The signs of the coordinates will depend upon which corner of the object you are focusing on. For instance, to set up a view looking at the front, right, upper corner of a 3D model, use the VPOINT coordinates of 1,-1,1. This often used viewpoint is listed as an SE Isometric in AutoCAD's View menu and View toolbar.

The foreshortened lines cause isometric projection drawings to be difficult to make with hand drafting techniques, and consequently they were seldom used when most drawings were done on drafting boards. *Isometric drawings* were much more common. They have their viewing plane positioned exactly as those for isometric projection drawings, but their lengths in the cardinal directions are drawn full size. This makes them much easier to draw and scale, although it does make objects larger than their actual size. Isometric drawings are what you get with Auto-CAD when the isometric snap mode is in use. To convert the isometric projection drawings you will get from SOLPROF to true isometric drawings, simply scale them 1.2247 times.

SOLPROF is easy to use and versatile. You set a viewpoint that shows the solid, or solids, as you want it to appear, invoke the command, and enter yes or no responses to three command line prompts for options. You must do this from the paper space side of AutoCAD through a floating viewport made with the MVIEW command, even though the results are in model space.

The wireframe objects are placed in blocks and in unique layers for easy management and transfer to other programs. You have a choice of placing hidden lines in their own layer and block or having them included with the layer and blocks used for visible lines. Most of the time you will choose to have hidden lines in their own block. Then you can use a linetype that is different from that used for the visible lines, and you can freeze their layer or erase their block to eliminate them altogether. SOL-PROF can also make 3D wireframe models from the edges of 3D solids. You are not likely to use this capability often, but it does provide you with one more conversion tool.

The length of lines in isometric projection views are 81.65 percent of the length of lines in true isometric views.

The blocks created by SOLPROF are anonymous blocks. Consequently, they have no name and cannot be inserted. However, if you want to use them in another drawing, you can make a named block from them through either the BLOCK or WBLOCK command. If the block is 2D, be certain to first set the UCS X-Y plane on the plane of the block. Since the block is on a plane that passes through the UCS origin and is perpendicular to the line of sight, you can do this with the View option of the UCS command, provided you have not changed the UCS or viewpoint after the block was created. If you have, you can use the 3point option of the UCS command, coupled with object snaps on the block.

SOLPROF also gives you the option of including tangential edges, which mark the transition between flat and curved surfaces and between two adjacent curved surfaces, on the profiles. Orthographic drawings seldom show tangential edges, but you will generally want them included when you are making isometric-type drawings.

Exercise One

In this exercise, you will create a 2D isometric drawing from the 3D solid model of a pipe fitting you created in Section Three. On the CD-ROM that accompanies this book, the completed model is in file mfe13205.dwg. Retrieve that file, open it, and immediately save it under another name of your choice. Later in this chapter, you will make a multiview drawing of the same model.

Set the layer named Vports to be the current layer. You should also load AutoCAD's HIDDEN linetype so that SOL-PROF will use it for the layer it will make for hidden objects.

Select the Layout1 tab to go into paper space. If there is already a viewport in Layout1, use the LAYOUT command, or its equivalent, to create a second layout, and click the new layout's tab to open it. Select a paper size for the layout of about 11 by 8 inches. If AutoCAD automatically creates a floating viewport, accept it. Otherwise, use VPORTS or MVIEW to make one floating viewport approximately centered in the graphics area that is roughly 5 by 5 units in size.

The 3D solid model will appear in the floating viewport, looking as it did in model space. Use the MSPACE command, or its equivalent, to go into model space through the floating viewport. Then, set an SE isometric view of the model, and zoom and pan as needed for the model to completely fill the viewport.

Now, use the following command line input to create a 2D isometric projection drawing of the model:

```
Command: SOLPROF (Enter)
Select objects: (Select the 3D solid.)
Display hidden profile lines on separate layer? [Yes/No] <Y>: (Enter)
Project profile lines onto a plane? [Yes/No] <Y>: (Enter)
Delete tangential edges? [Yes/No] <Y>: N (Enter)
```

Since AutoCAD must perform intensive calculations in projecting the 3D objects onto a plane, your computer may appear to be inactive for a few seconds. When the operation is complete, there will be no discernable differences within the viewport, but when you look through the list of layers in the drawing, you will notice that AutoCAD created two new ones having names such as Ph-2d6 and Pv-2d6.

The characters to the right of the hyphen in these names represent the handle of the floating viewport, and those in your drawing may be different. That is not important. What is important is that the hidden objects in the model are in the layer that has a name beginning with Ph and that the visible objects are in the layer whose name begins with Pv. Assign the HIDDEN linetype to the layer for hidden objects, if AutoCAD has not done so. When you freeze the layer that the solid model is in—Sol01—the image in your floating viewport should be similar to the one in the left figure above.

Since the numerous hidden lines tend to clutter and confuse the drawing rather than clarify it, you may want to freeze their layer also. Then, the drawing will look similar to the one in the right figure above.

On your computer screen, you are now viewing a 2D isometric projection drawing on a plane that is perpendicular to the line of sight and that passes through the UCS origin. If you want to export it to another drawing, use the View option of the UCS command so that the drawing is on the UCS X-Y plane, and use the WBLOCK command to save it in a new file. If you want the drawing to be a true isometric drawing, increase its size 1.277 times with AutoCAD's SCALE command.

On the CD-ROM that accompanies this book, the 3D model and the 2D isometric drawing of it—both within a floating viewport—are in the file mfe16104.dwg.

Command: SOLPROF

Purpose: SOLPROF creates blocks made of wireframe objects that are derived from the profile and edges of one or more 3D solids.

Initiate with:

- On the Command Line enter SOLPROF.
- From the Draw pull-down menu, select Solids, then Setup, and finally Profile.
- Select the Setup Profile button from the Solids toolbar.

Options:

SOLPROF must be initiated within a paper space floating viewport. The wireframe objects that will be created will be within model space, and they will be in either one or two layers (depending upon the command options you select) that AutoCAD will automatically create if they do not exist. One of these layers is for visible edges and profiles, while the other is

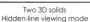

Two 3D solids
Hidden-line viewing mode

Two 3D solids
Wireframe viewing mode

Two 2D blocks created by SOLPROF
Visible edges are in one layer,
and hidden edges are in another.

for hidden edges and profiles (provided you specify that visible and hidden edges and profiles are to be in separate layers). Also, AutoCAD's HIDDEN linetype will be used for the layer for hidden objects, if that linetype is loaded.

The command first asks you to select the 3D solids that the wireframe objects are to be based on. You can select as many as you like, using any Auto-CAD selection method, with objects that are not 3D solids—including regions and blocks of 3D solids—being filtered out. Then, three options in the form of command line prompts for yes or no responses are offered:

```
Display hidden profile lines on a separate layer? [Yes/No]  <Y>:
(Enter Y or N, or press Enter.)
Project profile lines onto a plane? [Yes/No] <Y>: (Enter Y or N, or press Enter.)
Delete tangential edges? [Yes/No] <Y>: (Enter Y or N, or press Enter.)
```

- Display hidden profile lines on a separate layer?

  When a positive response is given to this prompt, AutoCAD will place the objects derived from hidden edges and profiles of the 3D solid, or solids, in a different layer than the one the visible edges and profiles are in. All of the visible edges and profiles will be in one block, regardless of how many 3D solids were in the selection set, while the hidden edges and profiles (including those hidden by other solids in the selection set) will be in a second block.

If you give a negative response, objects made from visible and hidden edges and profiles of the 3D solid, or solids, will be placed in the same layer used for visible objects. One block will be created for each 3D solid in the selection set. All edges, even those that are hidden, will be included in the block, or blocks.

Three 3D solids
Hidden-line viewing mode

Three 3D solids
Wireframe viewing mode

- Project profile lines onto a plane?

  If your answer to this prompt is yes, the 3D solid's edges will be projected onto a plane that passes through the UCS origin and is perpendicular to the floating viewport's line of sight. The resulting block, or blocks, will be 2D.

Two 2D blocks in two layers
Made with SOLPROF

Three 2D blocks in one layer
Made with SOLPROF

366

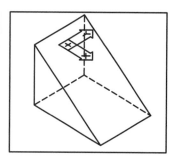

3D solid in wireframe viewing mode

The 3D solid's edges are projected onto a plane passing through the origin and perpendicular to the viewport's line of sight.

Resulting projected 2D blocks

If your answer to the prompt is no, wireframe 3D blocks that are derived from the edges and profiles of the 3D solids in the selection set will be made. Since the 3D blocks are based on the edges and profiles as they are seen, they may not be complete. For example, spherical solids produce a block that is simply a circle, and if a 3D solid wedge is seen from a plan view, only the edges of its slanted surface will be included in the 3D block.

- Delete tangential edges?

A tangential edge is the boundary between two curved surfaces, or between a curved surface and a planar surface. It represents the points of tangency between the two surfaces. If you give a positive answer to this prompt, tangential edges will not be shown, while a negative answer will cause the tangential edges to be included in the blocks made by SOL-PROF.

Notes:

- Wireframe objects created from visible edges and profiles of the

3D solid
Wireframe viewing mode
SE isometric view

View used for SOLPROF

Resulting 3D wireframe block
SE isometric view

Tangential edges kept

Tangential edges deleted

selected 3D solid, or solids, will be placed in a layer named PV-*handle*. Objects created from hidden edges and profiles will also be placed in that layer, unless you specify that hidden profile objects are to be placed in a separate layer. Then they will be placed in a layer named PH-*handle*. *Handle* in these layer names is the handle of the current floating viewport. For example, if the handle of the viewport used for SOLPROF is 8D7, the layer names will be PV-8D7 and PH-8D7. If these layers do not exist, AutoCAD will create them.

- The handle of an object is a hexadecimal number that serves as a name for the object. All AutoCAD objects, including floating viewports, have a unique handle that is assigned by AutoCAD. No two objects have the same handle, and as long as an object exists, it retains the same handle. The LIST command will display an object's handle.

- The blocks created by SOLPROF are anonymous blocks. Their names will not be displayed by the BLOCK, INSERT, or DDINSERT commands, and they cannot be inserted or written to a file.

Making Multiview 2D Drawings from 3D Solids

The Roles of SOLVIEW and SOLDRAW

Although you could use SOLPROF to make multiview 2D drawings from 3D solids, SOLVIEW and SOLDRAW are intended exclusively for that purpose and require much less work on your part. SOLVIEW sets up views of the solid model in paper space floating viewports, and SOLDRAW draws 2D objects that are suitable for dimensions in those viewports. These two commands also tie the 2D drawing closer to the 3D model than SOLPROF. After making a drawing with SOLVIEW and SOLDRAW, you can change the 3D model, rerun SOLDRAW, and the changes will be reflected in the 2D drawing.

Through SOLVIEW, you specify the basic scale of the drawing, the views that it is to have, and the locations of those views. Typically, multiview 2D drawings will have at least two orthographic views (such as a top, front, and perhaps a side view), plus any auxiliary and section views that are needed to fully define the part. SOLVIEW does a good job in

2D isometric-type drawing made with SOLPROF

setting up these fundamental views. It cannot, however, make magnified detail views (although SOLVIEW does allow section views to have a scale that is different from the other views). Another limitation is that section views must be full sections—partial and offset section views are not possible.

In using SOLVIEW, you specify the drawing's views one at a time. SOLVIEW makes a paper space floating viewport for each view, sets its 3D viewing direction and zoom level according to your input, and aligns the views with each other. While SOLVIEW doesn't draw anything other than floating viewport borders, it does create special layers that are used by SOLDRAW for drawing objects in the viewports. These special layers are for visible objects, hidden objects, and hatches (for section views only). The layers for hidden objects will use AutoCAD's HIDDEN linetype, if it is loaded. SOLVIEW also creates, as a convenience for the user, a layer for the

Views for a 2D drawing made by SOLVIEW

2D drawing views made by SOLDRAW

dimensions of each viewport. All of these layers are selectively frozen so that objects will appear only in the proper viewport.

When you have your drawing views established, you will exit SOLVIEW and move on to SOLDRAW. SOLDRAW is a command that requires very little user input but does a great deal of work. You simply pick the paper space floating viewports that were made by SOLVIEW, then sit back and watch as SOLDRAW goes about drawing objects in those viewports. When it is finished, the 3D solid model is no longer shown. In its place in each viewport will be a 2D drawing of the appropriate view of the model. If there are section views, the sliced areas will be hatched. To prevent objects from appearing in the wrong viewport, they are placed in a layer that is thawed only in the proper viewport.

The Steps in Making a 2D Drawing

Now that you have a general idea of what SOLVIEW and SOLDRAW do, we will outline the steps you will take in making a 2D multiview drawing from a 3D model.

1. Decide on the views that your drawing will have, the size of paper it will be printed on, and the scale it will have. This is a step you would do in setting up any 2D drawing, whether it is done directly on paper or with a computer.

2. Open the drawing file containing the 3D solid model. Load the HIDDEN line type so that AutoCAD will use it for the layers it will make for hidden objects.

3. Select a Layout tab to activate paper space. Invoke PAGESETUP and select a printer and paper size that will accommodate your drawing. If AutoCAD includes a floating viewport in the layout, erase it.

4. Start the SOLVIEW command. Use its UCS option to make the base view of the drawing. Often this will be the top view, but it doesn't have to be.

5. Make the drawing's other views from the base view. You can make all of the views during one call to SOLVIEW, or you can invoke the command several times.

6. Save your drawing file. Start the SOLDRAW command and select the floating viewports created by SOLVIEW as the viewports to be drawn.

7. Set the colors of the layers that SOLVIEW created so that they meet your standards and set the dimension parameters to your standards. The dimension parameters will be the same as for a 2D drawing, except for **dimscale**. You should set **dimscale** to 0, either directly or by checking the Scale to dimensions to Layout (paperspace) button in DDIM's Fit dialog box. When **dimscale** is set to 0, AutoCAD automatically uses a value that is appropriate for the viewport in which dimensions are being added.

8. Add dimensions to the drawing views. This one step will take more time than the previous seven steps. You will add dimensions within model space, working in one floating viewport at a time, using the following procedure:

   • Zoom in to get a good view of the viewport you are going to work in. Use the MSPACE command (in any of its several forms that we described in the previous chapter) to switch from paper space to model space and make the viewport you intend to work in to be the current viewport.

   • Use the View option of the UCS command to orient the X and Y axes to match the view. Follow this with the Origin option of the UCS command, and use an object snap on some object within the viewport. This will ensure that the dimensions will be on the same plane as the objects being dimensioned.

   • Set the layer for the dimensions to match the view. For example, if the view in the viewport you are working in is named Top, use the layer named Dim-top. This will cause dimensions to appear only in the proper viewport.

   • Add the dimensions as you would in any 2D drawing. If the viewport is too small to accommodate some dimensions, temporarily switch back to paper space and stretch the viewport's border. Do not zoom or pan within a floating viewport.

9. Erase the temporary border you made in Step 3. Insert a border and title block of your choice, and add general notes and annotation as you would in any 2D drawing. Since scale in paper space is one-to-one, all objects in paper space are entered in their true size.

10. If necessary, move the views to better fit the paper and borders you are using. While you can freely move viewports and change their size, you must make certain that you do not alter their scale or their alignment. When the views are as you want them, turn off or freeze the layer named Vports. The drawing is now done.

Exercise Two

In this exercise, you will make a 2D multiview drawing from the same 3D model you used in making an isometric drawing in Exercise One. The model, which represents a pipe fitting, is in file mfe13205.dwg on the CD-ROM that comes with this book. Find that file and open it.

   Our drawing will need four views to completely define the part. One view will look straight down toward the square base of the part, and another will be perpendicular to the part's bend radius. The drawing will also need an auxiliary view for showing the true size and form of the diamond-shaped face, and lastly, it will need a section view through the plane of the part's bend. We will use C-size paper (22 inches by 17 inches)—some back-of-the-envelope calculations based on the overall size of the part indicate that the four views will fit nicely on C-size paper when a two-to-one scale is used.

Select the Layout1 tab to activate paper space. To ensure that you start with a clean slate, open the Display tab of the Options dialog box and clear the check box labeled Create viewport in new layouts. Then, use any of the methods described in the last chapter to create a new layout. Activate that layout and use PAGESETUP to set the plot device to one that can handle C-sized paper, set the paper size to 22 by 17 inches, and the scale to 1:1. (Remember that this scale pertains to the layout scale, rather than to the drawing scale.) Exit the Page Setup dialog box. Draw a rectangular border that is about 19 inches in the X direction and 15 inches in the Y direction. This border, which will be erased later, will help you position the views you are about to make. This is also a good time to ensure that AutoCAD's HIDDEN line-type is loaded.

Now, we are ready to use SOLVIEW to make the four views we've decided on. We will create the top view first. The command line sequence of prompts and input to do this is

```
Command:  SOLVIEW (Enter)
Enter an option [Ucs/Ortho/Auxiliary/Section]:  U (Enter)
Enter an option [Named/World/?/Current] <Current>: W (Enter)
Enter view scale <1.0000>: 2 (Enter)
Specify view center: 9,12 (Enter)
Specify view center <specify viewport>: (Enter)
Specify first corner of viewport: 6,10 (Enter)
Specify opposite corner of viewport: 12,14 (Enter)
Enter view name:  TOP (Enter)
```

The Ucs option of the main SOLVIEW menu, which is the only option you can select when no viewports exist, creates a view that looks straight down on an X-Y plane. We specified that the X-Y plane of the WCS be used because the square base of the part sits on the WCS X-Y plane. Your responses to the prompts for viewport location and size are not especially important since the viewport can be easily moved and resized later.

Next, we will make the model's front view by using SOLVIEW's Ortho option. The command line input will be

```
Enter an option [Ucs/Ortho/Auxiliary/Section]:  O (Enter)
Specify side of viewport to project: (Pick the bottom edge of the top viewport.)
Specify view center:  9,7 (Enter)
Specify view center <specify viewport>: (Enter)
Specify first corner of viewport: 6,5 (Enter)
Specify opposite corner of viewport: 12,9 (Enter)
View name:  FRONT (Enter)
```

The ortho option makes a view that is folded 90 degrees from an existing one. From the top view that we created first, we could make a front view, a right-side view, a left-side view, or a back view by picking the appropriate edge of the viewport. Since we want a front view, we picked its bottom edge.

AutoCAD will display an image of the model's front view and will lock into the ortho mode to keep the image aligned with the top view as you drag it down to a convenient location. The Y location of the viewport's center is not critical, nor are the viewport's clip corners. We assigned the name Front to this view.

View names for mechanical parts such as this are rather arbitrary, having more to do with the interrelationships of the views than to the real-life orientation of the part. Some would call the view we just established a side view, and they would not be wrong.

Our third view will be an auxiliary view looking directly toward the diamond-shaped plane on the model. The command line input to create this view is

```
Enter an option [Ucs/Ortho/Auxiliary/Section]:  A (Enter)
Specify first point of inclined plane: (Use a quadrant object snap to pick point 1.)
Specify second point of inclined plane: (Use a quadrant object snap to pick point 2.)
Specify side to view from: (Pick Point 3.)
Specify view center: 5<90 (Enter)
Specify view center <specify viewport>: (Enter)
Specify first corner of viewport: 13,7 (Enter)
Specify opposite corner of viewport: 18,12 (Enter)
Enter view name:  AUX (Enter)
```

SOLVIEW's Auxiliary option creates a view that is perpendicular to a plane that is seen edge-on in the parent viewport. It is useful for showing true sizes on a plane that is askew to the principal planes. SOLVIEW will ask you to specify the plane by picking two points that are on its edge. These points must be in a viewport that shows an edge-on view of the plane. Generally you will use object snaps to specify the points. We used quadrant object snaps for this particular plane, but an endpoint object snap would have worked equally well. Once the plane is identified, SOLVIEW prompts for a point to indicate which side of the plane the viewpoint is to look toward.

AutoCAD will then rotate the paper space UCS around the Z axis to match the slope of the plane, lock into the ortho mode, and prompt for the auxiliary viewport's center location and its corners. After positioning the viewport, we named its view Aux.

The fourth, and final, viewport will be for a section view that slices the part along the curvature of its bend. The sequence of prompts and input to make this viewport are

```
Ucs/Ortho/Auxiliary/Section/<eXit>:  S (Enter)
Specify first point of cutting plane: (Use a midpoint object snap to pick point 1.)
Specify second point of cutting plane: (Use a quadrant object snap to pick point 2.)
Specify side to view from: (Pick Point 3.)
Enter view scale<2.0000>: 2 (Enter)
Specify view center: 9.5<270 (Enter)
Specify view center: (Enter)
Specify first corner of viewport: 6,.25 (Enter)
Specify opposite corner of viewport: 12,4.5(Enter)
Enter view name:  SEC (Enter)
```

Specifying a cutting plane is similar to specifying an auxiliary plane—you pick two points to identify the edge of the plane and a third point to indicate the view direction. The cutting plane will be perpendicular to the first two points. We used a midpoint object snap in specifying the first point and a quadrant object snap for the second. We used a two-to-one scale, just as we did in the top view. Then we showed AutoCAD the center and the corners of the section view, and lastly we named its view Sec. Although this section view appears to be identical to the front view, SOLDRAW will treat it differently.

You are now finished with SOLVIEW. If you look through the list of layers you will see that SOLVIEW has created thirteen new ones that have names such as Sec-hat, Top-vis, Top-hid, Aux-dim, and Front-vis. The first part of these layer names consists of the view names you assigned to the viewports, while the second part indicates the purpose of the layer. SOLDRAW will use the layers whose names end with vis for drawing visible lines, and those having names ending with hid for drawing hidden lines. The layer named Sec-hat will be used for hatches in the section view. Since these layers are for SOLDRAW, you should not use them. On the other hand, the layers with names ending with dim are for your use in adding dimensions. A layer named Vports was also created, and the borders of the four viewports are in this layer.

So far, the four floating paper space viewports contain just the 3D solid model. It is difficult to dimension such a model, and you have limited control over the display of hidden lines and edges. Therefore, SOLDRAW is used to draw a 2D version of the 3D model in each viewport. The command line input for SOLDRAW is

```
Command: SOLDRAW (Enter)
Select viewports to draw...
Select objects: (Pick the borders of the four viewports.)
```

AutoCAD's initial response to the command is a message reminding you of the type of object to select rather than a prompt for input. As soon as you pick the borders of the four viewports that were created with SOLVIEW, SOLDRAW goes to work. It may take a while, so be patient. When SOLVIEW is finished, the layer that the original 3D solid model is on is frozen in all of the viewports, and shown in its place are 2D versions of the model made from lines, arcs, and circles. Furthermore, the section view now shows the part's cross-section, and it is also hatched. All of these 2D objects are thawed, and therefore visible, only in the appropriate viewport. For instance, the Top-vis and Top-hid layers are frozen in all viewports except the one for the top view. Moreover, while the viewport for the section view does have objects in the Sec-hid layer, that layer is frozen because most drafting practices do not show hidden lines in section views.

Now you can add dimensions to the 2D objects that SOLDRAW has drawn in the floating viewports. The process works almost the same as for a fully 2D drawing, but since the objects are in model space and are not all on one plane, you will add dimensions within model space, and in one view at a time, rather than skip from one view to another as you might when dimensioning a pure 2D drawing.

You will probably need to enlarge the floating viewports to accommodate the dimensions, and you may even want to move them. Be certain, though, that you do not change their zoom level or their alignment (although you may want to move the section view so that it fits better on the paper).

Your completed drawing should look similar to the one in the next figure. The temporary border has been erased, and the Vports layer has been frozen. The title block and border in this figure is based on one from AutoCAD's MVSETUP command. One based on ANSI C title block.dwg in the Templates folder would work equally well.

We moved the section view and modified its hatch pattern. The layer for the center line that is shown in the front and section views is thawed only in those viewports. Other center marks are in the appropriate dimension layer. Since SOLDRAW does not draw tangential edges, the auxiliary view has some empty spots.

On the CD-ROM that accompanies this book, the completed drawing and model are in file mfe16206.dwg.

Command: SOLVIEW

Purpose: SOLVIEW creates and sets up floating viewports to be used for orthographic, section, and auxiliary views of a 2D multiview drawing of a 3D model. Generally, SOLVIEW is followed by the SOLDRAW command.

Initiate with:

- On the Command Line enter SOLVIEW.

- From the Draw pull-down menu, select Solids, then Setup, and lastly select View.

- Select the Setup View button from the Solids toolbar.

Options:

SOLVIEW sets up the views of a multiview 2D drawing based on a 3D solid model. It is an interactive command in which you specify, one at a time, the views that the drawing is to have, their scale (for some viewports only), and their relative location. SOLVIEW makes a paper space floating viewport for each view, sets the viewport's view direction and zoom level, and aligns the views with each other. SOLVIEW also creates special layers to be used for drawing visible objects, hidden objects, dimensions, and hatches within the floating viewports.

Although SOLVIEW creates viewports for orthographic, auxiliary, and section views, it does not draw anything in those viewports. When you are finished with SOLVIEW, you must use the SOLDRAW command to have objects drawn within the floating viewports.

SOLVIEW will set the **tilemode** system variable to 0 if it currently has a value of 1 and will display the command line menu

```
Enter an option [Ucs/Ortho/Auxiliary/Section]: (Enter an option or press Enter.)
```

AutoCAD will return to this menu when work within an option is completed. Press the Enter key to end the command. If no floating viewports exist, you must use the Ucs option to create one. The Ortho, Auxiliary, and Section options can be used only if at least one floating viewport exits.

- Ucs

  A viewport in which the view direction looks straight down on an X-Y plane—a plan view—is created with this option. It often is used for showing the top view of the 3D model. A submenu will be displayed for you to specify whether the plan view is to be based on the WCS, the current UCS, or a named UCS.

  ```
  Enter an option [Named/World/?/Current] <Current>: (Enter an option or press Enter.)
  ```

  The question mark suboption will bring up a list of existing UCSs that have been saved by the UCS command. After you specify which coordinate system you want the plan view based on, AutoCAD will prompt for the viewport's scale relative to paper space:

  ```
  Enter view scale<1.0000>: (Enter a number or press Enter.)
  ```

  Next, AutoCAD will prompt for the paper space location of the viewport's center:

  ```
  Specify view center: (Enter a location.)
  Specify view center <specify viewport>: (Enter a location or press Enter.)
  ```

  As soon as you specify a point for the viewport, AutoCAD will display the model centered at that point in the specified scale and will allow you to select a different point if your original location does not suit you. You can continue to move the center point until you find the location you want and press the Enter key to accept it.

  Then, AutoCAD will ask you to specify the size of the viewport by picking two points representing its opposite diagonal corners:

  ```
  Specify first corner of viewport: (Enter a location.)
  Specify opposite corner of viewport: (Enter a location.)
  ```

  A rubberband rectangle, anchored at the first corner, will help you specify the opposite corner. Lastly, AutoCAD will prompt for the name of the view:

  ```
  Enter view name: (Enter a valid view name.)
  ```

- Ortho

  This option creates a viewport having an orthographic view that is folded 90 degrees from the view in an existing view-port. You will first be prompted to select one side of the base viewport:

  ```
  Specify side of viewport to project: (Pick a point on
      the edge of a viewport.)
  ```

  The next prompt is for the location of the new viewport:

  ```
  Specify view center: (Enter a location.)
  Specify view center <specify viewport>: (Enter a
      location or press Enter.)
  ```

  AutoCAD will turn on the ortho mode and extend a rubber-band line from the midpoint of the base viewport border. When you pick a point for the viewport center, AutoCAD will display the model centered at that point, as seen from a viewpoint that is 90 degrees from that of the base viewport, and in the same scale as the base viewport. You may pick any number of view center locations until you signal acceptance of a point by pressing the Enter key.

  As soon as the viewport center has been established, AutoCAD will prompt for the viewport's opposite diagonal corners:

  ```
  Specify first corner of viewport: (Enter a location.)
  Specify opposite corner of viewport: (Enter a location.)
  ```

  A rubberband rectangle, anchored at the first corner, will help you locate the opposite corner. The last prompt by the Ortho option is for the name of the view:

  ```
  Enter view name: (Enter a valid view name.)
  ```

- Auxiliary

  The Auxiliary option creates a view that is perpendicular to a plane seen edge-on in a base viewport. It is useful for showing true sizes and shapes on a plane that is not aligned with any of the principal planes. AutoCAD will ask you to specify the angle of the auxiliary plane by picking two points on an edge view of it and will ask you to specify the side from which the plane is to be seen.

  ```
  Specify first point of inclined plane: (Specify a point.)
  Specify second point of inclined plane: (Specify a point.)
  Side to view from: (Specify a point.)
  ```

  Typically, object snaps will be used to specify the two points on the plane. The Side to view from point must be in the same viewport and off the line between the first two points. AutoCAD will then rotate the paper space UCS so that the X axis is perpendicular to the inclined plane, anchor a rubberband line on the plane, lock into the ortho mode, and prompt for a view center:

  ```
  Specify view center: (Enter a location.)
  Specify view center <specify viewport>: (Enter a location or press Enter.)
  ```

As soon as you pick a center location, AutoCAD will display the model as will appear in the auxiliary view, and will repeat the View Center prompt so that you can specify a location closer or further from the base viewport. When you have the location you want, press the Enter key. Once the viewport center has been established, AutoCAD will prompt for the viewport's opposite diagonal corners and the name of the view:

```
Specify first corner of viewport: (Enter
  a location.)
Specify opposite corner of viewport:
  (Enter a location.)
Enter view name: (Enter a valid view
  name.)
```

A rubberband rectangle, anchored at the first viewport corner, will help you specify the opposite clip corner.

- Section

This option sets up a cross-section view through the model. The section will slice completely through the model—partial sections and offset sections are not possible. You will be prompted to specify two points that will establish the edge of the cutting plane and to specify a third point indicating the side from which the section is to be seen. All three points must be in the same viewport.

```
Specify first point of cutting plane: (Specify a point.)
Specify second point of cutting plane: (Specify a point.)
Specify side to view from: (Specify a point.)
```

Next, AutoCAD will ask for the scale of the section view.

```
Enter view scale<1.0000>: (Enter a number or press Enter.)
```

AutoCAD will then anchor a rubberband line on, and perpendicular to, the cutting plane, turn on the ortho mode, and prompt for the paper space location of the viewport's center:

```
Specify view center: (Enter a location.)
Specify view center <specify viewport>: (Enter a location or press Enter.)
```

As soon as you specify a point for the viewport, AutoCAD will display the model centered at that point, in the specified scale. You can try different points until you are satisfied with the view location and press the Enter key. When the viewport's center has been established, AutoCAD will prompt for its opposite diagonal corners and for the name of the view:

```
Specify first corner of viewport: (Enter a location.)
Specify opposite corner of viewport: (Enter a location.)
Enter view name: (Enter a valid view name.)
```

A rubberband rectangle, anchored at the first viewport corner, will help you specify the opposite clip corner.

Notes:

- AutoCAD places all of the floating viewports in a layer named Vports. If that layer does not exist, SOLVIEW will create it.

- The names of the layers created by SOLVIEW for visible and hidden lines, for dimensions, and for hatches are based on the names assigned to the views by the user. The names begin with the view name and conclude with the extension of -vis, -hid, -dim, and -hat. For example, if the view within a viewport is named Top, AutoCAD will create layers having the names Top-vis, Top-hid, and Top-dim. Layers using the -hat name extension will be created only if a section view has been created.

- Layers are thawed only in the applicable viewport. Continuing with the previous example, the layers Top-vis, Top-hid, and Top-dim will be thawed in the viewport showing the top view and will be frozen in all other viewports.

- The layers AutoCAD creates for hidden lines will take on the HIDDEN linetype, provided that linetype has been loaded.

- The names assigned to the views become standard AutoCAD view names, so they must follow the VIEW command's rules for naming views and they cannot be the name of an existing view.

- SOLDRAW will delete and update objects in the layers SOLVIEW creates for visible objects, hidden objects, and hatches. Therefore, you should not use those layers.

- Section views will not look like section views until SOLDRAW is used. Although viewports for section views must initially be located at a point perpendicular to the cutting plane, they can be moved later.

Command: SOLDRAW

Purpose: SOLDRAW draws 2D objects that are suitable for dimensioning in viewports set up by the SOLVIEW command.

Initiate with:

- On the Command Line enter SOLDRAW.

- From the Draw pull-down menu, select Solids, then Setup, and lastly, select Drawing.

- Select the Setup Drawing button from the Solids toolbar.

Implementation:

SOLDRAW draws 2D objects in floating viewports that have been set up by SOLVIEW for orthographic, auxiliary, and section views. The command has no options. It issues a command line prompt for you to select the viewports that it is to work in, then draws objects within those viewports. The selected viewports must have been created by the SOLVIEW command, and the object in them must be a 3D solid that is not a block.

Within each viewport it draws the visible, and the hidden, edges and profiles of the 3D solid as seen within the viewport. Cross-section areas within section views are hatched using the current settings of the **hpname**, **hpscale**, and **hpang** system variables.

Notes:

- The objects are drawn using the appropriate layer for visible objects, hidden objects, and hatch patterns (these layers were created by SOLVIEW). Any existing objects that are in those layers within the viewports will be erased.

- Tangent lines, which delineate the transition between flat and curved surfaces or between two adjacent curved surfaces, are not drawn.

- Typically, the layers for hidden objects will use the HIDDEN line type. In each viewport, layers not needed to draw the objects specific to that viewport are frozen, and the layer of the 3D solid is frozen in all of the viewports. The layer for hidden objects is frozen in viewports for section views, since most drafting practices do not show hidden lines in section views.

- Objects within the orthographic views are drawn on the principal planes, while objects or auxiliary and section views are drawn on the planes selected during SOLVIEW.

Renderings from 3D Models

Renderings

T his is the first chapter in the section that explains how you can make realistic pictures from your 3D surface and solid models through AutoCAD's rendering module. In this chapter you will

- *get an overview of rendering—what it is, what you can do with it, and what its limitations are;*
- *learn about bitmap files, the various formats they come in, and their relationships to renderings;*
- *become acquainted with the steps and processes in making renderings;*
- *work through an exercise in rendering that involves both lights and materials.*

An Overview of Rendering

An AutoCAD rendering is a shaded, realistic-looking image of a 3D model. The figure on the right shows the same 3D surface model in four different viewing modes—its wireframe mode, when hidden lines have been removed, when SHADEMODE's flat face mode is in effect, and after it has been rendered. Not only have the surface mesh lines disappeared in the rendered image, its shapes and forms are more evident, and you have a better idea of what the object looks like.

Rendering in AutoCAD is handled by render.arx, an external program that is automatically activated the first time a command related to rendering is called. Rendering is a model space operation. None of the rendering commands are

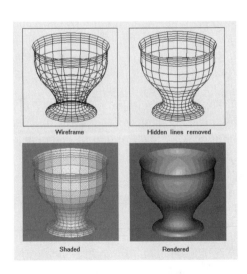

Wireframe   Hidden lines removed

Shaded   Rendered

allowed in paper space, although you can render within a floating viewport. Also, rendering works only on surface and solid models—wireframe objects vanish during a rendering.

Beginning with Release 14, render.arx is very versatile and powerful, having capabilities that were previously available only in extra-cost, add-on rendering programs. Here is a list of some of its capabilities:

- A variety of light types for obtaining different effects are supported. You can control the position, intensity, and color of these lights, and they can also cast shadows.
- You can enhance the realism of 3D models by adding texture and pattern images from bitmap files to their surfaces.
- AutoCAD can simulate materials that are transparent and materials that have mirrorlike surfaces.
- You can use images from bitmap files in the backgrounds of renderings, and you can add images of trees, shrubs, and other landscape objects to renderings.

Rendering without a background image, or landscape objects.

Rendering with a background image and landscape objects.

Rendering has two basic components—lights and materials. AutoCAD supports the four different types of lights shown in Table 17-1. Lights can also be given a specific color, and, with the exception of ambient light, can cast shadows. You can turn shadows on or off for each light you install. You will most likely install several lights to fully bring out the features of your 3D model. Lights for rendering will be described in more detail in Chapter Eighteen.

Materials, the second major component of renderings, control the appearance of specific surface objects of a 3D model. You can make surfaces appear to be shiny or dull, opaque or transparent; you can control their overall color as well as the color of their highlights; and you can make them reflective. To simulate objects that have patterns and textures—such as wood, brick, wallpaper, and marble—you can attach images from bitmap files to surface objects. Chapter Nineteen contains an extensive discussion of rendering materials.

Rendering is a more subjective process than most AutoCAD operations. There will seldom be a right or wrong selection of lights and their placement, and choices for materials will vary widely between individuals. You should, though, keep renderings as simple as you can. An abundance of lights and complicated materials does not necessarily make a better rendering.

Table 17-1 AutoCAD Rendering Light Types		
Light Type	**Purpose**	**Characteristics**
Distant	General illumination	Parallel light beams and constant intensity.
Spot	To brighten specific areas	Light beams radiate in a conelike pattern from the source. The relative brightness of the light can be set to diminish as distance from the source increases.
Point	To brighten specific areas	Light beams radiate in all directions from the source. Their intensity can be set to diminish at rates proportional to distance from the light.
Ambient	Relative brightness of shaded areas	No specific light source.

Bitmaps

Most AutoCAD objects are based on *vector graphics*, in which a few key points are used as anchors, with equations being used to define the object between the points. While vector graphics work well for depicting wireframe objects, as well as the edges and profiles of surface and 3D solid objects, they are not suitable for working with the broad colored and shaded areas of renderings. Consequently, renderings are based on *bitmap graphics*. Not only are renderings saved in bitmap files, images in bitmap files are used for material patterns and textures, as well as in backgrounds and as landscape objects. When you work with renderings, you work with bitmaps.

In bitmap graphics, the color of each dot on the computer screen (and on the printed output) is specified. In the word *bitmap*, *bit* refers to the binary digits used to specify the color of the dot, while *map* refers to the system for keeping track of each dot's location on the computer screen or printed output. Usually the dots on a computer screen are called *pixels*, which stands for picture element. Sometimes bitmap graphics are also called *raster graphics*.

Since binary numbers are used in specifying a particular color, the number of colors a pixel can have is 2 raised to the power of the number of bits available per pixel. In turn, the number of bits available for each pixel is dependent upon how much memory a computer's video system has and how many pixels are being used (the resolution of the screen or printed picture). Computer video systems often use the term *N-bit* in their specifications, where *N* is the number of bits per pixel that they support at a given resolution. This is often called *color depth*. Some commonly encountered color depths are

    8-bit   Maximum of 256 colors
    16-bit   Maximum of 65,536 colors
    24-bit   More than 16 million colors

Occasionally, you will even see references to 32-bit systems. However, in most cases differences between similar colors is not significant when you use more than sixty-five thousand colors. Some of AutoCAD's dialog boxes for rendering give you options related to color depth.

Bitmaps are usually generated on a horizontal, row-by-row basis. Often a bitmap file is able to reduce the overall number of bytes needed to store an image, especially if large areas in the bitmap have the same color. Rather than specifying the color of each pixel, the file can contain signals indicating the next so-many pixels that have color number such-and-such. This is called *compression*.

Unfortunately, there is no standard format for bitmap files. Many different formats exist; you will probably work with several different ones as you use them in renderings and as you export your renderings to output devices and to other programs. Commonly, each bitmap file format type will have a distinctive filename extension. The filename extensions of the formats, along with some information about the format, that AutoCAD's renderer is able to work with are as follows:

TIF   They are often called TIFF files, which stands for Tagged Image File Format. The format was developed to be portable across different computer platforms. Variations, however, exist within the format, and the variants are not necessarily compatible with each other.

GIF   GIF, which stands for Graphics Interchange Format, was developed by the Compuserve Information Network for exchanging graphic files electronically between different computer platforms and operating systems. For a given image, its file size tends to be small. It is, however, generally limited to 256 colors.

PCX   This format originated with an early personal computer paint program. It is a widely accepted format that has been kept updated and can be read by many modern paint programs, including the Windows paint accessory program.

BMP   Microsoft created this format for use in its Windows operating systems and accessories. Its images are stored uncompressed, which typically makes them fast to load, but large in size.

TGA   The TGA format was developed by Targa Truevision, a manufacturer of high-end computer graphics hardware. The files handle large numbers of colors well, but their file sizes tend to be large, even when they are compressed. Most of the files AutoCAD uses for materials, backgrounds, and landscape objects are in this format.

JPG   This format comes from an international standards committee—the Joint Photographic Experts Group (JPEG)—for digitizing photographs. It handles images having a large number of colors in relatively small file sizes.

Making Renderings

Although invoking the RENDER command is always the last step you take in making a rendering, we will discuss that command—and those associated with it—first. Actually, RENDER is the only essential command in making a rendering. If you do not install a light, AutoCAD

385

will automatically install one that has its light beams pointed in the current view direction. And, if you do not create or attach materials to your objects, AutoCAD will use some default global material characteristics.

The RENDER command gives you a choice of three different types of rendering. The most elementary type, called *Render*, supports the four types of lights we mentioned earlier, can do smooth shading, and can have materials with colors and various degrees of shininess. However, the lights cannot have shadows, and bitmaps are supported only for background images. The second rendering type is *Photo Real*. It supports all of the basic rendering features, plus shadows, transparent materials, bitmaps for materials, and bitmap landscape objects. The third rendering type, *Photo Raytrace*, supports everything that Photo Real does, plus reflective materials and light refraction (the bending of light beams as they pass through a transparent material).

Render is the fastest of the three rendering types, and you may sometimes use it for preliminary renderings or when you want to quickly obtain a smoothly shaded view of your 3D model. It is not, however, capable of making serious renderings. Most of the time you will use Photo Real rendering. You will probably use Photo Raytrace rendering only when you need its unique features, since it is usually (but not always) the slowest of the rendering types.

Your first step in making a rendering will be to set up a view of the 3D model. The viewing direction and the zoom level will depend on the shape of the model and on the features you wish to show. When you are working with large objects, especially buildings and structures, you will use a perspective view. Nothing prevents you from creating several different renderings of a model, each having a different view and combinations of lights. In fact, AutoCAD has a command, SCENE, that allows you to save and render specific combinations of views and lights.

Your second step will be to install the lights, and your third will be to create materials and attach them to surface objects. Within each of these steps, you will make numerous preliminary renderings. The sequence of these steps, however, is not absolute, and you will often change the lighting after you see its effects on materials. You may even tweak the view a little to improve the rendering.

Menu and toolbar buttons for RENDER and its related commands

As you try out combinations of lights and materials, your rendering destination will be the current viewport, and you will often use the rendering options that speed the rendering process—such as Query for Selections, Crop window, and Sub Sampling. Also, since rendering speed is related to the number of pixels in the rendering, dividing AutoCAD's graphics area into multiple viewports will significantly reduce rendering times. This also allows you to compare rendering results when you make changes in materials and lights.

When you have all of the parameters set to your liking, you will send the rendering to a file or to the render window, because, within the RENDER command, there is no provision for directly printing a rendering. Either of these two destinations work well for exporting the rendering to another file or document. Although the render window is a more direct method for printing the rendering with the system printer, the file destination gives you more choices for file type, color depth, and resolution. Renderings can also be saved to a file with the SAVEIMG command, but this command has no advantage over saving the rendering to a file.

Exercise

This exercise will give you an overall view of rendering—it will utilize shadows, bitmaps, transparent materials, and reflections. Start a new drawing. It does not need any special setup, and it is not one that you are likely to retain. Before you start this exercise, you should read through the descriptions of the RENDER and BACKGROUND commands in this chapter. You will also find it convenient to have the Render toolbar displayed on the screen for easy access when initiating rendering commands.

Before you can make a rendering, you need to create one or more objects that can be rendered. We will use a round ball that is sitting on a flat surface. Switch to a layer that has a red color, or simply set object color to red, then use the following command line input to make a surface model sphere that sits on the WCS X-Y plane:

```
Command: AI_SPHERE (Enter)
Specify center point of sphere: 0,0,1 (Enter)
Specify radius or [Diameter]: 1 (Enter)
Enter number of longitudinal segments for surface of sphere<16>: 24 (Enter)
Enter number of latitudinal segments for surface of sphere<16>: 24 (Enter)
```

A solid model sphere in the same location, and having the same radius, will work equally well. If you use a 3D solid sphere, though, you should set the system variable **facetres** to a value of 1.0. Once the sphere is drawn, change to an object color of white and draw a 3D face under the sphere by using the following command line input:

```
Command: 3DFACE (Enter)
Specify first point or [Invisible]: -2,-2 (Enter)
Specify second point or [Invisible]: 2,-2 (Enter)
Specify third point or [Invisible] <exit>: 2,2 (Enter)
Specify fourth point or [Invisible] <create three-sided face>: -2,2 (Enter)
Specify third point or [Invisible] <exit>: (Enter)
```

After drawing the 3D face, switch to an SE isometric view. Even though the sphere and 3D face will look the same from any of three other viewpoints, this particular one is important because we will set the direction of our rendering light to match it. After setting the viewpoint, you may want to zoom in to be closer to the sphere and 3D face. It will not hurt if the corners of the 3D face are even clipped a little. Your objects from this viewpoint should look similar to those in the figure on the right.

You may also want to divide the AutoCAD graphics area into multiple viewports. This will speed up rendering slightly, and it will enable you to compare the effects of different rendering settings. To divide the graphics area into four viewports, simply enter the word -VPORTS (be certain to precede the name with a hyphen) on the command line, then enter 4 in response to the list of options.

We will now use the LIGHT command to set up a light for the rendering. You can start this command in any of three different ways. You can enter the word *light* on the command line, select Render and then Light from the View pull-down menu, or click the Light button on the Render toolbar. Any of these actions will bring up the Lights dialog box. On the left side of this dialog box is a pull-down list of light types. Highlight Distant Light in this list by clicking on it, then click the New button.

This will bring up a dialog box titled New Distant Light. In this dialog box, give the light a name that has no more than eight characters, check the Shadow On check box, set Azimuth to 45, and set Altitude to 45. These last two parameters, which can be set by entering a value in their edit box or by moving their slider bar, aim the light. Azimuth is the light's angle in the X-Y plane from the Y axis, while altitude is its direction from the X-Y plane. Then press the OK button to leave the New Distant Light dialog box, and press the OK button in the Lights dialog box to leave the LIGHT command.

The distant light will appear in your drawing as a block containing the name you assigned to the light. It may be located almost inside your sphere, but that is of no consequence, since direction, not location, is what's important in aiming distant lights.

Start the RENDER command. We will use a neutral gray color for the rendering background, both to make the rendered objects stand out better and to free us from dependence on the current AutoCAD screen color. Click the Background button in the Render dialog box to display the Background dialog box. Select Solid from the row of radio buttons at the top of that dialog box, then clear the check box labeled AutoCAD Background. This will activate the Colors section of the dialog box. Set each of the three colors—red, green, and blue—to a value of about 0.30, then click the OK button to return to the Render dialog box.

In the Render dialog box, select Render as the rendering type. Make certain that Viewport is set as the rendering destinations and that Smooth Shade is on. Then click the button labeled Render.

Your rendering will look something like the one shown in grayscale in the figure on the right.

You are not likely to be impressed with the rendering. Although the sphere does look round, there is nothing to indicate that it is sitting on the 2D face. Therefore, start the RENDER command again. This time, select Photo Real as the rendering type. Then click the Shadows check box, and lastly click the button labeled Render to render the current view. Your rendering should look like the one shown in the next figure.

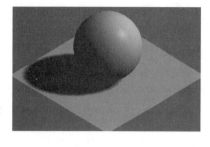

The shadow gives a better picture of the relative positions of the sphere and planar surface. Although the areas within the shadows are too dark now, they will become lighter when we add material properties to the objects. We have finished installing the lights for the rendering, and we will now begin working with materials.

Start the RMAT command. You can do this by selecting the button with a paint brush and green ball from the Render toolbar, by selecting Render/Materials from the View pull-down menu, or by entering RMAT on the command line. The Materials dialog box will appear. Press the button labeled Material Library that is in the middle of this dialog box.

In the large list box on the right side of the Materials Library dialog box will be the names of some ready-made materials that you can use with your surface objects. This list box may contain only four names, or it may contain about one hundred and fifty names, depending on how you installed AutoCAD. In any case there will be a material having the name CHECKER TEXTURE in the list. Find that material (they are arranged alphabetically), and click it so that it is highlighted. (If you

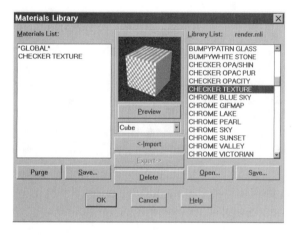

want to see what the material looks like, click the button labeled Preview.) Then, click the Import button. The name of the material will appear in the list box on the left side of the dialog box. Click the OK button to return to the Materials dialog box.

You now need to attach the material to a surface. The name CHECKER TEXTURE will be displayed in the list box on the left side of the Materials dialog box. This name should be highlighted, but if it isn't, click on the name to highlight it. Then click the Attach button. The dialog box will disappear to give you access to the entire AutoCAD graphics area. Pick an edge on the 3D face, and press the Enter key. This will restore the Materials dialog box. Press the OK button to end the RMAT command.

Invoke the RENDER command again. Make certain that the Apply Materials option is on, and click the Render button. Your rendering should look similar to the one in the next figure. The blue-and-white

tilelike pattern on the 3D face surface is from a bitmap
file named checkers.tga. If you were to view that file,
with either AutoCAD's REPLAY or IMAGE commands, or
with an external graphics program, you would see that it
looks exactly like the image on the 3D face in your rendering. AutoCD automatically scales bitmap images to fit
the size and shape of the surface they are attached to.

Next, we will add material properties to the sphere.
Invoke the RMAT command again. When the Materials
dialog box is displayed, notice that on
its right side is a button labeled New.
Make certain that the word *Standard* is
shown in the list box directly below
the New button, then click the button
labeled New. A dialog box titled New
Standard Material will appear.

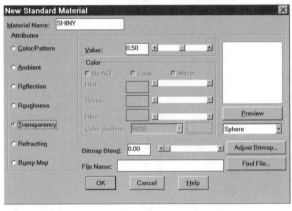

Enter any name you like in the
Material Name edit box, as long as it
has sixteen or fewer characters and
spaces. On the left side of the dialog
box is a cluster of radio buttons for
setting material attribute parameters.
Check the attribute labeled
Transparency and go to the Value edit box. For transparency, value represents the fraction of
light that passes through material. When transparency is 0, no light will pass through the material—it will be completely opaque. Conversely, when transparency is 1, all light will pass through
the material—it will be completely clear. Set a value of about 0.50 by entering it directly in the
edit box or by using the slider bar. Then check the OK button to leave the dialog box.

When you are back in the Materials dialog box, highlight the name of your new material if it
is not already highlighted and click the Attach button. When the dialog box temporarily disappears, pick a point on the sphere and press the Enter key to bring back the dialog box. Lastly,
click the OK button to end the RMAT command.

When you render the current viewport this time, your rendering with the transparent sphere
should look similar to the figure on the right. You will notice that as you add features to the rendering, rendering times take progressively longer. You can use the STATS command to see exactly
how long each rendering takes, as well as other details
about the rendering and the current rendering settings.

The last changes we will make in material attributes
will cause the sphere to be reflective as well as transparent. Start RMAT. In the Materials dialog box highlight the
name you assigned to your transparent material and click
the Modify button. This will bring up a dialog box identical to the New Standard Material dialog box you used
before, but it will be titled Modify Standard Material.

Activate the Reflection attribute radio button, and set the value of reflection to 1.00. Below the slider bar for value is a check box labeled Mirror that was grayed-out until you selected the

reflection attribute. Click this check box, then click the OK button to return to the Materials dialog box, and click its OK button to exit the RMAT command.

Start the RENDER command. This time, set Rendering Type to Photo Raytrace, then click the Render button to render the view in the current viewport. The rendering will take a relatively long time, perhaps around two minutes, depending upon your computer and the number of pixels involved in the rendering. Your rendering should be similar to the one shown in grayscale in the figure on the right.

That finishes our activities in this exercise. On the CD-ROM that accompanies this book, the 3D model and the rendering parameters associated with it are in the file mfe17110.dwg. We will not use this model in the future, so there is no compelling reason for you to keep it. Before you discard it though, you may want to try out some of the other options of the RENDER command—such as Query for Selection, Crop Window, and Sub Sampling.

Command: RENDER

Purpose: Rendering operations for making shaded images of 3D models are implemented through this command.

Initiate with:

- On the command line enter RENDER.

- From the View pull-down menu, select Render, and from the resulting flyout menu, select Render.

- Select the Render button from the Render toolbar.

Options:

Unless rendering preferences have been set to not display the Render dialog box, the dialog box shown on the right will be displayed for you to select rendering options and to initiate the rendering operation. Changes made to the settings in this dialog box remain in effect until they are specifically changed. The rendering parameters also remain in the drawing file's data base.

- Rendering Type

  Select one of the three rendering types from this drop-down list box.

  ° Render

    Only basic shading, lights, and materials are supported by this rendering type. It does not support shadows, transparent or reflective materials, or materials with bitmaps. It is, however, considerably faster than the other two rendering types.

  ° Photo Real

    This rendering type has all of the features of the Render type, plus it supports shadows, transparent materials, bitmap-based materials, and landscape objects.

  ° Photo Raytrace

    In addition to the features of Photo Real rendering, Photo Raytrace rendering supports reflective materials and refracted light beams.

- Scene to Render

  All existing scenes will be displayed in this list box. The current viewport's view and light installations will be listed as *current view* in this list box. Highlight the name of the scene you wish to render.

- Rendering Procedure

  ° Query for Selections

    When this toggle is checked, you will be prompted to select objects after you press the Render button. Only the selected objects will be rendered, and the other objects will disappear during the rendering.

  ° Crop Window

    When this toggle is checked, AutoCAD will clear the screen after you click the Render button and ask you to draw a rectangular window. Only objects within the window will be rendered. This option is available only when the rendering destination is the current viewport.

  ° Skip Render Dialog

    In subsequent calls to the RENDER command, the Render dialog box will not be displayed when this toggle is checked. The current render settings will be used for the rendering. Once this toggle is set, you must use the RPREF command to turn it off.

- Light Icon Scale

  Use this edit box to change the relative size of the blocks AutoCAD uses to mark the locations of distant, spot, and point lights.

- Smoothing Angle

  The value in this edit box tells the renderer the size of the angle between faces on polygon mesh surfaces at which their common edge is to be interpreted as a sharp edge. If the angle between two faces is equal or less than this value, their edge will be smoothed. If the angle is greater than this value, their common edge will be kept sharp. This value has an effect only if the Smooth Shade rendering option is on. Also, it has no effect on objects other than polygon mesh surface. Its default setting is 45 degrees.

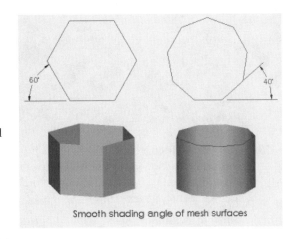

Smooth shading angle of mesh surfaces

- Rendering Options

  ○ Smooth Shade

    When this check box is checked, rendered edges between faces on polygon mesh surfaces will be smoothed, provided the angle between the faces is equal or less than the current smoothing angle. When this check box is off, each face on a polygon mesh will appear as a distinct facet.

  ○ Apply Materials

    Unless this toggle is turned on, materials that have been created and attached to objects through the RMAT command will have no effect. All objects will be rendered using AutoCAD's default material properties.

Faceted shading   Smooth shading

  ○ Shadows

    Shadows will be generated in the rendering when this box is checked, provided shadows have been specified within one or more installed lights within the scene to be rendered. This option is available only for Photo Real and Photo Raytrace rendering.

  ○ Render Cache

    When this option is selected, AutoCAD will write some of the information it needs for renderings in a cache file on the computer's hard disk. This can save time in subsequent renderings, especially when 3D solids are involved. The cache file is rewritten whenever changes in

Shadows off   Shadows on

the view or object geometry have been made.

° More Options

Clicking on this button will bring up one of three dialog boxes having options appropriate to the rendering type. All of these boxes will have an option to discard back

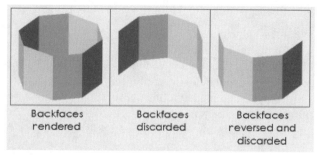

Backfaces rendered

Backfaces discarded

Backfaces reversed and discarded

faces and an option to reverse back faces. Only surface objects have back faces. By default they are rendered, and you will probably never need to discard them during renderings, or switch back faces with front faces.

Photo Real and Photo Raytrace renderings also have the following options:

Anti-aliasing. This sets the level of control for smoothing jagged diagonal lines in renderings. You can choose between Minimal, Low, Medium, and High, with Minimal being the default setting. Setting anti-aliasing to High results in the smoothest lines, but rendering times will increase.

Texture Map Sampling. This option lets you choose the sampling method for bitmap images used in materials when the view is very close or very distant. You will probably always use the default method.

Shadow Map Controls. This option allows you to set the minimum and maximum bias levels for shadow maps. The default values generally work satisfactorily.

In addition to these options, Photo Raytrace rendering also has the following two options:

Adaptive Sampling. Photo Raytrace rendering can use a special sampling technique to accelerate the anti-aliasing process when anti-aliasing is set above the minimal level. You can enable or disable this method, and you can also set its sampling sensitivity. Most likely, you will always accept the default settings.

Ray Tree Depth. This option has two controls that affect the ray tree. You are not likely to ever change the default settings.

• Destination

The pull-down list box offers three different output options.

° Viewport

This output option renders the selected scene in the current viewport. The dimensions of the viewport, in pixels, are listed below the list box, along with the bitmap color depth.

° Render Window

The rendering is sent to a special window titled Render, where it is displayed using the pixel resolution and color depth listed below the Destination list box. From the Render window, you can print the rendering, save it in a BMP bitmap file format, or save it in the Windows clipboard. AutoCAD automatically opens the Render window when you send your rendering to it. You can also open it yourself by clicking the Render button on the Windows task bar.

394

○ File

This option saves the rendering in a bitmap file. The default resolution of the file, in pixels, and its color depth will be displayed below the Destination list box. The More Options button will be activated, and from there you can choose to save the rendering as a BMP, PCX, Postscript, TGA, or TIFF file. Additional options allow you to control the file's resolution and color depth. You can even set the rendering's resolution and color depth to values that exceed those of your computer system.

- Sub Sampling

This option allows you to reduce rendering time while retaining such features as shadows and reflections by combining rows of pixels in the rendering. It is useful when you are

establishing parameters in a preliminary rendering. Select a ratio from the drop-down list box to set the number of rows that are to be combined. These ratios range from 1:1 (which renders every row) to 8:1 (which combines eight rows in one).

- Background

Clicking this button will bring up the same dialog box used by the BACKGROUND command.

- Fog/Depth Cue

When this button is pressed, the same dialog box used by the FOG command will be displayed.

- Render

Click this button to start the rendering process and end the RENDER command. AutoCAD will report the progress of the rendering on the command line as it performs its calculations, and you can stop the rendering at any time by pressing the Esc key.

If you are rendering to the current viewport, the rendered scene will remain until a redraw or screen regen takes place. If the rendering destination is to a file, AutoCAD will display a file dialog box for you to specify the name and location of the file. If the destination is the Render Window, that window will be displayed in front of the AutoCAD graphics screen.

Command: RPREF

Purpose: The RPREF command allows you to establish rendering parameters without performing a rendering operation.

Initiate with:

- On the command line enter RPREF.
- From the View pull-down menu, select Render, and from the resulting flyout menu, select Preferences.
- Select the Rendering Preferences button from the Render toolbar.

Options:

This command uses a dialog box that is the same as the one used by the RENDER command, except for its title (it is titled Rendering Preferences rather than Render), and that it has a button labeled OK instead of one labeled Render. See the discussion on the RENDER command for a description of the dialog box and the options it contains.

Notes:

- You will occasionally use the RPREF command to establish rendering parameters when you do not want to perform a rendering. You will have to use RPREF when the Skip Render Dialog toggle is on and you want to change the current rendering parameters.

Command: BACKGROUND

Purpose: This command controls the appearance of areas within the rendering that are not filled with objects.

Initiate with:

- On the command line enter BACKGROUND.

- From the View pull-down menu, select Render, and from the resulting flyout menu, select Background.

- Select the Background button from the Render toolbar.

Options:

The BACKGROUND command uses a dialog box, titled Background, for you to specify how areas within the rendering that are not filled with objects are to appear. You can also access this dialog box from the REN-DER command.

The dialog box gives you three options for controlling the background, plus one for controlling whether the render buffer is cleared before rendering and one that

affects the relationship between objects with reflective (mirrorlike) materials and the background. The first four options—solid, gradient, image, and merge—are selected through four radio buttons at the top of the dialog box. When you select the solid, gradient, or image options, appropriate clusters of buttons and edit boxes in the Background dialog box will be activated. Pressing the Preview button of the dialog box will show the effects of the current background settings. The option affecting objects with mirrorlike finishes is accessed through the cluster of buttons labeled Environment.

When you specify a color within the Background dialog box, you can use the edit boxes and slider bars for either the RGB (Red, Green, Blue) or the HLS (Hue, Lightness,

396

Saturation) color systems. You can also click the Select Custom Color button to bring up a dialog box titled Color. Within this dialog box, you can choose from forty-eight basic colors that are shown in image tiles or you can specify a color by picking a point within a large image tile showing blended bands of colors.

- Solid

This, the default option, assigns one color to the background. If the check box labeled AutoCAD Background is on, the current color of the AutoCAD graphics window will be used for the rendering background. If this check box is cleared, the Colors section of the Background dialog box will be activated for you to specify a color. The color you choose will be reflected in the color tile labeled Top, as well as in the preview panel when you click the button labeled Preview.

- Gradient

This background option uses two or three colors in bands that blend together. To select the color of a particular band, click the color tile labeled Top, Middle, or Bottom, then specify a color. The color tile will change in accordance with your selected color. Use just the top and bottom colors for a two-color gradient.

The relative location, width, and orientation of the color bands are controlled through the three edit boxes, and their corresponding sliders, located in the lower-right corner of the Background dialog box.

- Horizon establishes the center of the color band gradient. It represents the percent of viewport height.

- Height, which also represents a percent of screen height, determines where the second color of a three-color gradient begins. To use a two-color gradient, set Height to 0 and ignore the middle color.

- Rotation allows you to slant the color bands. You can specify any angle value between 90 degrees and -90 degrees. Positive angle values place the top color to the left, while negative angle values place it to the right.

- Image

Select this option to use the image in a bitmap file for the rendering background. The cluster of buttons labeled Image will be activated for you to specify the bitmap file. You can enter the bitmap file's name directly in the edit box labeled Name or press the Find File button to search for the file you want. The types of bitmap file formats you can use for background images are BMP, TGA, TIF, GIF, JPG, and PCX.

When you click the Adjust Bitmap button, AutoCAD will display a dialog box titled Adjust Background

Bitmap Placement. The default setting in this dialog box is to fit the image to the screen. If the Fit to Screen check box is cleared, you can adjust the relative size of the image through the edit boxes and sliders labeled Scale, and you can establish its relative location through the Offset edit boxes and sliders. Scale values greater than 1 reduce the image size, while values smaller than 1 increase the image size.

When the Use Image Aspect Ratio check box is on, the proportions of the image are maintained. When this check box as well as the one labeled Maintain Aspect Ratio are cleared, you can distort the image by using different scales in the X and Y directions. You can center the image by setting the X and Y offsets to 0 or by pressing the Center button.

When scale values are greater than 1 (thus reducing the relative image size), the image will be repeated to fill the entire background when the radio button labeled Tile is checked. When the radio button labeled Crop is checked, the image will appear just one time, and it will not completely fill the background if the image scale is greater than 1.

- Merge

Normally, AutoCAD clears the render buffer at the beginning of each rendering and will repaint the entire viewport. If the Merge radio button is checked, though, the current render buffer is retained, and any differences in the new rendering will be combined with the existing rendering. This can be useful when you are working with complicated renderings. Merge, however, does not work well when the Crop Window option of the RENDER command is in effect, since AutoCAD clears the screen before it prompts you to specify the crop window.

- Environment

When either Photo Real or Photo Raytrace rendering is used, objects that have a mirrorlike material attached will reflect the background (see the discussion of the RMAT command in Chapter Nineteen for information about mirror-like materials). This occurs when colors, either solid or gradient, and bitmap images are used for the background.

You can, however, have the mirrorlike object reflect the image within a bitmap file rather than the rendering background. To do this, clear the check box labeled Use Background. The Name edit box and the Find File button will then be activated for you to use in specifying a file to be reflected from the mirrorlike objects in the rendering. The same bitmap file formats that can

Object with a mirror-like surface reflecting the background image's checkerboard pattern

Same object reflecting an environment map image rather than the background image

398

be used for background images can be used for environment maps. As long as the Use Background check box is cleared and a file for the environment map has been specified, AutoCAD automatically attaches the file's image to all objects in the rendering that have mirrorlike surfaces—you do not need to explicitly attach the image to objects.

Notes:

The dialog boxes that AutoCAD uses to find bitmap files that are to be used as background images and as environment maps are initially set to display only BMP files. Use the drop-down list box to specify bitmap files having other formats.

Command: SAVEIMG

Purpose: SAVEIMG saves the image within the current viewport to a bitmap file.

Initiate with:

- On the command line enter SAVEIMG.

- From the Tools pull-down menu, select Display Image, and from the resulting flyout menu, select Save.

Options:

SAVEIMG displays a dialog box that allows you to save the image within the current viewport in any of three bitmap formats: BMP, TGA, or TIF. Options for the TGA and TIF formats also allow you to compress the files. By default, the entire viewport is saved, but you can specify an area within it to be saved by picking two points in the image tile labeled Active Viewport. AutoCAD will draw a box representing the viewport area to be saved and will display the coordinates, in pixels, in edit boxes. You can also specify the area by entering numbers in the edit boxes. When the OK button is pressed, AutoCAD will display a dialog box for you to specify a name and location for the bitmap file.

Notes:

- In Release 13 and earlier versions of AutoCAD, SAVEIMG had an option for saving the contents of the current viewport, the contents of all viewports in the graphics area, or of the entire screen, including the menus. Beginning with Release 14, however, SAVEIMG can save the contents of only the current viewport.

- SAVEIMG is probably more useful for saving wireframe, outline, or shaded images than for saving rendered images, since the RENDER command offers more options for file type, resolution, and color depth.

Command: REPLAY

Purpose: REPLAY displays the image within a bitmap file in the current viewport.

Initiate with:

- On the command line enter REPLAY.

- From the Tools pull-down menu, select Display Image, and from the resulting flyout menu, select View.

Options:

REPLAY is strictly for viewing the image in a bitmap file. You cannot use the image in any way, and it will disappear when the viewport is redrawn. The bitmap file formats that can be displayed are BMP, TGA, and TIF. Each pixel of the bitmap file is mapped to a pixel in the current view-port—there is no provision for enlarging or reducing the image. You can, though, specify the location of the image within the viewport, and you can also clip part of the image. If the image is larger than the size of the current viewport, the image will be clipped at the viewport borders.

Notes:

- REPLAY is a convenient way to view the contents of a bitmap file, especially if you do not have a graphics file viewing program.

- You can also view the contents of bitmap files through AutoCAD's IMAGE command. However, that command is for inserting bitmaps in a drawing, not just for viewing them. Consequently, it is more involved to use.

Command: STATS

Purpose: This command displays information and data about the last rendering.

Initiate with:

- On the command line enter STATS.

- From the View pull-down menu, select Render, and from the resulting flyout menu, select Statistics.

- Select the Statistics button from the Render toolbar.

Implementation:

The information about the last rendering is displayed in a read-only list box within a dialog box titled Statistics. You can save this information by selecting the Save Statistics to File check box and entering a file name. You must supply the extension to the file name. If the file exists, AutoCAD will add the data from the most recent rendering to the end of the file. The file is in ASCII format, which can be read and edited by Windows' Notepad text editor.

Lights in Renderings

T*his chapter is devoted entirely to rendering lighting.
When you have finished it, you will*

- *know the properties of rendering lighting;*
- *be familiar with the four types of AutoCAD rendering lights—ambient lighting, distant lights, point lights, and spotlights;*
- *be acquainted with the different types of shadows in AutoCAD renderings;*
- *have practical experience in installing lights after completing three exercises;*
- *know how to use the many dialog boxes of the LIGHT command;*
- *know what scenes are, how to use them, and how to create them.*

Lighting is an essential component of renderings, and each of your renderings will probably require that you install a variety of them to obtain a realistic representation of your model. Therefore, most of this chapter is devoted to the one AutoCAD command—LIGHT—that both creates lights and modifies them after they have been installed. A second essential component of renderings is the view of the object that is to be rendered. Since lights and views are such important components of a rendering, AutoCAD has a special command—SCENE—for combining and managing them.

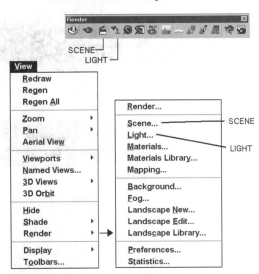

Menus and toolbar buttons for lights and scenes

Properties of Rendering Lighting

A key characteristic in AutoCAD lighting, as well as in real-world lighting, is that surfaces directly facing a light are brighter than surfaces that are inclined to the light. This is illustrated by the sixteen-sided extruded polygon in the figure on the right

The face on the polygon that directly faces the incoming light beams, which are traveling in the same direction as the view's line of sight, is the brightest, and the brightness of the other faces is directly proportional to their angle with the light beams. The more a face is inclined to the light beams, the dimmer it is. This characteristic is what shading is all about, and you will want to place your lights to take advantage of it.

The 3D cube on the left side of this figure is illumi-nated by a single light whose beams are at the same angle to the three visible surfaces of the cube. The rendering of the cube is simply a blob, with no evidence that it is a 3D object. In the rendering on the right side, though, the light has been rotated so that its light beams strike the three visible surfaces at different angles. In this rendering, there is no doubt that the object is a cube, even though the viewpoint is the same as in the other rendering.

Although AutoCAD's lights are able to simulate this property of real lights, as well as some others that we will mention shortly, they are unlike real lights in other ways. For one thing, you cannot see an AutoCAD light. You can see the results of the light as it shines on objects, but you cannot see the light itself, as you can a glowing lightbulb or the sun.

Also, AutoCAD lights pass completely through objects to illuminate other objects. This is shown on the left in the next figure, where the same sixteen-sided polygon solid shown earlier now has a round hole through it.

An AutoCAD light aimed directly at the side of this object illuminates the outside faces of the solid as you would expect, but it also illuminates the inside hole in the solid. This characteristic can be annoying at times and beneficial at other times. When you add shadows to lights, this effect is diminished, as shown in the rendering on the right.

While AutoCAD's rendering lights are white by default, they can be given color. However, colored lights significantly add to the complexity of renderings, and the results do not necessarily follow the standard rules for mixing colors. A blue light shining on a yellow surface, for instance, will not make the surface green, or even blue. Furthermore, since you cannot see rendering lights, the effects are not the same as those of colored lights in a theater or on an electrical panel. For example, you cannot simulate a warning light by placing a red point light on the surface of a model. You must instead reflect a light from an object that represents the warning light, and the results will be the same regardless of whether a white light is reflected from a red surface or a red light is reflected from a white surface. As you will see in the next chapter, you can use rendering materials to assign colors to specific surface objects, and in almost all cases it is better to handle color through material than through lights. Generally, you will leave rendering lights white.

AutoCAD's rendering lights can vary in brightness, or intensity, just as real lights do. Each light is assigned an intensity value that has no units. Its effect is on the relative brightness of the objects illuminated by the light. Thus, surfaces reflecting a light that has an intensity of 0.5 will be darker than those reflecting a light that has an intensity of 1.0. The maximum intensity value that you can assign to a light depends on the light's type and sometimes on the extent of the AutoCAD drawing area. For many types of rendering lights, intensity can range from 0 to 1, but a point light for the model of a large structure can have an intensity of several hundred thousand. You can assign an intensity value of 0 to a light, which has the effect of turning the light off (we will discuss the specifics of intensity values in a few pages).

All real light becomes dimmer as distance from the light source increases. This is true even for the sun, although it is not apparent to those of us on Earth because of the great initial intensity of the sun's light. Similar to real lights, AutoCAD point lights and spotlights can be set to become dimmer with distance. AutoCAD refers to this falloff of intensity as *attenuation*. AutoCAD distant lights, which imitate sunlight, cannot be attenuated.

Attenuation in point lights and spotlights can be set to have one of two falloff rates:

- Inverse linear attenuation. The light's intensity is inversely proportional to distance from the light. For instance, an object twice as far from the light source as another object will be one-half as bright.
- Inverse square attenuation. The light's intensity decreases in inverse proportion to the square of the distance from the light. Thus, an object twice as far from the light source as another object will be one-fourth as bright.

You can also turn off attenuation in point lights and spotlights so that objects far from the light are just as bright as objects close to the light.

AutoCAD Light Types

AutoCAD supports four different types of rendering lights, each with characteristics that make them suitable for specific rendering lighting tasks. With the exception of ambient light, each light is given a unique name, and you can install as many lights in as many combinations as you like. Only one ambient light can exist, and it does not have a name. You can use the SCENE command to associate particular lights with particular views of a 3D model.

AutoCAD inserts a block at the location of each light (again, with the exception of ambient light). The type of block inserted indicates the type of light installed, and the name assigned to a light is shown as a visible attribute of the block. Other information AutoCAD needs about the light's parameters are stored as invisible attributes. You can adjust the scale of these blocks through the Light Icon Scale edit box used by the RENDER and RPREF commands.

Ambient Light

Ambient light sets the overall level of illumination in a rendering. It has no particular source, no light beams, and it cannot cast shadows. Even though ambient light is not able to shade objects or produce realistic renderings by itself, it does give you some control over the relative brightness of shaded areas, as shown in the figure on the right. Its effects are subtle.

High ambient light   Low ambient light

Ambient light, which is set from the main Lights dialog box of the LIGHT command, applies to the entire rendering. Its intensity can range from 0 to 1, and its default intensity is 0.30. Generally, you will leave ambient light set to its default value. You can assign a color to ambient light. Ambient light is not assigned a name.

Distant Lights

A distant light is comparable to light from the sun as it strikes the Earth. Its light beams are all traveling in the same direction, and the light source seems far away. Although each distant light has a specific location, the direction in which the light is pointing is the important parameter. Location is of no consequence because, as shown in the figure on the right even objects that are behind a distant light will be illuminated by it.

AutoCAD places a block named DIRECT at the installed location of a distant light. This block is in the form of a circle with five parallel lines, indicating the light's direction on one side of the circle and the assigned name of the light in the middle of the circle. Initially, AutoCAD aims a new distant light in the current view direction, and it inserts the block in the center of the viewport. You can move and rotate the block to move and re-aim the distant light, and you can reposition or re-aim the light through several options in the LIGHT command's dialog box for distant lights.

The intensity of distant lights can be set to any value between 0 and 1. Their light intensity cannot be attenuated. Distant lights can cast shadows, and you can give them a color.

Distant light is useful for providing general illumination in a rendering, and generally each of your renderings will have at least one distant light. In renderings of exterior scenes, sunlight will generally be simulated with a distant light. Since distant lights are so often used for sunlight, AutoCAD's LIGHT command uses the terms *azimuth* and *altitude* in aiming distant lights, and it provides a special sun angle calculator for aiming them according to the position of the sun at a specific time and date for various geographic locations.

Point Lights

Light beams from a point light radiate in all directions from a point in 3D space. The lights are similar to a candle or to a bare incandescent lightbulb. When installing a point light, you simply specify its location—you do not aim it.

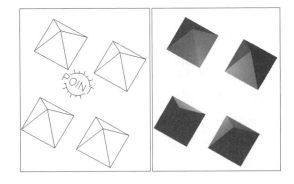

AutoCAD inserts a block, named OVERHEAD, at the point light's location. This block looks like a circle with short lines, representing light beams, pointing in all directions from its perimeter. The name of the light is shown in the middle of the circle. AutoCAD locates a new point light in the center of the current viewport. You can move it by moving its block or by specifying a point through an option in the LIGHT command's dialog box for point lights.

The intensity of point lights can be attenuated, using either inverse linear or inverse square falloff rates. Maximum allowed intensity varies according to the extent of the drawing area and to the falloff rate used. When attenuation is set to 0, intensity can range from 0 to 1.

Point lights are useful for emphasizing local areas of a model and for simulating street lamps and ceiling lights. Point lights can cast shadows, and they can be given a color.

Spotlights

An AutoCAD spotlight sends out light in the shape of a cone, similar to a desk lamp or a theater spotlight. You must specify both a target point and a light point when you install a spotlight. By default, AutoCAD places the target for a new spotlight in the center of the current viewport and the light about 1 unit from the target toward the viewer.

A block, named SH_SPOT, is inserted by AutoCAD at the spotlight's location. It is in the form of a square, with five short lines pointing toward the target and with the name of the light in the center of the square. You can move the block to move the light, and you can rotate it to re-aim the light. The target will move as the block is moved or rotated. You can also specify point location coordinates for the target and light through the dialog box that the LIGHT command uses for creating and modifying spotlights.

Spotlights send out two concentric cones of light. The inner cone is called the *hotspot cone*, and the outer one is called the *falloff cone*. The intensity of light in the hotspot cone is constant throughout the disk of the cone, while the intensity of light in the falloff cone diminishes from the center of the cone to its edges.

The angle of the hotspot cone can equal that of the falloff cone, but it cannot exceed it. When the two cones have the same angle, the edge of the spotlight will be sharp. When the hotspot cone is smaller than the falloff cone, the edge of the light gradually fades away, producing a soft edge. You must use Photo Real or Photo Raytrace rendering for these effects to be evident. The cone angles, which are specified through the LIGHT command, can range from 0 to 160 degrees.

This fading in light intensity across the falloff cone is not the same as attenuation, which is the loss of intensity as distance from the light source increases. You can, though, specify either inverse linear or inverse square attenuation for spotlights. Their maximum allowed intensity varies according to the extent of the drawing area and the falloff rate used. When attenuation is set to 0, spotlight intensity can range from 0 to 1.

Spotlights are useful for brightening specific areas of a 3D model and for simulating the effects of artificial lighting. They can cast shadows, and they can be colored.

Installing a spotlight is more involved than installing a distant light or a point light because more parameters must be specified. You must locate the light and its target, set its cone angles, and set its intensity. Furthermore, the size of the area illuminated by a point light depends upon its distance from the surface

Use relative spherical coordinates from the target to place the spotlight:

@ Dist < H_Ang < V_Ang

and on the size of the cone angles. One good technique for positioning a spotlight is to place the target in a spot that will be approximately in the center of the light beams and on the surface you want to illuminate. Then, use relative spherical coordinates to specify the light's location. This can be done through the Modify button of the New/Modify Spotlight dialog box.

Shadows

Photo Real and Photo Raytrace rendering allow you to have one of two types of shadows. When you use Photo Real rendering, AutoCAD's lights can cast shadows either by generating *volumetric shadows* or by using *shadow maps*. Photo Raytrace rendering can also use shadow maps to generate shadows, but the other choice for shadow type is *ray traced shadows* rather than volumetric shadows.

You make your choice for a shadow type within the LIGHT command by picking the Shadow Options button in the New/Modify dialog box for the light type you are working with. This will bring up the Shadow Options dialog box. If you want volumetric or ray traced shadows, click the check box labeled Shadow Volumes/Ray Traced Shadows. If you want the shadows generated from shadow maps, clear the Shadow Volumes/Ray Traced Shadows check box.

Visually, the differences between the shadow types are that volumetric and ray traced shadows have sharp edges, while shadow map shadows have soft, or blurred, edges. Volumetric and ray traced shadows can also transmit color from transparent and translucent objects. Shadow map shadows can be more accurate than volumetric shadows, but they tend to pull away from the object casting

Volumetric shadows and ray traced shadows   Shadow map shadows

the shadow, and they sometimes affect the appearance of objects outside the shadows. Furthermore, shadow map shadows slow rendering speeds significantly. Ray traced shadows have the same appearance as volumetric shadows, but they are more accurate, and in complex renderings they can even be faster.

The Shadow Options dialog box contains several options that apply only to shadow map shadows. The Shadow Map Size option gives you some control over the accuracy of the shadows. You can pick the shadow map size from a list of set values ranging from 64 to 4096 pixels through a pull-down list box. The larger the shadow map, the greater its accuracy and the slower its rendering. You can also control the softness of the shadow edges. And for point and distant lights, you can pick specific objects that are to cast shadows. This option is not available for spotlights. Additional controls for shadow maps can be accessed through the More Options button in the Render and Render Preferences dialog boxes.

To have shadows in renderings, Photo Real or Photo Raytrace rendering must be used, and shadows must be enabled in the Render or Render Preferences dialog box as well as in the dialog box for the lights that are to make the shadows.

Installing Lights

Although nothing is inherently difficult about installing rendering lights, it is almost a trial and error process, and it can be a tedious process. Typically while installing a light, you will go through several cycles of adjusting its properties, then rendering the scene to view the results. Furthermore, there will always be an infinite combination of light types and properties, and there will be many combinations that are equally satisfactory. Installing lights, like most rendering steps, is a subjective process.

The best strategy for lighting a rendering is to first install a key light that will provide general illumination. Often this will be a distant light, and you should aim it so that as many surfaces and edges as possible in the rendering stand out. If you want this light to cast shadows, then you need to also consider which direction the shadows are to be in. When the parameters of this key light are as you want them, you should look the rendering over closely to determine which areas need further illumination—perhaps to make a surface brighter or perhaps to make edges stand out. Then, if needed, you should take care of one of these areas by installing a second light, using a light type suitable for the area and what you want to accomplish. When the lighting for that area is as you want it, you can install a third light, perhaps a fourth one, and maybe even a fifth one. Too many lights, though, can make the rendering overly complicated, and the lights will begin to cancel each other's effects.

Using multiple small viewports will help reduce rendering times as you adjust lights, and they will also help you compare results when you add or change lights. If you are rendering a perspective view, you will find it helpful to have at least one viewport that has a non-perspective view so you can use your pointing device when setting light and target locations.

Exercise One

This first exercise will be very simple, but nevertheless it will still demonstrate some important principles that you should consider when you install rendering lights. Locate file mfe18101.dwg on the CD-ROM that accompanies this book and open it. This file contains the 3D solid model of a small mechanical part that is lying on the WCS X-Y plane as shown in the figure on the right.

Use AutoCAD's VIEW command to switch to the view named ISO_SE _50. Then, you may want to use the 4 option of the VPORTS command to divide the AutoCAD graphics area into four viewports. This step is optional, but it will help you compare the effects of various lighting parameters.

First make a rendering without any installed lights. Just invoke the RENDER command and render the current viewport. AutoCAD will make the rendering using a single distant light pointed in the view direction. The results will not be bad, but the rendering will have little contrast between surfaces on the model, and some of the model's edges will not show up.

Start the LIGHT command, select Distant Light from the pull-down list box, and press the New button. Enter DIST_1 in the name edit box, and set the light's parameters as follows:

Intensity:	1.0
Azimuth:	90 degrees
Altitude:	45 degrees
Shadows:	On
Shadow Options:	Shadow Volumes/Ray Traced Shadows
Color:	White

Leave ambient light set to its default value of 0.30. Render the current viewport. Make certain that rendering type is set to Photo Real and that Shadows are activated. Set the rendering background to any solid color of your choice. Your rendering of the current viewport should resemble the one shown in the figure on the right.

Having shadows and the light shine from the right side improve the rendering, but there are still some edges that are not distinct, and the left side of the model is a little dark. Therefore, we will install another distant light. Name this second distant light DIST_2 and assign the following parameters to it:

Intensity:	0.33
Azimuth:	180 degrees
Altitude:	25 degrees
Shadows:	On
Shadow Options:	Shadow Volumes/ Ray Traced Shadows
Color:	White

Your rendering should now look like the one in the figure on the right. The shadows of the second light help delineate the upper round edges on the model, and they brighten up its left side. This model with the lights installed is in file mfe18102.dwg on the CD-ROM that comes with this book. These two lights represent just one of an infinite combination of lights and viewpoints that could be used in a rendering of this model, and you may want to experiment further on your own.

Exercise Two
This second exercise in installing lights will be more complicated. We will place some lights in the surface model of a kitchen and dining room that we used in an exercise in Chapter Seven of this book. In this exercise, we will use a different version of the model, so you should find and open the file mfe18201.dwg on the CD-ROM that comes with this book. This model has a table, some chairs, a floor lamp, and a ceiling light in the dining area. Also, the color of all of the layers has been set to white. We will install the lights in the dining area.

Use the VIEW command to restore the view named DINING_ROOM. This is a perspective view of the dining room as seen from the kitchen. Since it is a perspective view, you will have to specify point coordinates from the keyboard. The drawing uses architectural units, so coordinates can be entered either as feet (which we will use) or as inches. Also, you may want to divide the graphics area into four viewports, so that you can see the effect that each light has.

Install one distant light, one point light, and two spotlights using the parameters listed below. Leave ambient light set to its default of 0.30. To better see the effects of each light, you should render the current viewport after installing each light. Use Photo Real rendering, and make certain that shadows are activated in the Render dialog box.

Light type:	Distant
Name:	FILL
Intensity:	0.45
Azimuth:	105.0
Altitude:	-20.0
Shadows:	None
Color:	White
Remarks:	Notice that this light points up.

Light type:	Point
Name:	CEILING
Intensity:	75.0
Attenuation:	Inverse Linear
Position:	8',8',8.5'
Shadows:	On
Shadow Options:	Shadow Volumes/Ray Traced Shadows
Color:	White

Light type:	Spotlight
Name:	LMP_TOP
Intensity:	13.0
Attenuation:	Inverse Linear
Target Position:	2',9',9'
Light Postion:	2',9',5.5'
Hotspot cone:	150
Falloff cone:	160
Shadows:	None
Color:	White
Remarks:	Simulates light from the top of the floor lamp.

Light type:	Spotlight
Name:	LMP_BTM
Intensity:	50.0
Attenuation:	Inverse Linear
Target Position:	2',9',0
Light Position:	2',9',5.5'
Hotspot cone:	125
Falloff cone:	160
Shadows:	On
Shadow Options:	Shadow Volumes/Ray Traced Shadows
Color:	White
Remarks:	Simulates light from the bottom of the floor lamp.

With all four lights installed, your rendering should resemble the one illustrated in the figure on the right. On the CD-ROM, the model with the installed lights is in file mfe18202.dwg.

Exercise Three

In this exercise, we will install some lights for a rendering of the 3D house we built as a surface model in Section Two. Find the file mfe18301.dwg on the CD-ROM that accompanies this book. This version of the model has some 3D surfaces that will serve as backgrounds for the rendering. Open the file and restore the view named DIST_80. (This is the perspective view we set up during an exercise in Chapter Seven.) The model as seen in this view is shown in the figure below.Since this is a perspective view, you will not be able to use your pointing device.

Install three distant lights, using the parameters listed below. Leave ambient light set to its default value of 0.30. To see the effects of the lights, you should render the current viewport after installing each light. You may also want to divide the AutoCAD graphics area into four viewports so you can better compare the effects of the lights.

Light type:	Distant
Name:	SUN
Intensity:	1.00
Azimuth:	136.0
Altitude:	45.0
Shadows:	On
Shadow Options:	Shadow Volumes/Ray Traced Shadows
Color:	White

Light type:	Distant
Name:	FILL
Intensity:	0.20
Azimuth:	-90.0
Altitude:	21.0
Shadows:	Off
Color:	White

Light type:	Distant
Name:	FRONT
Intensity:	0.33
Azimuth:	-155.0
Altitude:	0
Shadows:	Off
Color:	White

Light type:	Point
Name:	POINT_1
Intensity:	15.0
Attenuation:	Inverse Linear
Position:	25',4',7'
Shadows:	Off
Color:	White

Your final rendering will look similar to the one in the figure on the right. At this stage, the rendering is not especially impressive. It will look more realistic when we add some materials and landscape objects to it. On the CD-ROM, the model with the three distant lights is in file mf318302.dwg.

Command: LIGHT

Purpose: Rendering lights are installed and modified through this command.

Initiate with:

- On the command line enter LIGHT.

- From the View pull-down menu, select Render, and then Light.

- Select the Lights button from the Render toolbar.

Options:

All three different types of AutoCAD lights are installed and modified through this command. It also controls the intensity and color of ambient light. Dialog boxes are used in establishing all light parameters. When the LIGHT command is initiated, a dialog box titled Lights will be displayed, and as you select options from that dialog box, appropriate secondary dialog boxes will appear.

The names of all lights currently installed in the drawing will be displayed in a list box in the upper-left corner of this dialog box. A specific light in this list can be selected for modification or deletion by clicking on its name or by using the Select button (as explained below).

- Modify

This button brings up a dialog box for modifying the selected light. Double-clicking the name of the light has the same effect as selecting the Modify button.

- Delete

  Pressing this button will delete the selected light. An alert box will ask you to confirm the action.

- Select

  When you press this button, AutoCAD will temporarily dismiss the Lights dialog box and issue a command line prompt asking you to select a light. Select one light by picking a point on the block AutoCAD has inserted at its location. The Lights dialog box will reappear with the name of the light in the list box highlighted.

- New

  Press this button to create a new point, spot, or distant light. AutoCAD will replace the Lights dialog box with one appropriate for the type of light specified in the drop-down list box that is to the right of the New button.

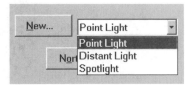

- North Location

  AutoCAD uses the metaphor of compass directions when aiming distant lights, and by default north points in the WCS Y axis direction. You can change that by pressing this button. Auto-CAD will display a dialog box named North Location, in which you can specify another direction on the X-Y plane as north, or specify that the Y axis of a saved UCS will be used rather than the Y axis of the WCS.

- Ambient Light

  This cluster of buttons, edit boxes, and sliders is for control-ling the intensity and color of ambient light. Use the edit box labeled Intensity, or the slider just below the edit box, to set the intensity of ambient light. Its minimum allowed value is 0, its maximum value is 1, and its default value is 0.30.

  You can use any one of three methods in setting the color of ambient light. One method is to specify values, ranging from 0 to 1, for the red, green, and blue color components either by entering them in the edit boxes or by using the sliders. Another method is to click the Select Custom Color button. This will bring up a dialog box titled Color that has forty-eight basic colors shown in image tiles for you to choose from, along with a large image tile showing blended bands of colors from which you can pick a point to specify a color. The third way to specify ambient light color is to press Select from the ACI button. This will cause the same dialog box used by the DDCOLOR command, titled Select Color, to be dis-played for you to use in specifying one of the 255 colors in the AutoCAD Color Index (ACI). The default color of ambient light is white.

Point Light

AutoCAD will display a dialog box titled New Point Light when you create a point light, and it will display a dialog box titled Modify Point Light when you modify an existing point light. These two dialog boxes are the same, except for their title.

- Light Name

  Use this edit box to enter the name of the
  new light or change the name of an
  existing light. Each light must have a name
  that has no more than eight characters.
  Spaces, asterisks, and question marks are
  not allowed in names.

- Intensity

  The relative brightness of the point light is
  controlled through this edit box. You can
  enter values directly or with the slider
  below the edit box. The maximum intensity
  allowed depends on the light's attenuation
  and on the drawing extents.

  ○ When attenuation is none, maximum
    intensity is 1.

  ○ When attenuation is Inverse Linear, maximum intensity is equal to one-half the distance
    between the coordinates in the **extmin** and **extmax** system variables.

  ○ When attenuation is Inverse Square, maximum intensity is equal to one-fourth the square
    of the distance between the coordinates in the **extmin** and **extmax** system variables.

- Position

  The two buttons in this cluster are related to the point coordinates of the light's location.
  When you press the button labeled Show, AutoCAD will display the coordinates of the
  light's location in an information box. You can change the location of the point light by
  pressing the Modify button. AutoCAD will temporarily dismiss the dialog box and issue a
  command line prompt for you to specify a new location. You may use any point selection
  method. Initially, AutoCAD places the point light in the center of the viewport.

- Color

  This cluster of buttons and sliders for setting the color of the point light is the same as the
  one in the main Lights dialog box for setting the color of ambient light. The default color of
  point lights is white.

- Attenuation

  These three radio buttons control the type of attenuation—the light intensity falloff rate—
  for the point light.

- Shadows

  The check box and button in this cluster control
  whether the light will cast shadows, as well as its parameters for casting shadows. To enable shadows, click
  the check box labeled Shadows On. When you press
  the Shadows Options button, AutoCAD will display a
  dialog box titled Shadows Options.

414

When the Shadow Volumes/Ray Traced Shadows box is checked, AutoCAD will use volumetric shadows when Photo Real rendering is in effect and ray traced shadows when Photo Raytrace rendering is in effect. Both of these shadow types make sharp-edged shadows. When that check box is cleared, AutoCAD will use shadow maps, which make shadows having blurred edges. You can control the accuracy of the shadows through the Shadow Map Size pull-down list box, and you can control the relative fuzziness of their edges through the Shadow Softness edit box and slider. Generally, the default settings give satisfactory results.

The Shadow Bounding Objects button is available only when shadow maps are being used. When you click this button, AutoCAD will temporarily dismiss the dialog boxes and issue a command line prompt for you to select the objects that are to cast shadows. The light will not cast shadows for objects that are not selected.

Distant Light

When you install a new distant light, AutoCAD will display a dialog box titled New Distant Light, and when you modify an existing distant light, AutoCAD will display a dialog box titled Modify Distant Light. Except for their titles, these two dialog boxes are the same.

- Light Name

  Use this edit box to enter the name of the new light or to change the name of an existing light. Names cannot have more than eight characters and cannot contain spaces, asterisks, or question marks.

- Intensity

  Set the intensity of the distant light with the slider or by entering a value in the edit box. The maximum intensity allowed is 1. Distant light intensity cannot be attenuated.

- Color

  Set the color of the distant light through the buttons, edit boxes, and sliders in this cluster. See the discussion for setting the color of ambient light in the main Lights dialog box for a description of this cluster. The default light color is white.

- Shadows

  See the discussion of point lights for a description of the options available in this cluster.

- Azimuth/Altitude

  These two parameters are used to aim the distant light. Azimuth is the light's horizontal angle from north, while altitude is its vertical angle from the X-Y plane. By default, north is in the direction of the WCS Y axis, but you can change it through the North Location dialog box accessed through the Lights dialog box. You can set azimuth and altitude by entering values in their edit boxes, by picking a point within the image tiles, or by moving the sliders located below the image tiles. A negative altitude is allowed, but you must enter it in the edit box. Initially AutoCAD aims the light in the current viewing direction.

- Light Source Vector

  The values in these three edit boxes are the coordinates of a direction vector. The distant light points in the same direction as that of a line drawn from the direction vector coordinates to the UCS origin. If you press the Modify button, AutoCAD will temporarily dismiss the dialog box and issue command line prompts for two points:

```
Enter light direction TO <current>: (Specify a point.)
Enter light direction FROM <current>: (Specify a point.)
```

  The light will point in the direction from the second point to the first point. In these prompts, *current* is the actual word used—AutoCAD does not display the current target and direction vector points. You may use any method to specify the points. Relative coordinates are often useful for specifying the location of the second point.

- Sun Angle Calculator

  When you press this button, AutoCAD will display the Sun Angle Calculator dialog box for you to use in finding the angle of the sun for a specific date, time, latitude, and longitude. The azimuth and altitude of the distant light will be set to correspond to the sun's angle.

  The Geographic Location button in this dialog box brings up a dialog box that enables you to set the latitude and longitude by selecting the name of a city from a list or by picking a point on a map in an image tile. Most regions of the world are included.

Spotlight

AutoCAD displays a dialog box titled New Spotlight when you install a new spotlight, and it displays a dialog box titled Modify Spotlight when you modify an existing one. Except for their titles, these two dialog boxes are the same.

- Light Name

  Enter the name of the new light or change the name of an existing light through this edit box. Light names can have up to eight characters. Spaces, asterisks and question marks are not allowed in light names.

- Intensity

  This parameter controls the relative brightness of the spotlight. You can specify intensity by entering a value in the edit box or by moving the slider below the edit box. The maximum intensity allowed is dependent on the light's attenuation and on the drawing extents.

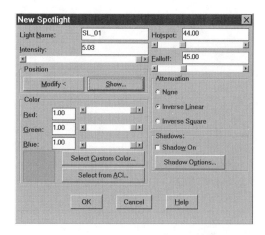

° When attenuation is none, maximum intensity is 1.

° When attenuation is Inverse Linear, maximum intensity is equal to one-half the distance between the coordinates in the **extmin** and **extmax** system variables.

° When attenuation is Inverse Square, maximum intensity is equal to one-fourth the square of the distance between the coordinates in the **extmin** and **extmax** system variables.

- Position

Two points are required for positioning spotlights. One is the location of the spotlight, and the other is the location of its target. When you press the button labeled Show, AutoCAD will display the coordinates of the light and of its target in a read-only dialog box.

You can change these points by pressing the Modify button. AutoCAD will temporarily dismiss the dialog box and issue command line prompts for you to specify two points:

```
Enter light target <current>: (Specify a point.)
Enter light location <current>: (Specify a point.)
```

In these prompts, *current* is the actual word used—AutoCAD does not display the current light target and location points. You may use any method to specify the points. Relative coordinates are often useful for specifying the location of the second point. Initially, Auto-CAD places the target on the X-Y plane in the center of the current viewport and places the light about 1 unit away on the line of sight toward the viewer.

- Color

This cluster of buttons and sliders for setting the color of the spotlight is the same as the one in the main Lights dialog box for setting the color of ambient light. The default color of spotlights is white.

- Hotspot

Set the edge-to-edge taper angle of the spotlight's interior cone of uniform light by entering a value within this edit box or by moving the associated slider. The angle can range from 0 to 160 degrees, but it cannot exceed the falloff cone angle.

- Falloff

Specify the edge-to-edge taper angle of the spotlight's full cone of light by entering a number in this edit box or by moving the slider below the edit box. The angle can range from 0 (which effectively turns the light off) to 160 degrees. If the angle of the hotspot cone equals the angle of the falloff cone, the edge of the light beam will be sharp.

- Attenuation

  The three radio buttons in this cluster control the type of attenuation—the light intensity falloff rate—for the spotlight.

- Shadows

  The controls for spotlight shadows work the same as those for point lights, except that the Shadow Casting Option is not available for spotlights.

Notes:

- Once a light has been installed in a drawing, AutoCAD's HIDE command no longer works.

Using Scenes

A scene is the association of a view with one or more lights. If you create a scene when no named views exist and no lights are installed, the scene consists of the current view and all of the lights (even if none exist). However, to obtain any benefit from scenes, at least one named view should exist and at least one light should be installed. Views for scenes are created through AutoCAD's VIEW command. (Since VIEW is a 2D command that has long been part of AutoCAD, we will not describe it.)

Once a scene has been created, its name will be shown in the list box that is labeled Scenes to Render in the dialog box used by the RENDER command. You can render a scene—using the current viewport, the render window, or a file as a destination—even if the view for the scene is not currently displayed.

Command:	SCENE
Purpose:	This command associates a view with one or more lights. Scenes are named, and you can render a specific scene even if the view for the scene is not currently shown.

Initiate with:

- On the command line enter SCENE.
- From the View pull-down menu, select Render, then Scene.
- Select the Scene button from the Render toolbar.

Options:

The initial dialog box used by the SCENE command displays the names of existing scenes in a list box. A scene named *NONE* will always be included. This scene consists of the current view and all of the existing lights. If no light has been installed, AutoCAD will use a single distant light pointed in the viewport's view direction during renderings.

418

Press the button labeled New to create a new scene. To modify an existing scene, click its name in the list box, then click the button labeled Modify. To delete a scene, click its name, then click the button labeled Delete.

The buttons labeled New and Modify lead to dialog boxes that are identical except for their titles. Use the edit box in the upper-right corner of this dialog box to enter or modify the name of the scene. Scene names must be eight or fewer characters long. They cannot contain spaces, question marks, slashes, or asterisks.

The names of all existing views will be displayed in the left-hand list box. A view named *CURRENT*, representing the view in the current viewport, will always be included. The names of all installed lights will be shown in the right-hand list box. This list will include the name *ALL*, which represents all of the installed lights, or the default distant light if none have been installed.

You may select only one view from the left-hand list box for each scene, but you can have any number of lights from the right-hand list box to be part of the scene. To select multiple lights, hold your computer's Control key down as you pick light names. Renderings of the scene will use the scene's view and only those lights that have been specified for the scene.

419

Rendering Materials

W hether objects look real in renderings depends largely on the properties of their surfaces. Collectively, the properties that have been assigned to a surface are referred to as a rendering material, and we will explore rendering materials extensively in this chapter. Specifically, this chapter will

- describe the properties, or attributes as they are generally called, that can be assigned to a material;
- explain how bitmap images can be incorporated into rendering materials;
- tell you how to adjust the scale and location of bitmap images to accommodate various geometric shapes and orientations;
- discuss the mechanics of attaching and managing materials;
- help you gain experience in creating and working with materials through three hands-on exercises;
- describe how to assemble and save a collection of rendering materials.

An AutoCAD rendering material is a set of properties assigned to a surface object for controlling the appearance of the object during a rendering. If, for example, you create a material that is shiny and red, every surface object—such as a polygon mesh, a 3D face, or a 3D solid—that you attach that material to will appear to be shiny and red when it is rendered. AutoCAD has a large assortment of properties (or attributes, as AutoCAD often calls them) that you can incorporate in materials, and we will spend much of this chapter describing them and explaining how you can use them.

Materials are created through the RMAT command. Similar to the LIGHT command that we discussed in the previous chapter, RMAT is a flexible command that uses numerous dialog boxes in defining a material. Since creating a material can be an involved process, each material is given a unique name, and you can save a material in a file so that it can be retrieved and used in other drawings. AutoCAD refers to these files of saved materials as material libraries and has a command, MATLIB, for managing them.

For simulating objects that have texture or patterns—such as wooden boards, brick walls, shingled roofs, galvanized steel, and tiled floors—you can include images from bitmap files in the properties of a material. Since bitmapped images are basically 2D rectangles, you will often need to adjust them to fit surfaces that are cylindrical or spherical and to fit planar surfaces that are not aligned with the coordinate system axes. These adjustments are made through the SETUV command.

Menus and toolbar buttons for materials

Material Attributes

Every material is created by assigning values to certain properties or attributes. Attributes affecting colors allow you to specify their color as well as their value. Descriptions of these attributes, along with the meaning of their values, are given in the following paragraphs.

Color

Although all objects in the real world, except for those that are completely transparent, have color, their color is seldom uniform, especially if they are not planar. Their main color will be darkened on surfaces that are inclined to incoming light beams, and surfaces directly facing incoming light beams may reflect the color of the light source. Because of these surface color variations, AutoCAD has three different attributes for controlling material color:

- *Color.* In the dialog boxes for setting material attributes, the name of the main color of the material is called simply Color. You can assign virtually any color you wish to this attribute. The finish of the color will be diffuse, or matte, similar to that of a flat wall paint. The relative brightness of surfaces having this base color depends on the value assigned to color, as well as the surface's angle to incoming light beams. (We described this phenomenon in the previous chapter when we discussed the properties of rendering lighting.) You can assign color a value ranging from 0 to 1.

- *Ambient.* This is the base color of shaded areas. You can use an ambient color that is different from the material's main color. You can also control its relative brightness by assigning it a value between 0 and 1.

- *Reflection.* When you look directly into the light beams that are reflected from a surface, you will indirectly see the color of the light source, as shown in the diagram below. As a result, areas of reflected light on a surface may have a different color than the object's main color. To simulate this, you can assign a color to areas of reflection on a surface that correspond to the light's color. Since most light is white, you will often use white as a reflection color. This attribute is most noticeable on rounded and curved surfaces. If, on the other hand, you want a surface to have a diffuse, matte finish, you will generally use the same color, or a similar color, for the reflected light that you use for the material's main color.

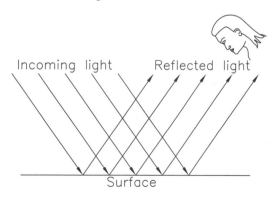

Incoming light   Reflected light

Surface

421

The reflection attribute also enables you to give a mirrorlike finish to a surface. This is handled through an on-off toggle in the dialog boxes that create and modify materials. When the mirror toggle is checked, the material will cause surfaces to which it is attached to reflect other objects in a rendering. Raytraced rendering must be used to enable mirrorlike reflections. Similar to the other two attributes for color, you can assign reflection a value ranging from 0 to 1.

Roughness

If a surface is perfectly smooth, all light beams will be reflected from the surface at the same angle at which they struck the surface, as illustrated in the previous figure. Consequently, you will see just a narrow band of light reflecting from a cylinder that is highly reflective, and you will see just a small spot of reflected light from a highly reflective round surface. The

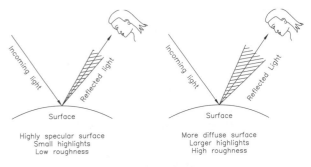

highlights caused by reflected light are small but intense on highly reflective surfaces. Such extremely smooth, reflective surfaces are called *specular surfaces*. Few surfaces, however, are perfect reflectors, and some of the reflected light from them will be scattered. Their highlights will be larger, but less intense than those from highly specular surfaces.

AutoCAD lets you control the relative degree of specular reflection through an attribute called *roughness*. You can assign a value ranging from 0 to 1 to the roughness attribute. Small roughness values result in small, bright highlights that make the surface look shiny. Large roughness values result in large highlights that blend with the surface's main color, and the surface appears to have a matte finish.

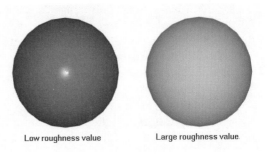

Low roughness value   Large roughness value.

Transparency

When light beams pass through an object rather than reflect from its surface, the object is transparent. Many objects are semitransparent—some light beams pass through the object, while others are reflected from its surface. AutoCAD allows you to set the transparency of a material to a value between zero and one. Objects assigned a transparency of 0 will be opaque, while objects having a transparency of 1 will be completely transparent; they will not even be visible in a rendering.

Refraction

Light beams bend when they enter a transparent material, and they return to their original direction when they exit on its far side. This phenomenon, which is called *refraction*, causes objects viewed through a transparent material to be offset or distorted. The degree to which the light beams bend is a material property called *refraction index*.

You can set the degree of refraction for a rendering material by giving the refraction attribute a value other than 1. When a material has a refraction of 1.0, the light beams do not bend as they pass through a transparent material. Refraction values greater or less than 1 cause objects on the opposite side of a transparent material to be shifted, and the degree to which they are shifted increases as the deviation of refraction from 1.0 increases. Raytraced rendering must be used for the refraction attribute to have an effect.

Mapping

The material attributes we have just described work great for materials that have uniform surfaces and color, but they cannot simulate wood, marble, wallpaper, or other materials that have texture or patterns. Therefore, AutoCAD's renderer lets you supplement a material's attributes with bitmap images. This use of bitmap images is often referred to as *mapping*, and the images themselves are called *maps*. Photo Real or Photo Raytrace rendering must be used to enable mapping. Some sophisticated rendering and animation programs, such as 3D Studio, also support bitmaps, and AutoCAD's maps can be exported to some of them.

AutoCAD comes with a good supply of bitmap files that you can use in rendering materials. They are all in the TGA bitmap file format, although you can also use images in the bitmap file formats of GIF, PCX, BMP, TIF, GIF, and JPG.

If you used the default AutoCAD 2000 installation folder names, all of the bitmap files for mapping will be in the Program Files\Acad2000\Textures folder. Unfortunately, if you used the typical AutoCAD installation, there are likely to be only three files in that folder. If that is the case in your system, you should copy all of the files that are in the Acad\Textures folder on the AutoCAD 2000 CD-ROM to your computer. This will give you more than 140 bitmap files to work with. Many of the files in this folder—such as the ones of a TV set, an aquarium and the face of a chimpanzee—will be of little value to you. Others, though, will be useful for materials and backgrounds. The names of the files you are most likely to use are listed in Table 19-1, found at the end of this chapter.

You should also find the file render.mli on the AutoCAD 2000 CD-ROM and copy it to your computer's Program Files\Acad2000\Support folder. This file, which has a size of 47KB, will be in the Acad\Support folder on the CD-ROM, and it will replace a file that has a size of 2KB. It contains about 150 ready-made materials in a materials library that you can use for your models. We will refer to this materials library later in this chapter when we discuss the MATLIB command.

Types of Mapping

AutoCAD supports four different types of mapping. Each type serves a specific purpose, and the interface of each type is through a specific material attribute.

Texture Maps

Texture maps make surfaces appear to have patterns or texture. Wood, concrete, tile floors, shingled roofs, rusted or oxidized metal, and furniture fabric are just a few of the materials that can be simulated by texture maps. You do, of course, need to have a bitmap file with a suitable image. Texture maps are connected to a material through the color attribute, and since texture maps are used so often, AutoCAD has added the word *pattern* to the color attribute in its dialog boxes for creating and modifying materials.

Reflection Maps

Reflection maps simulate mirrorlike reflections on shiny surfaces, such as the reflection of clouds on a polished automobile hood. They are not the same as the mirror reflections you can have in raytraced renderings. Their interface with the material is through the reflection attribute. Three conditions are necessary for reflection maps to render well. First, the surface must be curved; second, the value of the material's roughness attribute must be set to a low number; and third, the bitmap used must have a relatively high resolution.

Hemisphere without
reflection map

Hemisphere with reflection
map of clouds

Opacity Maps

Opacity maps are for making transparent areas on surfaces. When rendered, pure white areas of an opacity map will be completely opaque, black areas will be completely transparent, and the transparency of gray shades will be proportional to their darkness. Colors take on their equivalent grayscale values.

The figure on the right shows the image of a typical opacity map. It is simply six black squares on a white rectangle, but when it is projected onto a 3D face, it makes holes in the face, as illustrated in the rendering in the next figure. The image seen through this window is from another bitmap file that is used as a rendering background.

Although AutoCAD supplies almost no bitmap files that are suitable for opacity maps, it is not difficult to custom make your

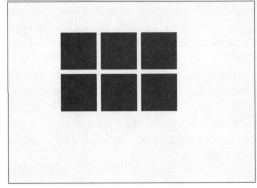

424

own for simulating the panes of a window or a hole through a surface. One way to make them is to use a white AutoCAD background and black as an object color as you make planar surface objects in the shape of the holes you want. Circles make good round holes, 3D faces work well as rectangular holes, and regions can be used for more complex shapes. When the objects have been drawn and arranged as you want them, invoke the SHADE command so that the surfaces will become black objects on a white background, then save the viewport image with the SAVEIMG command. A paint program can be helpful in touchingup and cropping the image, but it is not necessary. The opacity file for the image and rendering shown above was made using this method.

Bump Maps

AutoCAD uses the brightness values of pixels in bump map images to create the illusion of a slight change in height; as if the surface were embossed. A bump map is always used in conjunction with a texture map.

Sometimes, the same bitmap file is even used for both the texture map and the bump map. By themselves, bump map images are rendered black and white, even if the image in the bitmap file has colors. Consequently, the bitmap blend of the bump map is always set to a low value—usually to 0.10 or less. In the rendering in the figure on the right, the material for the bottom half of the brick wall uses a straight texture map, while the material for the top half of the wall uses the same texture map plus a bump map. The added realism is noticeable, even in this grayscale illustration.

Tiling and Cropping

When a bitmap image is projected onto a surface, it will, by default, adjust its size and shape to completely fill the surface. In the figure below, for instance, the bitmap image attached to the cylinder on the left is stretched so that it completely wraps around the cylinder. As a result, the image is distorted. You can, though, adjust the scale and the insert point of the bitmap image so that it fits the surface better, as shown on the other two cylinders. When the image is reduced in size, as it is on these two cylinders, you can have the image either repeated as many times as necessary to completely fill the surface, as shown on the middle cylinder, or you can have the image displayed just once, as shown on the right-hand cylinder. The repeated image effect is called *tiling*, while the single image effect is called *cropping*.

Mapping Projections

Bitmap images are 2D rectangular objects, yet in a rendering they are often projected onto surfaces that are curved and rounded and surfaces that are triangular-shaped or have wavy edges. They are also projected onto surfaces that are oriented at odd angles to the principal planes of the WCS.

Mapping projection and scale is handled by AutoCAD's SETUV command. SETUV also allows you to rotate an image and to move its insert point. The letters *U* and *V* in the name of this command refer to the labels used for the mapping coordinates. These coordinates are roughly comparable to the X and Y coordinates of the WES and UCS, but their orientation is independent of them. Furthermore, since the U and V directions correspond to the edges of the surface being mapped, they are not necessarily perpendicular to one another, or even straight.

The SETUV command has provisions for three projection types: planar, cylindrical, and spherical. When the surface you are mapping does not match any of these basic geometric shapes, you must pick the projection type that comes closest to the shape of your surface. These projection types are described in the following paragraphs.

Planar Projection

If an image is projected onto a plane that is parallel with the WCS X-Y plane and has proportions similar to those of the image, no adjustments will be needed, unless you want to change the scale of the projected image. On the other hand, if the planar surface is not parallel with the WCS X-Y plane, you will have to use the SETUV command to tell AutoCAD what the orientation of the surface is. Moreover, if the plane's proportions are different from those of the image, you will have to also adjust the scale of the image (unless the distortion of it does not matter). You can adjust the scale of an image one of two ways—through the RMAT command for the material or through the SETUV command for the surface object.

In the next figure, no adjustments are needed when the bitmap image of a square checkerboard is projected onto a square 3D face that is lying on the WCS X-Y plane. However, when that same image is projected onto the rectangular 3D face that is parallel with the WCS Y-Z

plane, you must use SETUV to tell Auto-CAD what the orientation of the surface is. You must also do that for the polygon mesh surface in this figure that is parallel with the WCS Z-X plane.

Neither of the vertical surfaces in this rendering are square. And, since no adjustments were made in the scale of the image projected onto the rectangular 3D face, the image is compressed in the vertical direction. The scale of the image projected onto the polygon mesh, however, was set to be half-size in the vertical direction. Consequently, the size and shape of each square of the checkerboard on that surface matches those of the checkerboard on the square 3D face that is on the WCS X-Y plane. Notice, also, that the image is simply clipped at the curved edge of the polygon mesh rather than being distorted to conform to it.

Cylindrical Projection

When a bitmap is projected onto a cylinder, the image is wrapped around the cylinder. You do, however, have to tell AutoCAD, through the SETUV command, that the surface is cylindrical.

Furthermore, if the axis of the cylinder is not pointing in the Z axis direction, you must also tell Auto-CAD how the cylinder is oriented.

The figure on the right shows a rendering of four different cylinders, each with the same square bitmap image attached as a texture map. The cylinders are all surface models, with the texture map attached to just the circumference of the cylinder (not to the ends of the cylinders).

Notice the following about the cylinders in this figure:

- AutoCAD was not told that the cylinder in the upper-right corner is a cylinder. Consequently, the image that is projected on it is distorted beyond recognition.
- The scale of the image projected onto the cylinder in the upper-left corner was not changed from its one-to-one correspondence, and therefore, the image is elongated as it wraps around the circumference of the cylinder.
- The scale of the image projected onto the cylinder in the lower-left corner, however, was set so that its size around the cylinder is about one-third its size along the cylinder. As a result, the image comes closer to matching its original square shape.
- The scale of the image on the cylinder in the lower-right corner was adjusted in both directions to achieve an even different effect. Moreover, since the axis of this cylinder is not parallel with the Z-axis, its orientation had to be specified as well.
- Although the object in the center is not a true cylinder, that is its closest geometric shape. The image is distorted, and there isn't anything you can really do about it. This has more to do with conflicting geometries than limitations of AutoCAD's renderer.

Spherical Projection

If you do not tell AutoCAD that an image is attached to a sphere, the image will be projected onto the top and bottom halves of the sphere, as shown on the left-most sphere. When you specify through SETUV that the surface is a sphere, though, the image will be compressed to a point at the poles of the sphere, and at the same time it will be stretched to fit around the sphere's equator, as shown on the right-most sphere in the figure.

Images mapped onto spheres generally look better when they are scaled down in relative size, as shown on the other two spheres—one has been tiled, while the other has been cropped.

When images are mapped onto a sphere, AutoCAD assumes by default that the pole of the sphere is parallel with the Z axis, but you can specify another direction.

Template Materials

Bitmap images do not work very well on 3D solid objects. AutoCAD considers the entire surface of the 3D solid to be a single surface object and attempts to map the image on all sides of the

solid. Consequently, while the image may be satisfactory on
one face of the 3D solid, it will be severely distorted on
most of its other faces.

AutoCAD, however, does support three special rendering
materials that do work well on 3D solids. They are generally
called *template* materials, although AutoCAD sometimes
refers to them as *solid* materials. The three materials simulate wood, granite, and marble. The figure on the right
shows an example of a material based on the wood template when it is applied to a 3D solid.

Although these template materials look much like
bitmap images, their patterns are generated at the time of rendering—they are not based on
bitmap files. One consequence of this is that template materials cannot be exported to other
programs. Materials using these templates are created through an option of the RMAT
command.

Creating Materials

If no material is attached to an object, AutoCAD uses one that is named *GLOBAL*, which has
its attributes set as follows:

Attribute	Value	Color
Color	0.70	By ACI
Ambient	0.10	Same as that for Color
Reflection	0.20	Same as that for Color
Roughness	0.50	
Transparency	0.00	
Refraction	1.00	

No bitmaps are used with the *GLOBAL* material. When the color attribute is set to By ACI
(which stands for AutoCAD Color Index), the rendering material takes the color of the surface
object's AutoCAD color. This default material is opaque and has a slightly glossy appearance.

Actually, the number values for the color, ambient, and reflection attributes have little effect
on the material's appearance, and you can generally set all three of them to 1.00. If you want
the material to have a matte finish, set roughness to a high value, such as 1.00, and set the
color of the reflection attribute to one that is either similar to that of the color attribute or one
that has a dull, graylike hue. If, on the other hand, you want the material to be shiny, set
roughness to a value below 0.50 and set the color of the reflection attribute to white, or
another bright color.

To create a transparent material, set the value of transparency somewhere between 0.50 and
0.80, depending upon how transparent you want the surface to be. If transparency is set to
1.00, you will not be able to see the object that the material is attached to.

You will use the refraction attribute only in special circumstances. While you can set refraction to any value between 0 and 100, those that are very close to 1.00 produce the best results,
and you may find that values less than 1.00 (in the 0.80 to 0.90 range) work better than values

greater than 1.00. When refraction is set to 1.00 (its default value), no light refraction occurs. You must use Photo Raytraced rendering for the refraction attribute to have any effect.

You will also use the mirror toggle only in special circumstances. When you want the material to reflect other objects, click the Mirror check box. This check box is available only through the reflection attribute. Furthermore, Photo Raytraced rendering must be used for the objects to actually have mirrorlike reflections. If an object does have a mirrorlike material attached, it will not reflect other objects when Photo Real rendering is being used. It will, however, reflect the color of the background, which can be undesirable.

The vast majority of your maps will be texture maps. Texture maps are incorporated into a material through the Color/Pattern attribute. If the texture map is the only thing that is important for the material, you can leave the settings of the other attributes at their defaults. Occasionally, though, you may want to have some color show through the bitmap image. You will then assign a color to the color attribute, and perhaps to the reflection attribute as well, and make the image (not the material) somewhat transparent by reducing its bitmap blend value from its default setting of 1.00. You will also want to give the material some color if you are going to crop the texture map. Otherwise, the unmapped areas on the surface will be rendered in the object's color.

Bump maps are very good for adding realism to materials for stones, bricks, and embossed metal. You will use them in conjunction with a texture map from the same bitmap file, or from a companion file. The bitmap blend for the texture map will be 1.00, while the bitmap blend for the bump map will be 0.10, or even less. See Table 19-1 at the end of this chapter for a list of files supplied by AutoCAD that are suitable for bump maps.

Only rarely will you use reflection maps. Nevertheless, you should keep them in mind for the time when you do need one to simulate a reflection on a rounded surface. If you want to use an image to simulate a reflection on a planar surface, such as a mirror or a window, you will use a texture map.

You will not use opacity maps often either, and when you do need to use one (to make a hole in a surface), you will generally have to make your own bitmap file (using the method we described earlier) for the opacity map.

Most problems in mapping are related to having the image conform to the shape and size of the surface. To solve these problems, you will use the SETUV command extensively.

3D solid objects do not work well with bitmaps. AutoCAD considers their surface to be a single object, and the bitmap image is projected onto all sides of the solid. The image may be recognizable on some faces of the solid, but on many faces it will be just a blur. You can, though, use the template materials to add patterns to 3D solids during renderings. These are truly 3D images, but you are restricted to only three different materials—granite, marble, and wood. Also, they are not as realistic looking as are bitmap images based on photographs of real materials.

Although there is nothing inherently difficult in the individual steps for creating materials and for attaching them to objects, the number of materials and the number of objects involved can make the process complicated. You should keep your rendering materials as simple as possible, and you should match them to the scale of your renderings. For instance, there is no point in creating a complicated material, complete with a reflection map, for the knob of a door handle that will be seen 40 feet away. Also, you must be organized when you work with materials, and you must keep track of which materials are attached to which objects.

Exercise One

This exercise will show you how to project a bitmap image onto a cylindrical surface and how to create tiled and cropped images. Start a new drawing. Its initial setup is not important, and you are not likely to save the drawing file when you have finished the exercise.

Before we start with the rendering material, we will create a surface model cylinder to be used for the rendering. Draw a circle having a radius of 1 unit, and place a copy of that circle 1 1/2 units in the positive Z direction. Then, use any method you like to set an SE isometric view. Set the value of the **surftab1** system variable to 18, and finally, use the RULESURF command to create a surface between the two circles.

You may want to divide the AutoCAD graphics area into four viewports so you can compare the results from different material settings.

Start the RMAT command and begin a new standard material. Assign any name you like to the material. Make sure that the Color/Pattern attribute is checked and click the Find File button to locate the file named 3d.tga. It will probably be the very first file in the folder \Program Files\Acad2000\Textures.

When you locate this file, double click on it to associate the file with your material and restore the New Standard Material dialog box. If you use the preview panel with a cube, you will see that the image in this file is simply the characters *3D* on a red background. Click the OK button to return to the Materials dialog box. If the name of your new material is not highlighted in the Materials list box, highlight it by clicking once on its name. Click the Attach button, and pick one of the vertical surface mesh lines when AutoCAD asks you to select objects to attach your material to. Be certain that you do not include either of the circles in your selection set. Press the Enter key to return to the Materials dialog box and press the OK button to end the RMAT command.

Start the RENDER command. Be certain that Photo Real is the rendering type, and render the current view. Your rendering will probably resemble the one shown in the figure on the right. The image is not at all evident in the rendering.

To fix the image, start the SETUV command. Select the tube surface when you are prompted to select objects, and press the Enter key. When the Mapping dialog box appears, you will notice that the bitmap projection is planar, which does not match the shape of our surface. Click the radio button labeled Cylindrical, then click the OK button to exit the SETUV command. When you render the scene this time, your model should look similar to the one shown in the next figure. The characters in the image are now evident, although they are distorted.

Start the SETUV command, and again pick the surface mesh when you are prompted to select objects. This time, click the Adjust Coordinates button in the Mapping dialog box. (Notice that the dialog box now reports that the projection is cylindrical.) A dialog box titled Adjust Cylindrical Projection will appear. If the axis of our tube was not pointed in the Z direction, we would use this dialog box to make some changes, but we are just passing through now, and we do not need to change anything. Therefore, click the button labeled Adjust Bitmap to move to a dialog box titled Adjust Object Bitmap Placement.

This dialog box looks like and performs the same functions as the Adjust Material Bitmap Placement dialog box of the RMAT command. The difference is that one controls the global parameters of a material, while the other controls the bitmap image parameters for specific objects.

Set the bitmap Scale in the U direction to a value of 6.0 and the Scale in the V direction to 2.0. This will cause the image to be repeated six times around the tube and two times along its length. Also, set the Offset in the V direction to a value of 0.25. Since AutoCAD starts the bitmap in the middle of the tube's length, this offset in the V direction will prevent the image from being clipped at the ends of the tube. Click three OK buttons to exit the SETUV command. Your rendered tube should now look like the one in the upper-right figure.

The image in this rendering is tiled; that is, it is repeated as often as necessary to completely fill the surface. For the last rendering of this cylinder, we will crop the image so that it appears just once. Start the SETUV command, pick the tube, click the Adjust Coordinates button, and click the Adjust Bitmap button to bring up the Adjust Object Bitmap Placement dialog box. Do not change the U and V scales, but return the V Offset to 0 so that the image will be centered along the length of the tube. Finally, click the radio button labeled Crop, then click three OK buttons to leave the SETUV command. This time, your rendering should be similar to the one shown in the second figure.

The bitmap image looks as if it were a label on a can. Autodesk sometimes refers to cropped images as the *decal effect*. The rest of the surfaces are rendered in their object color, which on our model is white.

That finishes our work in this exercise. You may, however, want to further experiment with the model and the material on your own. One thing that you might try is to rotate the cropped image. This is done through the SETUV command's Adjust Cylindrical Coordinates dialog box, and it moves the image around the circumference of the cylinder. Rotating it -45 degrees, for instance, will make the image face the SE isometric view direction.

Exercise Two

In this exercise, we will experiment with one of AutoCAD's template materials. These are useful for adding patterns to materials for 3D solid objects. Start a new drawing. This is not going to be a drawing that you will want to keep, and its initial setup is not important.

Our model will be that of a short wooden beam, and the easiest way to make it is with the following command line input:

```
Command: BOX (Enter)
Specify corner of box or [CEnter]: (Enter)
Specify corner or [Cube/Length]: 6,24,4 (Enter)
```

That's all there is to making the beam. Now switch to an SE isometric viewpoint. In the wireframe viewing mode, your model should look like the one in the figure on the right.

Start the RMAT command. In the Materials dialog box's drop-down list box below the button labeled New, highlight Wood and click the New button. A dialog box titled New Wood Material will be displayed. Give the new material any name you like. The attributes of the material are in a column of radio buttons on the left side of the dialog box. We will change only the Scale attribute, leaving the others at their default settings. Click the Scale button, and enter 0.50 in the edit box labeled Value. Click the OK button to return to the main Materials dialog box.

Make certain that the name of your material is highlighted in the Materials list box, and click the Attach button. When AutoCAD asks you to select objects to attach your material to, pick an edge of the 3D solid and press the Enter key. When the Materials dialog box reappears, press the OK button to end the RMAT command.

Begin the RENDER command. Set the rendering type to Photo Real, and render the current viewport. Your rendering of the wooden beam should look like the one in the figure on the right, and it's probably not what you expected. It is highly unlikely that a 24″ by 6″ by 4″ wooden beam would ever be like this one. In real lumber, the grain of the wood invariably lies along the length of the beam or board, and the circular growth rings occur on the ends of the beam or board.

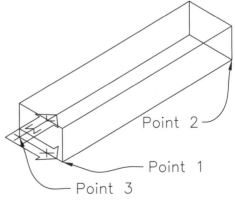

The problem in our rendering occurs because of the directions AutoCAD uses in mapping the wood pattern on the model. AutoCAD always places the end view of the growth rings in its wood template material on a plane that is parallel with the V-W plane of the bitmap projection coordinate system, and the grain of the wood extends in the U direction. By default on wood material, the U projection direction is in the WCS X direction, V is in the WCS Y direction, and W is in the WCS Z direction. We just need to change the U and V directions relative to the WCS.

Start the SETUV command, and pick the 3D solid when you are prompted to select an object. When the Mapping dialog box appears, click the Projection radio button that is labeled Solid, then click the Adjust Coordinates button.

A dialog box titled Adjust UVW Coordinates will be displayed. In this dialog box, turn the Maintain Aspect Ratio check box off, then click the button labeled Pick Points. The dialog box will disappear, and on the command line you will be prompted to specify three points and a distance.

Using the points shown in the figure on the right, respond to these prompts as follows:

```
Place the origin of the mapper: (Specify point 1)
Place the U axis of the mapper: (Specify point 2)
Place the V axis of the mapper: (Specify point 3)
Length of W axis: 4 (Enter)
```

The Adjust UVW Coordinates dialog box will reappear. Press its OK button, and press the OK button in the Mapping dialog box to end the SETUV command. When you render the current viewport this time, your wooden beam should look similar to the one shown in the next figure. The grain in the wooden beam is now aligned as you would expect it to be.

Point 2

Point 1

Point 3

This finishes the exercise. You may, however, want to experiment further with the model and its material on your own by changing the values of the wood material's attributes to see how they affect the appearance of the rendering.

Exercise Three

In this exercise, you will add materials to the 3D model house you have been working on throughout this book. You last worked on this model in Chapter Eighteen, when you installed some rendering lights. We will divide this exercise in adding materials to the house into three parts. The first part will consist of creating and attaching some standard materials that have only color. In the second part, you will create and attach a material that includes a bump map for making a brick wall. And, in the third part, you will create and attach a material with a texture map simulating roofing shingles.

Part One of Exercise Three

Retrieve file mfe180302.dwg from the CD-ROM that accompanies this book and open it. We will create five standard materials and assign them to layers in the drawing. None of these materials will have bitmap files associated with them. In each material, set the values of the color, ambient, reflection, and roughness attributes to 1.00. Also have the color of the ambient and reflection attributes locked to that of the color attribute. The only differences between these materials will be their color. To establish the color of the color attribute in each material, set its red, green, and blue color components to the values shown below:

Material	Red	Green	Blue
BACKDROP	0.0	0.25	0.0
TRIM	0.35	0.20	0.10
GARAGE_DR	0.55	0.30	0.20
GLASS	0.10	0.10	0.10
SIDING	0.75	0.50	0.40

When you have created these materials, press the By Layer button in the Materials dialog box to bring up the Attach by Layer dialog box. In this dialog box, attach the materials to the layers as follows:

Material Name	Layer(s)
BACKDROP	BACKDROP
TRIM	FRAME_SIL,
	FRAME_WIN,
	FRAME_DOOR,
	FRAME_GAR_DOOR,
	EAVES
GARAGE_DR	DOOR_GAR
GLASS	GLASS
SIDING	SID01

Remember, the procedure to attach a material to a layer, or to several layers, is to highlight one material, along with the layers you want to attach the material to. Then press the Attach button.

Once the materials have been attached, exit the RMAT command, and start the RENDER command. We will use a bitmap image for the background from now on, so press the Background button in the Render dialog box to bring up the Background dialog box. Click the radio button labeled Image, then click the Find File button. The file you want is named cloud.tga. Once you find it, double-click its name to bring it into the Background dialog box. Then click the OK button to restore the Render dialog box. Make certain that Photo Real rendering is in effect and press the Render button to render the current viewport. A grayscale version of the rendering is shown in the figure on the right.

Part Two of Exercise Three

In this part of Exercise Three, you will create a brick material that will be attached to the surfaces below two windows on the front of the house. Start by invoking the VPOINT command with the view rotation angles of 245 degrees from the X axis and 10 degrees from the X-Y plane. In addition to establishing a convenient view direction, this action will turn the perspective viewing mode off, which will allow you to use your pointing device. It will leave you far from the house, though, so you will need to zoom in until the house looks similar to the figure above.

As soon as you have established a good view of this part of the house, you may want to freeze all of the layers in the drawing except for the layer named Brick. Just two 3D faces will then be visible.

Start the RMAT command and start a new standard material. Name the material BRICK_WALL. With the Color/Pattern attribute's radio button checked, press the Find File button. The file you want will be named bmbrick.tga. When you find it, double-click its name to bring it into the New Standard Material dialog box. Leave the Bitmap Blend value for this file set to its default of 1.00.

Next, turn on the Bump Map attribute's radio button. The name of the file you want to associate with this attribute is bmbricb.tga. After you have brought this file into the dialog box, set the value of Bitmap Blend to 0.10. Lastly, click the OK button to return to the main Materials dialog box. Attach this new material to the two 3D faces.

The next step is to adjust the projection and scale of the bitmaps on each of the 3D faces. We will work on the smaller face first.

- Start the SETUV command, and pick an edge on the small 3D face when you are prompted to select objects. When you press the Enter key to complete the selection set, the Mapping dialog box will appear.
- Make certain that the projection type is Planar, and press the Adjust Coordinates button.
- Tell AutoCAD how the plane is oriented by clicking the radio button labeled WCS XZ Plane.
- Click the Adjust Bitmap button.
- In the Adjust Object Bitmap Placement dialog box, set U Scale to 2.25, V Scale to 1.50, and V Offset to 0.05. (Leave U Offset at 0.00.)
- Click three OK buttons to exit the SETUV command.

The the figure on the right shows a grayscale rendering of this 3D face.

Follow the same procedure to adjust the projection and bitmap placement of the images on the larger 3D face. All of its parameters will be the same, except for the U Scale of the image. Set U Scale to a value of 4.50. (This 3D face is twice the length of the other one.) We are now finished with the brick facing, so you can thaw all of the drawing's layers.

Part Three of Exercise Three

Our last task in creating, attaching, and adjusting materials for the house will be to add one that has a texture map of wooden shingles to its roof. Although AutoCAD does supply one bitmap file of roof shingles (it is file ishingl2.tga), it is a small image that doesn't work well when it must cover a large surface. Therefore, we will use one named shing1.tga from the CD-ROM that accompanies this book. See Appendix A for help in locating this file. When you find it, copy it to the folder on your computer that contains your rendering texture files.

Before you begin working on the roof, you may want to freeze all of the layers in the drawing except for the one named ROOF01. The next figure shows a plan view of the roof. Surfaces one, three, and four of the roof are 3D face objects, while surface two is a polygon mesh object (made with the PFACE command).

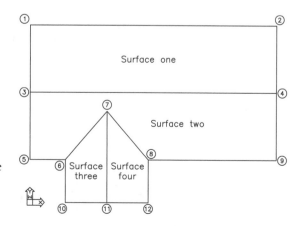

Use the RMAT command to create a new standard material. Name the material SHINGLES. The only attribute you will use in this material will be Color/Pattern. Be certain that its radio button is on, then locate and bring the file shing1.tga into the material as a texture map. Attach that material to the four objects that make up the roof of the house, and exit the RMAT command.

You will have to use the SETUV command four times to set the orientation and scale of the texture map on each surface. Since none of these surfaces are parallel with any of the WCS principal planes, you will have to use the Picked Plane option to establish their orientation. You will also have to set the U and V scale, and the V offset, for each surface. Use the parameters below as a guide. The numbers for the corners of the surfaces correspond to those shown in the previous figure.

Lower Surface	Lower Left	Upper Right	Scale Left	U	Offset V	U	V
One	2	1	4	5.00	2.74	0	0
Two	5	9	3	5.00	2.74	0	0
Three	6	10	7	2.50	2.50	0	0.05
Four	12	8	11	2.50	2.50	0	0.05

When you thaw all of the layers in the drawing, your rendering of the house should resemble the one shown in grayscale in the figure on the right. Rendering will take several minutes.

That finishes this exercise. On the CD-ROM that comes with this book, the surface model house with the materials attached and the bitmap images attached, is in file mfe19305.dwg. To make the file as compatible with as many AutoCAD versions as possible, it was saved in in Release 14 format. Therefore, if you are opening it in AutoCAD 2000, you will need to modify the BRICK_WALL and SHINGLES materials by changing the path for their Color/Pattern maps, and for the bump map of BRICK_WALL, from \AutoCAD R14\Textures to \Acad2000\Textures (or where ever your material texture files are stored). You will also need to update the path to the the image (cloud.tga) used for a rendering background. In the next chapter, we will add some landscape items to the rendering so that the house will not look quite so barren. If you do not like the colors or the bitmap images we selected for the rendering, don't hesitate to change them. You have all the knowledge and experience you need to make any modifications you like—both to the rendering and to the 3D model.

Command: RMAT

Purpose: Rendering materials are created and attached to objects through this command.

Initiate with:

- On the command line enter RMAT.

- From the View pull-down menu, select Render, then Materials.

- Select the Materials button from the Render toolbar.

Options:

The RMAT command starts and ends through a dialog box titled Materials. Generally, when options in this dialog box are selected, dialog boxes appropriate for the option will be displayed.

The names of all existing materials will be displayed in a list box. A material named *GLOBAL* will always be included, and all surface objects in a rendering will assume the properties of that material, unless another material is specifically attached to it. The *GLOBAL* material has the default standard material attribute settings.

To perform an action on a material, click on its name to highlight it, then select the action by clicking the appropriate button. Material names can also be selected through the Select button, as described below. You may select only one material in the list at a time. Double-clicking a name is equivalent to highlighting a name and pressing the Modify button.

- Preview

  When the Preview button is pressed, the highlighted material will be displayed as it would appear on a 3D solid sphere or cube. Every one of the dialog boxes used by the RMAT command has a similar preview panel for the material.

- Materials Library

  This button will display the Materials Library dialog box. See the discussion beginning on page 452 of the MATLIB command for a description of this dialog box.

- Select

  When the Select button is pressed, the Materials dialog box will be dismissed, and AutoCAD will issue a prompt for you to select one object. You must select the object by picking a point on it. When you do, AutoCAD will restore the Materials dialog box with the name of the material highlighted in the list box. The material's name will also be displayed in the lower-left corner of the dialog box, along with the method that was used in attaching it.

- Modify

  Pressing this button will bring up a dialog box appropriate for the type of material selected. All of the material's properties will be displayed in the dialog box, and they can be modified. Double-clicking the name of a material in the list box is equivalent to highlighting it and pressing the modify button.

- Duplicate

  Click this button to create a new material based on the properties of the highlighted material. A dialog box for a new material will be displayed. Except for the new material's name, all of the properties of the highlighted material will be preset in the dialog box.

- New

  To create a new material, select a material type from the pull-down list box, then press the New button. A dialog box appropriate for the type of material will be displayed.

- Attach

  When this button is pressed, AutoCAD will dismiss the Materials dialog box and issue a command line prompt to select the objects that are to receive the properties of the specified material. You may use any object selection method, and objects will be highlighted as they are selected. Objects that already have the specified material attached are also highlighted. Press the Enter key to restore the Materials dialog box.

- Detach

  This option detaches an object from its material. The Materials dialog box will temporarily disappear, and AutoCAD will display a command line prompt for you to select objects. Use any object selection method, and press the Enter key to return to the Materials dialog box. All objects selected will have their material detached, even if the name of their material was not specified.

- By ACI

  You can attach a material to all objects that have a specific color through this button. A dialog box titled Attach by AutoCAD Color Index will be displayed. On the left side of this dialog box is a list of all materials in the drawing, while the 255 AutoCAD color numbers will be displayed on the right side of the dialog box. You may select as many colors as you like by clicking their name or number, but you can select only one material at a time. Press the Attach button to

  assign the selected material to AutoCAD objects that have the specified colors. You can remove the association between a material and an ACI color by pressing the Detach button. Objects drawn in that color will no longer have any material attached.

- By Layer

  Pressing this button brings up a dialog box titled Attach by Layer. On the left side of this dialog box will be a list of materials, and on the right side will be a list of the layers in the drawing. Although you can select just one material at a time, you can select as many layers as you wish. Press the Attach button to associate the selected material with the selected layers.

All objects within the selected layers will be attached to the selected materials. Pressing the Detach button will detach any material currently attached to objects in the selected layers.

New/Modify Standard Material

The same dialog box used for creating a new standard material is used for modifying an existing standard material. Only the titles of the dialog boxes are different.

- Material Name

  Enter the name of a new material in this edit box or modify the name of an existing one. Names may have up to sixteen characters and may contain spaces.

- Attributes

  Select an attribute from this column of radio buttons. Then set the features of that attribute. Features that are not appropriate for an attribute will be grayed out.

  Color/Pattern

  ◦ Set a Value from 0 to 1. The default value is 0.70.

  ◦ Color is By ACI by default. Clear the By ACI check box to specify a color.

  ◦ A texture map may be specified through the File Name edit box.

  Ambient

  ◦ Set a Value from 0 to 1. The default value is 0.10.

  ◦ By default, ambient color is locked to that of the Color attribute. To assign a color to ambient, clear the Lock check box. To specify a particular color, clear the By ACI check box.

  Reflection

  ◦ Set a Value from 0 to 1. The default value is 0.20.

  ◦ By default, reflection color is locked to that of the Color attribute. To assign a color to reflection, clear the Lock check box, and to specify a particular color, clear the By ACI check box.

  ◦ Check the Mirror check box to give the material a mirrorlike finish. Raytraced rendering must be used to obtain mirror images.

  ◦ A reflection map may be specified within the File Name edit box.

  Roughness

  ◦ Set a Value from 0 to 1. The default value is 0.50. Smaller values result in smaller reflection highlights.

  Transparency

  ◦ Set a Value from 0 to 1. The default value is 0. When the value is 0, the material is completely opaque; when the value is 1, the material is completely transparent.

  ◦ An opacity map may be specified by entering a file name in the File Name edit box.

Refraction

° Set a Value from 0 to 100. With the default value of 1.0, no refraction occurs. Raytraced rendering must be used for this attribute to have an effect.

Bump Map

° Specify the name of the bump map in the File Name edit box.

- Value

The meaning of the number in this edit box varies by attribute. Value can be entered directly, or with the slider.

- Color

This cluster of check boxes, edit boxes, and sliders controls the color of the color, ambient, and reflection attributes. When the By ACI check box is turned on, the attribute's color will be the same as the color of the AutoCAD object that the material is attached to. The Lock check box applies only to the ambient and reflection attributes. When it is turned on, the attribute will have the same color as the color attribute. The Mirror check box is enabled only for the reflection attribute. When it is checked, the material will have a mirrorlike reflection (when raytraced rendering is used).

If the By ACI check box is cleared, you can specify a color for the attribute through the three edit boxes and sliders for color. When the RGB color system is in effect, the three color parameters are red, green, and blue. When the HLS color system is used, the three color parameters are hue, lightness, and saturation. If you click within the color swatch, a dialog box titled Color will be displayed and can be used to specify a color.

- Bitmap Blend

This edit box and slider controls the extent to which the attribute's color shows through the bitmap image of texture maps and reflection maps. For opacity maps, bitmap blend controls their transparency; for bump maps, it controls the degree of bumpiness. Values can range from 0 to 1; the higher the value, the greater the effect of the bitmap. Bump maps generally work best with bitmap blends of 0.10 or less.

- File Name and Find File

Enter the name of a bitmap file for a texture, reflection, opacity, or bump map in the file name edit box, or initiate a search for a file by clicking the Find File button.

- Adjust Bitmap

Press this button to adjust the scale and insert a point of the bitmap image of texture, opacity, and bump maps. A dialog box titled Adjust Material Bitmap Placement will be displayed.

Scale represents the number of times the bitmap image fits on the surface objects in the specified direction. Thus, if the scale in the U direction is 3.0, the image will be one-third of its one-to-one size in that direction. You can set the scale of both directions with the slider bars above and to the left of the image tile or by entering a value in the edit boxes. If the Maintain Aspect Ratio toggle is checked, changing the scale in one direction will change it in the other as well.

Offset is the displacement of the insert point of the image in the specified direction. For instance, if the offset in the V direction is 0.25, the image will be shifted in the V direction by a distance that is one-fourth of its projected size. You can set the offsets with the slider bars that are below and to the right of the image tile or by entering numbers in the offset edit boxes.

When scale is greater than 1 (which means that its size will be less than one-to-one), the image will be repeated as necessary to fill surfaces when the radio button labeled Tile is checked. When Crop is checked, the image will be shown just once. Surface areas outside the image will be rendered in the material's color.

New/Modify Granite Material

Granite is one of the three template materials that generate bitmap images during rendering. A dialog box named New Granite Material is displayed when a new granite material is being defined, while one named Modify Granite Material is displayed when an existing granite material is being changed. Both dialog boxes are the same, except for their title.

- Material Name

  Enter the name of a new granite material in this edit box, or modify the name of an existing one. Names may have up to sixteen characters, and they may contain spaces.

- Attributes

  Select an attribute from this column of radio buttons. Then set the features of that attribute. Features that are not appropriate for an attribute will be grayed out.

  ○ First, Second, Third, and Fourth Color

    The image for granite material has random shaped patches of four colors, as shown highly magnified in the next figure. Click the radio button for a color, and use the same procedure used for a standard material to give it a value and a color. The By ACI toggle will be grayed out. To use fewer than four colors, set the value of the unwanted colors to 0, or set their color to be the same as another's.

441

○ Reflection

This attribute is the same as the reflection attribute for standard materials. You can assign a value and a color to reflection, and you can have the material reflect other objects by checking Mirror. Photo Raytraced rendering must be used to enable mirror-image reflections.

○ Roughness

This attribute accepts a value from 0 to 1 for controlling the size of reflected light highlights, just as the roughness attribute of standard materials does.

○ Sharpness

This attribute can be assigned a value ranging from 0 to 1. When sharpness equals one, the edges between the granite grains is sharp, as shown in the figure above. At the other extreme, when sharpness is set to zero, the edges between grains will be blended together.

○ Scale

The relative size of the grains, or color patches, in the granite is controlled by this attribute. You may assign it any value from 0 to 100, with larger values resulting in larger grain sizes.

○ Bump Map

This attribute allows you to use a bump map with the granite material. The controls for the bump map are the same as those for standard materials.

New/Modify Marble Material

Marble is a template material that simulates marble. A dialog box titled New Marble Material is used when a new marble material is being defined, and one titled Modify Marble Material is used when an existing marble material is being modified. Both dialog boxes are the same, except for their title.

• Material Name

Enter the name of the marble material, or edit the name of an existing one, through this edit box. The name can have up to sixteen characters, including spaces.

• Attributes

Materials are defined through these eight attributes. When an attribute is selected, appropriate edit boxes, sliders, and toggles for setting its parameters will be available.

- ◦ Stone Color and Vein Color

  The Stone Color attribute controls the overall color of the marble, while the Vein Color attribute controls the color of the marble's veins. Only the edit boxes and sliders in the Color section of the dialog box will be available. The By ACI button and the edit box and slider for Value will be disabled. The default stone color is white, and the default vein color is black.

- ◦ Reflection

  Just as with standard materials, you can set both the value and color of reflected light. If the By ACI toggle is selected, the color of reflected light will be the same as the object's color. You can also give the marble material a mirrorlike finish, and you can use a reflection map with it.

- ◦ Roughness

  The relative size of reflected light highlights is controlled by this attribute. Only the Value edit box and slider will be available.

- ◦ Turbulence

  This attribute controls the relative distance between the peaks of the squiggly, wavelike veins in the marble. Although it accepts any value between 0 and 100, values between 1 and 10 generally give the best results. The veins are straight lines when turbulence is set to 0.

- ◦ Sharpness

  When sharpness is set to its maximum value of 1, the veins in the marble consist of distinct squiggly lines that blend into the surrounding stone color. When sharpness is set to its minimum value of 0, the lines are not distinct and the blend area of the veins dominate. The default sharpness is 1.

- ◦ Scale

  This attribute sets the overall size of the marblelike features and the relative distance between the veins. You can specify any value between 0 and 100.

- ◦ Bump Map

  Through this attribute, you can assign a bump map to the marble material.

New/Modify Wood Material

This template material simulates the annual growth ring patterns of wood. A dialog boxed titled New Wood Material is used for creating a new material, and one titled Modify Wood Material is used for modifying existing materials. Both dialog boxes are the same, except for their title.

- • Material Name

  Enter the name of the wood material in this edit box, or change the name of the existing material. Names may have up to sixteen characters, including spaces.

- Attribute

  To establish the characteristics of the wood material, set the parameters of each of these ten attributes. When the radio button for an attribute is selected, the parameters appropriate for it will be available, while the others will be grayed out.

  ○ Light Color and Dark Color

    Dark Color controls the color of the dark rings of summer wood in the material, while the Light Color attribute controls the color of the spring wood rings. The Value and By ACI parameters are not available.

  ○ Reflection

    This attribute is the same as the reflection attribute for standard materials. You can assign both a value and a color to reflection, and you can have the material reflect other objects when Photo Raytraced rendering is used by checking the Mirror check box.

  ○ Roughness

    This attribute accepts a value from 0 to 1 for controlling the size of reflected light highlights, just as the roughness attribute of standard materials does.

  ○ Light/Dark

    This attribute, which takes a value between 0 and 1, controls the relative width of the rings of dark wood and light wood. When low values are used, the dark wood bands will be wider than the light wood bands. When high values are used, the dark wood bands will be narrower than the light wood bands. The default value is 0.50.

Low light/dark ratio   High light/dark ratio

  ○ Ring Density

    The number of annual growth rings for a set scale is controlled by this attribute. You may assign it any value between 0 and 100, with larger values resulting in more rings.

  ○ Ring Width

    This attribute controls the variation in the distance between the growth rings. It accepts any value from 0 to 1. When

Low ring density value   High ring density value

444

ring width is set to 0, the distance between each ring is the same. As higher ring width values are assigned, the spacing between the rings becomes increasingly varied. The greatest variation occurs when ring width is set to 1. The default setting is 0.40.

° Ring Shape

By default, the wood's growth rings are almost perfect circles or arcs. You can, though, make them irregular by increasing the value of this attribute. Ring Shape accepts any value from 0 to 1, and its default value is 0.20. Higher values result in more irregular rings.

° Scale

The overall scale of the wood's pattern is controlled by this attribute. You may assign it any value between 0 and 100, with larger values resulting in relatively larger growth ring patterns. The default scale is 6.25.

° Bump Map

A bump map may be assigned to the wood material through this attribute.

Low ring width value   High ring width value

Low ring shape value   High ring shape value

Low scale value   High scale value

Notes:

- You must use the Materials Library dialog box to delete a material. See the discussion of the MATLIB command for details.

- Material attachment to objects by ACI takes precedence over attachment by layer, and a material explicitly attached to an object through the Attach button takes precedence over both ACI and layer attachments.

- You can detach an object from a material through the Attach button of the Materials dialog box. When you press the Attach button, the AutoCAD objects that are already attached to the specified material will be highlighted as AutoCAD asks you to identify objects for a selection set. Any object you remove from the selection set will be detached from the material.

Command: SHOWMAT

Purpose: This command shows the name of the material attached to an object and the method used to attach it.

Initiate with:

• On the command line enter SHOWMAT.

Implementation:

This command performs the same function as the Select button in the Materials dialog box. You will be prompted from the command line to pick one object. AutoCAD will then display one of the following responses on the command line:

```
Material <material name> is explicitly attached to the object.
Material <material name> is attached by ACI to ACI <color number>.
Material <material name> is attached by layer to layer <layer name>.
Material *GLOBAL* is attached by default or by block.
```

Command: SETUV

Purpose: This command controls the mapping of texture maps, opacity maps, bump maps, and template materials on specific objects.

Initiate with:

• On the command line enter SETUV.

• From the View pull-down menu, select Render, then Mapping.

• Select the Mapping button from the Render toolbar.

Options:

The SETUV command starts with a command line prompt for you to select the AutoCAD objects that are to be mapped. Although you may freely select as many objects as you like, the objects should have similar geometric properties and similar orientation in 3D space. The objects selected do not need to have a material attached—you can establish the mapping properties of an object and attach a material to it later. The objects selected will retain the mapping properties if they are moved, and copies of them will have the mapping properties also. See the note at the end of this command description for a method to detach mapping properties from an object.

When you press the Enter key to signal completion of the object selection process, AutoCAD will display a dialog box titled Mapping.

446

- Projection

  From this set of four radio buttons, select the geometry—planar, cylindrical, spherical, or solid—that comes closest to matching the geometry of the selected objects. Solid is for objects having one of the three template materials.

- Preview

  Unlike the preview panels of the other rendering dialog boxes, those of the SETUV command show the selected object rather than a solid cube or sphere.

- Acquire From

  This option allows you to assign the mapping properties of another object to the currently selected objects. The Mapping dialog box will temporarily disappear, and AutoCAD will issue a command line prompt for you to select objects. You should select only one object, even though AutoCAD permits you to select as many as you wish. Press the Enter key to restore the Mapping dialog box. The newly acquired properties can be modified or accepted as they are.

- Copy To

  You can assign the mapping properties of the current selection set to other objects through this option. AutoCAD will hide the Mapping dialog box and will ask you from the command line to select the objects that are to acquire the current mapping properties. Press the Enter key to end the selection process and return to the Mapping dialog box.

- Adjust Coordinates

  Pressing this button brings up a dialog box (one of four) that is appropriate for the specified projection type. Through it, you can orient the map's projection, shift and rotate the image, and adjust the scale of the image.

Adjust Planar Coordinates

When the Planar projection radio button in the Mapping dialog box is selected, pressing the Adjust Coordinates button brings up a dialog box titled Adjust Planar Coordinates.

- Parallel Plane

  Specify the orientation of the plane by selecting one of these radio buttons. The default orientation is that the plane is parallel with the WCS X-Y plane. If the plane is not parallel with any of the principal WCS planes, select the Picked Plane button. AutoCAD will hide the dialog box and prompt for the lower-left, lower-right, and upper-left corners of the plane. The angle between the upper-left, lower-left, and lower-right corners does not have to be 90 degrees.

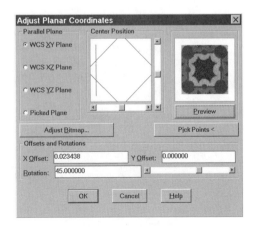

- Center Position

    The center of the bitmap's projection is shown as a dot in this image tile, and you can move it with the sliders that are beside the image tile. The outline of the projected image is also shown.

- Preview

    The bitmap image with the current settings is displayed in this image tile. It is not updated automatically, so you must press the Preview button to view the effects of current settings.

- Pick Points

    Use this button to change the orientation of a plane that is not parallel with any of the three principal planes of the WCS. AutoCAD will temporarily dismiss the dialog box and issue command line prompts for the lower-left, lower-right, and upper-left corners of the plane.

- Offsets and Rotations

    You can move the center of the bitmap by entering values in the X Offset and Y Offset edit boxes. Moreover, you can rotate the bitmap by entering an angle in the Rotation edit box or by moving the slider. The rotation angle limits are 180 degrees and -180 degrees. The Center Position image tile will be updated when you change the center offsets and rotation angle.

- Adjust Bitmap

    Pressing this button brings up a dialog box titled Adjust Object Bitmap Placement.

    This dialog box is very similar to the Adjust Material Bitmap Placement dialog box used by the RMAT command. It has an additional radio button, labeled DEFAULT, for tiling. When DEFAULT is selected, the image will be either tiled or cropped, depending on the setting for the material as a whole. You can override the material's setting by specifying that the image on the selected object will be tiled or that it will be cropped.

The offsets specified in this dialog box are added to the offsets for the material, while the scales specified in this dialog box are multiplied with those of the material. Thus, if the U scale for a material is 2.0 and the U scale for the object is 3.0, the scale of the image will be 6.0 when it is rendered.

448

Adjust Cylindrical Coordinates

When the Cylindrical projection radio button in the Mapping dialog box is selected, pressing the Adjust Coordinates button brings up a dialog box titled Adjust Cylindrical Coordinates.

- Parallel Axis

  Select one of these radio buttons to specify the direction of the cylindrical surface's axis direction. The default direction is that of the WCS Z axis. If the axis is not parallel with any of the three cardinal axes, select the Picked Axis button. AutoCAD will hide the dialog box and prompt for two points that will define the direction of the axis and a third point to specify the seam of the bitmap (the point at which the image wrapped around the cylinder begins and ends).

- Central Axis Position

  This image tile shows the cylinder projected onto a plane parallel with the cylinder's axis, as well as a cross-section of the cylinder. You can use the two sliders next to the image to move the axis. A line from the center of the cylinder indicates the image seam line. The seam is in the minus Y direction when the cylinder's axis is in the Z direction, and the minus Z direction when the axis is in either the X or Y directions.

- Preview

  The bitmap image, based on the current projection settings, can be seen in this panel.

- Adjust Bitmap

  Pressing this button brings up the Adjust Object Bitmap Placement dialog box. See the earlier description for adjusting planar coordinates for a description of this dialog box. The U direction of the bitmap is around the circumference of the cylinder, while the V direction is in the direction of the cylinder's axis.

- Pick Points

  You can respecify the direction of the cylinder's axis and wrap line by pressing this button. AutoCAD will hide the dialog box and issue prompts for points to specify the bottom of the axis, the top of the axis, and the direction of the seam line.

- Offsets and Rotation

  You can move the projection axis by entering values for the X Offset and Y Offset in the edit boxes. Rotation refers to the direction of the seam line. You can change it by entering a value in the edit box or by moving the slider. The rotation limits are -180 degrees and 180 degrees.

Adjust Spherical Coordinates

When the Spherical projection radio button in the Mapping dialog box is selected, pressing the Adjust Coordinates button brings up a dialog box titled Adjust Spherical Coordinates.

- Parallel Axis

  Specify the direction of the sphere's axis by picking one of these radio buttons. When Picked Axis is selected, AutoCAD will temporarily dismiss the dialog box and issue command line prompts for three points. The first point is for the center of the sphere, the second is for the sphere's north pole, and the third is for the image seam line.

- Polar Axis Position

  The projection of the image onto the sphere is shown in this panel, and the seam line is indicated by a line from the center of the sphere. You can move the image insert point by moving the sliders beside the panel.

- Preview

  This panel displays the sphere with the current mapping settings.

- Adjust Bitmap

  When this button is pressed, the Adjust Object Bitmap Placement dialog box will be displayed. See the earlier description of adjusting planar coordinates for a description of this dialog box. The U direction of the bitmap is around the equator of the sphere, while the V direction is in the direction of the sphere's axis.

- Pick Points

  This button enables you to respecify the axis and the seam line of the sphere. The dialog box will be hidden while AutoCAD issues three points from the command line. The first point is for the center of the sphere, the second is for the sphere's north pole, and the third is for the direction of the image wrap line.

- Offsets and Rotation

  You can move the projection center by entering values for the X Offset and Y Offset in the edit boxes. Rotation refers to the direction of the seam line. You can change it by entering a value in the edit box or by moving the slider. The rotation limits are -180 degrees and 180 degrees.

Adjust UVW Coordinates

When the Solid projection radio button in the Mapping dialog box is selected, pressing the Adjust Coordinates button brings up a dialog box titled Adjust UVW Coordinates. This dialog box is for adjusting the coordinate scales and the orientation of the image for the three template materials—granite, marble, and wood.

- U Scale, V Scale, and W Scale

  Use the edit boxes or the sliders to change the scale of the pattern in the specified direction.

- Pick Points

  By default, the U direction is in the WCS X direction, V is in the WCS Y direction, and W is in the WCS Z direction. You can change those directions, though, with this option. AutoCAD will hide the dialog box and prompt you from the command line to enter three points and a distance:

```
Place the origin of the mapper: (Specify a point.)
Place the U axis of the mapper: (Specify a point.)
Place the V axis of the mapper: (Specify a point.)
Length of W axis: (Specify a distance.)
```

  The three points control the orientation of the plane as well as the direction of its axes and the scale in the U and V directions, while the distance sets the scale in the W direction.

  The figure below shows two identical 3D solid objects that have the same wood template–based material attached. The mapping axes have been twisted, however, on the solid on the right so that they no longer match the edges of the solid. This skews its pattern and gives the material a different appearance.

- Maintain Aspect Ratio

  When this check box is cleared, you can change the scale independently in the three directions. When it is checked, the scales of the three directions are linked together so that if one is changed, the scales in the other two directions also change to maintain their original proportions.

Notes:

- To remove mapping properties from an object, enter the following AutoLISP function on the command line:

```
(c:setuv "D" (ssget))
```

  A command line prompt will be displayed on the command line asking you to select objects. Mapping properties will be deleted from the objects you select.

A Materials Library

Since the creation of a material can be an involved process—one that you do not want to repeat unnecessarily—AutoCAD allows you to save materials in a file so that they can be used in other drawings. MATLIB is the command that manages such a file. With it, you can save a newly created material, import a material from the file into your current drawing, and remove unwanted materials from your current drawing or from the file.

You can have any number of different material files—each having a filename extension of .mli—to make a library of material files. You can, for example, have your materials for building interiors in one file, materials for exteriors in another, materials for metals in another, and so forth. You create and manage the files in this library also through the MATLIB command.

AutoCAD comes with a ready-made collection of about 150 materials in the file render.mli. If the version of render.mli in your computer has only about four materials, read the instructions at the beginning of the mapping section for loading the larger version of render.mli from the AutoCAD 2000 CD-ROM. As you have time, you will want to look at the materials in this file. The file encompasses a wide range of material types, and you are likely to find that some will be useful but many will not be. As you find materials that are useful, you will probably want to trans-fer them into your own files so that the materials are better organized and easier to find.

Command: MATLIB

Purpose: This command enables you to create, manage, and use a collection of render-ing materials.

Initiate with:

- On the command line enter MATLIB.

- From the View pull-down menu, select Render, then Materials Library.

- Select the Materials Library button from the Render toolbar.

- Press the Materials Library button in the Materials dialog box of the RMAT command.

Options:

The MATLIB command uses the Materials Library dialog box. You can also access this dialog box through the RMAT command, and you are likely to often use that approach since it allows you to both retrieve materials and attach them to objects. It also allows you to delete unwanted materials from your drawing file.

All of the materials in the current draw-ing are shown in a list on the left side of the dialog box, while a list of the mate-rials in the library file are shown on the

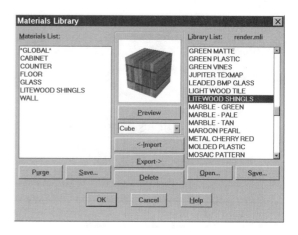

right side of the dialog box. You can select any number of items in either list (to make multiple selections, hold down the computer's Control key as you click item names), but you can work in only one list at a time. Once materials have been selected, they will be highlighted, and buttons for appropriate options will be available.

The following options are available for items in the materials list:

- Purge

  When you press this button, all unattached materials in the materials list will be deleted, even if they are not highlighted.

- Save

  All materials in the material list, whether they are highlighted or not, will be saved in a file having a .mli file name extension when this button is pressed. AutoCAD will prompt for the name and the location of the file.

- Export

  When this button is clicked, the highlighted materials will be added to the library list. If the exported material has the same name as a material in the library list, AutoCAD will display a dialog box for you to use in reconciling the duplication.

The following options are available for items in the library list:

- Open

  You can switch to another material file by pressing this button. A dialog box for finding and specifying the file will be displayed.

- Save

  Press this button to save the materials in the library list in a new materials file. The file will have a .mli extension, and AutoCAD will display a dialog box for you to use in specifying a name and location for the file.

- Import

  Highlighted materials in the library list will be added to the materials list when this button is pressed. If a name conflict occurs, AutoCAD will display a dialog box to help you resolve it.

The following options are available for items in either list:

- Preview

  This panel gives you an idea of what the selected material looks like when it is attached to a solid sphere or cube.

- Delete

  The selected items will be deleted when this button is pressed. If the material is attached, AutoCAD will display a warning and ask you to confirm the deletion.

Table 19-1 AutoCAD Supplied Bitmap Files That Are Useful in Renderings

File	Size in Pixels	Description
Wood:		
ashsen.tga	320 x 200	light-colored wood pattern
bubinga.tga	320 x 200	dark wood pattern
oak_bed1.tga	256 x 131	light-colored wood veneer
oak_bed2.tga	310 x 135	light-colored wood veneer
teak.tga	320 x 200	dark wood pattern
whiteash.tga	320 x 200	light-colored wood pattern
Brick and concrete:		
cement.tga	125 x 100	gray finished cement
grybrick.tga	128 x 78	gray brick with white mortar
Stone and marble:		
benediti.tga	320 x 200	light gray mottled compound marble
granite.tga	73 x 65	polished gray granite
gravel1.tga	64 x 64	polished pink and blue gray granite
graymarb.tga	320 x 200	gray marble w/black and white veins
Stone and marble:		
marbpale.tga	320 x 200	light gray polished marble with pink veins
marbteal.tg	320 x 200	blue-green marble with white veins
pinkmarb.tga	178 x 146	bright pink marble in four squares
Tile and patterns:		
bmmarop.tga	99 x 81	four square gray tiles
brwmmarb.tga	101 x 83	four square brown tiles with marble pattern
checker.tga	161 x 153	four squares—two black and two white
checkers.tga	394 x 319	16-by-13 set of light blue and white squares
checkop.tga	391 x 390	16-by-16 set of black and white squares
conctile.tga	93 x 69	single light gray tile with darker gray border
idkwood.tga	32 x 32	light and dark square wood tiles
inlay3.tga	103 x 108	wood inlay pattern
inlay4.tga	103 x 108	wood inlay pattern
tile*.tga	106 x 106	single floor tile with black border
pat*.tga	various	various geometric patterns for tile or wallpaper

Table 19-1 AutoCAD Supplied Bitmap Files That Are Useful in Renderings (cont.)

File	Size in Pixels	Description
Miscellaneous:		
lattice1.tga	40 x 40	single white X on black background
lattice2.tga	40 x 40	single white X, shaded, on black background
Bluchina.tga	258 x 194	random white patterns on a dark blue background
fence.tga	320 x 200	chain-link fence
Bump maps:		
bmbricb.tga	128 x 78	bump map for bmbrick.tga
bmbrick.tga	128 x 78	texture map, dark red/brown brick
camoflab.tga	140 x 114	bump map for camofla.tga
camoflag.tga	138 x 112	texture map, green camouflage pattern
imarble1.tga	64 x 64	light brown and white—no distinct veins
istone2.tga	64 x 64	light gray rounded stone
imetalb.tg	64 x 64	bump map for imetal.tga
imetal.tga	64 x 64	texture map, metal tread plate
iltwood1.tga	86 x 88	light-colored wood pattern
ishingl2.tga	64 x 64	reddish-brown cedar shingles
ipavers.tga	64 x 64	dark gray brick with white mortar
ivines.tga	66 x 65	green foliage
Backgrounds:		
biglake.tga	320 x 200	lake- and snow-covered mountain
cloud.tga	320 x 200	deep blue sky with white lacy clouds
Backgrounds:		
house.tga	512 x 241	Victorian house, front view
sky.tga	320 x 200	blue sky with fluffy clouds
sunset.tga	320 x 200	stratus clouds at sunset
valley_i.tga	512 x 480	yellow tree, sagebrush, and mountains

CHAPTER 20

Landscape Objects and Depth Perception

*I*n this chapter, we will discuss some tools for making renderings of exterior objects, such as buildings, more realistic looking. When you have finished the chapter, you will be able to

- *insert realistic bitmap images of trees, shrubs, people, and so forth in renderings;*
- *enhance the illusion of distance in renderings by making far objects hazy or dim.*

In addition to tools for incorporating lights and materials in renderings, AutoCAD's Renderer contains tools for adding external objects to renderings. If, for instance, you would like to have a tree within a rendering, you do not need to construct a 3D tree; instead, you can simply insert one of these external objects that looks like a tree.

Often these external objects represent trees and shrubs, and therefore, they are generally referred to as *landscape objects*. Despite the name, though, the objects can also represent people, automobiles, signs, and so forth. They are based on bitmap images from photographs of real objects. All you need is a suitable pair of images. (As we will explain later in this chapter, two bitmap images are needed for each object.)

These landscape objects are comparable to cardboard cutouts used in a department store window or as scenery in a stage play in that they are 2D surfaces with an image that resembles a 3D object. Nevertheless, they are able to cast shadows, just as if they were a 3D object.

Menus and toolbar buttons for landscape objects and fog

456

Furthermore, you can have them always face the current viewing direction. Thus, when you switch from a front view of a house to a side view, the landscape objects will automatically rotate to face the new view direction.

AutoCAD has three commands relating to landscape objects. LSNEW is for installing a landscape object, LSEDIT is for modifying the features of an installed object, and LSLIB is for managing the bitmap files used as landscape objects.

AutoCAD's renderer also has a tool for simulating the visual effects of distance. Just as real objects, such as hills and city skylines, become hazy and dim when they are far away, you can have objects in a rendering become hazy and dim. The AutoCAD command that manages this effect is FOG.

As you would expect, Photo Real or Photo Raytraced rendering must be used for the landscape and fog features to have an effect. In this chapter, we will first explore landscape objects, then we will see how the tools for creating distant effects work.

Landscape Objects

Installing landscape objects is a straightforward process that you will have little or no trouble with. You install them one at a time with the LSNEW command. This command uses a dialog box, through which you specify the following parameters:

- *The landscape object.* Although landscape objects are based on bitmap files that often have cryptic names, such as 8tree44l.tga, they go by names that are reasonably descriptive, such as Quaking Aspen. The names of available objects will be shown in a list box, and you click the name of the object you want. Moreover, you can use a preview panel to see what an object looks like.

- *Geometry style.* The landscape object will be projected onto a planar object that AutoCAD will create. As an alternative, you can have the image projected onto two planes that intersect at right angles. This can enhance the realism of some objects, such as a tree. If your landscape object is a sign, though, you will want to stick with a single plane.

- *View Aligned.* You can choose whether you want the landscape object to always face the same direction or to automatically rotate to match the current view direction. Generally, you will have 3D objects, such as trees and shrubs, be view-aligned. However, if the object represents a 2D object, such as a stop sign, you may want its orientation to be fixed. If you ever want to change the orientation of a non-view-aligned object, you can rotate it with the AutoCAD ROTATE command.

- *Height.* You specify a height for the landscape object, using the current drawing units. The height of a tree, for example, might be 240 inches (20 feet), and the height of a bush might be 48 inches (4 feet). Height, as you would expect, is in the Z axis direction. If you do not specify a height, AutoCAD will make the object 20 units tall.

- *Position.* By default, AutoCAD inserts landscape objects at the UCS origin. You can, however, specify any base point you want. You can also move objects, through the move command or through their grips, after they have been inserted.

Landscape objects are able to cast shadows when Photo Raytrace rendering is in effect. Once a landscape object has been inserted, you can use AutoCAD commands and its grips to erase it, move it, make copies of it, and even (with some trouble) change its height. You can also rotate it, provided it is not a view-aligned object. You can also modify the landscape object through the LSEDIT command. This command uses a dialog box that is identical to that used by the LSNEW command. You cannot, however, change the image of an inserted landscape object.

Every landscape object is based on two bitmap files. One, called the image file, contains the image you will see in the rendering on a black background. The other, called the opacity file, has the area of the image filled with white. It too has a black background. See the figure in the discussion of the LSLIB command in this chapter for an example.

This image file and opacity map combination is similar to a texture and opacity map combination in a rendering material. In fact, you can use the bitmap file pairs intended for landscape objects in a material and attach it to a 3D face plane to create your own landscape object. There is no reason to do this, though, since it involves more work than the renderer's landscape objects, and the results are not as good.

The image file and its companion opacity file are linked together with the LSLIB command. This command also allows you to assign a meaningful name, such as Quaking Aspen, to the pair of files. Similar to the material libraries, you can group any number of landscape objects together and save them in a landscape library file. They always have a filename extension of LLI.

When you begin the LSNEW command, the landscape objects it lists as being available for installation are those in the current landscape library. If the landscape object you want is not in the list, you will have to exit the LSNEW command and use the LSLIB command to open the landscape library file that contains the object you want. Then that landscape library will be the current one, and the LSNEW command's list of landscape objects will include the object you want to install. This is somewhat awkward, but it is not really a problem since AutoCAD supplies the files for only eleven landscape objects, and they conveniently fit in one library.

The default current landscape library is render.lli, and if you used the typical AutoCAD installation, there will be only one landscape object in it. You should replace your abbreviated render.lli file with the one on the AutoCAD 2000 CD-ROM. This will give you access to all eleven landscape objects. On the CD-ROM, render.lli is in folder \Acad\Support. The render.lli file it should replace in your computer is in folder \Program Files\Acad2000\Support. The bitmap files needed for the landscape objects are already in your computer, provided you followed the instructions for loading all of AutoCAD's bitmap files in your computer that were in the section on mapping in Chapter Nineteen.

Exercise One

We will add some trees and shrubs to the rendering of the 3D surface model house that we have been working with. Retrieve file mfe19305.dwg from the CD-ROM that comes with this book, and open it. To make the file as compatible with as many AutoCAD versions as possible, it was saved in in Release 14 format. Therefore, if you are opening it in AutoCAD 2000, you will need to modify the BRICK_WALL and SHINGLES materials by changing the path for their Color/Pattern maps, and for the bump map of BRICK_WALL, from \AutoCAD R14\Textures to \Acad2000\Textures (or where ever your texture files are stored). You will also need to update the path to the the image (cloud.tga) used for a rendering background. This version of the drawing file has lights installed and has materials attached to its surface objects.

This drawing file has a view named DIST_80, and you should make certain that this view is the current one. It is a perspective view. Then use the 4 option of the VPORTS command to divide the AutoCAD graphics area into four equal-sized viewports. In one of these viewports, invoke the PLAN command so that the viewing direction is straight down on the WCS X-Y plane. This will allow you to use your pointing device to position the landscape objects in one viewport and to make renderings in the other viewports.

Start the LSNEW command. If the list box of the Landscape New dialog box does not contain the names of eleven landscape objects, stop and replace your render.lli file with the one on the AutoCAD 2000 CD-ROM. The instructions for doing this were given a few paragraphs ago.

In the Landscape New dialog box select the landscape object named Wandering Yew by clicking on its name. Click the Crossing Faces radio button and the View Aligned check box. Set the object's height to 48 (4 feet). Click the Position button, and place the base of the object at the coordinates of 5'-0",5'-0",0'-0". Then, click the OK button. Two intersecting triangles will appear in the perspective views. We want two of these plants, so use the AutoCAD COPY command to make a duplicate of the one you just created. Locate the copy at the coordinates of 8'-0",5'-0",0'-0".

Rendering times for this model are becoming increasingly longer. If you want to see how these two landscape objects look when they are rendered, you may want to use the Crop Window option of the RENDER command to render just the area around the two plants. You should also use Photo Raytrace rendering. This will actually speed up rendering times a little, but more importantly it will enable the landscape object to cast shadows.

Invoke the LSNEW command again. This time select Bush #1 as the landscape object. Click the Crossing Faces geometry radio button and the View Aligned check box. Although there isn't much difference in the appearance of crossing faces and a single face with this bush, crossing faces will cast better shadows. Set its height to 36, and position its base at the coordinates of 30'-0",-1'-0",0'-0". Then make two copies of the plant—one placed at the coordinates of 30'-0",-7'-0",0'-0" and the other at the coordinates of 30'-0",-13'-0",0'-0".

Next, we will place a tree in the rendering. Select Sweetgum, Summer, from the list of objects in the Landscape New dialog box. Set its geometry to Crossing Faces and View Aligned. Give it a height of 360 (30 feet), and position it at the coordinates of 25'-0",-21'0",0'-0".

Lastly, we will place a tree in back of the house. Select Quaking Aspen from the Landscape New dialog box's list of landscape object. Use a Single Face (this will make the tree broader than crossing faces), and set it to View Aligned. Set its height to 360, and place it at the coordinates of 3'-0",43'-0",0'-0".

Your rendering of the model should now resemble the one shown in grayscale in the figure on the right. On the CD-ROM that accompanies this book, the model and the landscape objects are in file mfe20101.dwg. This file also has been saved in AutoCAD's Release 14 format, so you will need to modify the file's paths to the texture, bump map, and rendering background as described at the first of this exercise.

Command: LSNEW

Purpose: This command installs new rendering landscape objects in a drawing.

Initiate with:

- On the command line enter LSNEW.

- From the View pull-down menu, select Render, then Landscape New.

- Select the Landscape New button from the Render toolbar.

Options:

This command uses a dialog box titled Landscape New. Objects in the current landscape library file will be shown in a list box in the upper-left corner of this dialog box. (See the upcoming description of the LSLIB command for instructions in establishing the current landscape library file.) Select the object in this list box that you want installed in the drawing by clicking once on its name.

In non-rendered views, the landscape object will have either a triangular or a rectangular shape, depending upon the installation options selected. The name of the landscape object will be displayed on the object.

- Preview

When you press this button, an image of the selected landscape object will appear in the panel.

- Single Face/Crossing Faces

You must select one or the other of these two radio buttons. In the middle figure, the rendered tree on the left has a single face, while the tree on the right has crossing faces.

In non-rendered views, single face landscape objects appear as a single triangle or rectangle, depending on whether the object is view-aligned. Double-faced objects appear as two triangles that intersect at right angles. In the bottom figure, the object on the left has a single face, and the object on the right has crossing faces. These are the same objects shown previously in a rendered view.

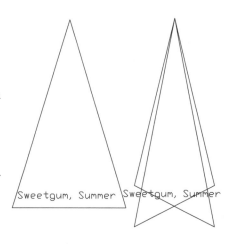

Sweetgum, Summer   Sweetgum, Summer

460

- View Aligned

  When this toggle is on, the landscape object will always face the current horizontal view direction. When the toggle is off, the orientation of the landscape object is fixed. The left-hand sign in the first figure below is fixed, while the right-hand is view-aligned. Regardless of what the view direction is, the right-hand sign will rotate itself to be seen face-on.

  In non-rendered views, single-faced fixed landscape objects appear as rectangles, as shown on the left in the second figure. You can rotate these objects. Single-faced view-aligned objects, on the other hand, are triangular, as shown on the right in the figure. You cannot rotate view-aligned objects.

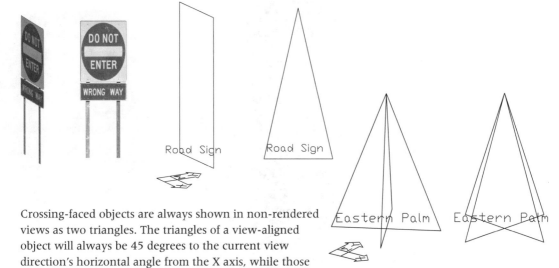

  Crossing-faced objects are always shown in non-rendered views as two triangles. The triangles of a view-aligned object will always be 45 degrees to the current view direction's horizontal angle from the X axis, while those of fixed objects will be oriented as specified. In the third figure, the orientation of the crossing-faced landscape object on the left is fixed, while the crossing-faced object on the right is view-aligned. You can rotate fixed crossing-faced objects.

- Height

  Specify the height of the landscape object with the slider or by entering a value in the edit box. The maximum value you can specify using the slider is 100, while the maximum height you can enter in the edit box is 9999. The default height is 20. Height is always in the positive Z axis direction of the UCS.

- Position

  You can specify the base location of the landscape object when you press this button. Auto-CAD will hide the dialog box and issue a command line prompt for you to specify the base of the landscape object. The default location is the UCS origin.

Notes:

- Use Photo Raytrace rendering to enable shadow casting by landscape objects.

Command: LSEDIT

Purpose: This command modifies rendering landscape objects that are in a drawing.

Initiate with:

- On the command line enter LSEDIT.
- From the View pull-down menu, select Render, then Landscape Edit.
- Select the Landscape Edit button from the Render toolbar.

Options:

This command starts with a command line prompt for you to select a landscape object. You can select only one object, and you must do so picking a point on it. As soon as you pick a landscape object, AutoCAD will display a dialog box titled Landscape Edit.

The type of object you selected will be highlighted in the landscape object list box. The other landscape object types in the current landscape library will also be listed, but they will be grayed-out and cannot be accessed. You can edit only the object you selected, and you cannot change its landscape object type.

The options in the Landscape Edit dialog box are the same as those in the Landscape New dialog box of the LSNEW command. You saw the description of that command in the previous section.

Command: LSLIB

Purpose: This command creates and manages files containing landscape objects.

Initiate with:

- On the command line enter LSLIB.
- From the View pull-down menu, select Render, then Landscape Library.
- Select the Landscape Library button from the Render toolbar.

Options:

The LSLIB command displays a dialog box titled Landscape Library.

The name of the current landscape library file will be shown in the upper-left corner of the dialog box, and the names of the objects in that file will be shown below it in a list box. You can highlight a name in this list box by clicking on it. The highlighted object can then be modified or deleted.

- Modify/New

The Modify option is for changing the parameters of the landscape object highlighted in the landscape objects list box. The New option is for defining a new landscape object that will be added to the contents of the list box. Both of these options use a dialog box that is the same except for its title. Modify uses a dialog box titled Landscape Library Edit, while New uses one titled Landscape Library New.

- Default Geometry

These two radio buttons and one check box determine the default settings for the landscape object's geometry options in the Landscape New dialog box of the LSNEW command. See the discussion of that command for their description.

- Name

Enter a descriptive name for a new landscape object, or modify the name of an existing one, in this edit box. The name can have up to seventeen characters, including spaces. This name appears in the Landscape Library list box, as well as the Landscape New list box of the LSNEW command.

- Image File

Two bitmap files are needed for every landscape object. One contains a full color image of the landscape object on a black background—this is the image file. In the other file, the area of the landscape object is pure white, while the rest of the file image is pure black—this is the opacity map file. In a rendering, the image is projected onto the white area of the opacity map file, and the black area of both images is completely transparent. The image in an image file is shown on the left in the figure, and the image in its companion opacity map file is shown on the right.

Enter the names of the two files for the landscape object you are creating in the appropriate edit box, or press the Find File button to browse for the files. The files AutoCAD supplies for landscape objects all have .tga filename extensions, but bmp, gif, tif, jpg, and pcx files are also accepted.

- Preview

  When you click this button, the image in the specified files will be displayed in the panel.

- Delete

  When you press this button, the highlighted landscape object will be removed from the current landscape library file.

- Open

  Use this option to change from the current landscape library file to another. A folder and file dialog box will be displayed to help you locate the file you want. All landscape library files have an .lli filename extension.

- Save

  This option saves the contents of the current landscape library file. A dialog box will be displayed to help you specify the location and name of the library file. The filename extension of the file will be .lli.

Fog and Depth Cueing

If you anticipate that the FOG command will produce an effect in your renderings similar to that of mist rising from the ground, you will be disappointed. Much like real fog, it results in an overall coloration of the rendering. You can make the fog white to produce a hazy effect, you can make it black to darken the rendering (when black is used, AutoCAD refers to the results as *depth cueing*), and you can use any color between these two extremes. You can have rose-colored fog if you like. The purpose of fog is to create an illusion of distance. Just as distant hills and buildings often appear hazy, you can make distant objects in renderings appear hazy.

AutoCAD bases distances at which fog takes effect on the back cutting plane of a view. You will recall from Chapter Seven that cutting planes are established as an option of the DVIEW command. They are perpendicular to the line of sight, and they are located relative to the target point (which is also set by the DVIEW command). The purpose of a back cutting plane is to hide everything that is behind it. Once a cutting plane has been setup, it can be turned on and off. For the FOG command, you will want a back cutting plane established, but you will not want it turned on. If it is, all objects that are behind it will disappear during a rendering.

Exercise Two

Find the file named mfe20201.dwg on the CD-ROM that comes with this

book, and open it. As with the file for Exercise One, you may
need to modify the paths to the texture maps used in the
BRICK_WALL and SHINGLES materials, as well as for the
image used for the rendering background. This file contains the
surface model house we have been working with, plus a couple
of sheds that have been placed behind the house. The view has
also been panned to the left, and the tree that was behind the
house has been removed. A rendering of the house, without any
fog effects, is shown in the preceding figure.

This view has been saved under the name FOG_TEST. The
diagram in the figure on the right shows the relationship
between the objects in the rendering and the camera, target,
and cutting plane. The distance from the camera to the target is
80 feet, and the back clipping plane is 70 feet behind the target.
These points were all established with the DVIEW command.

To compare the effects of various fog settings, use the 4
option of the VPORTS command to divide the graphics area into four viewports. Start the REN-
DER command, set the rendering type to Photo Raytrace (it will render faster than Photo Real,
and also cast shadows from the landscape objects), and render one of the viewports without
any fog effects. This rendering will serve as a comparison base.

Move to another viewport, and start the RENDER command again. Click the button labeled
Fog/Depth Cue to bring up the Fog dialog box. In this dialog box, click the Enable Fog toggle.
Leave the Fog Background toggle cleared so that none of the fog settings will affect the sky image
background of the rendering. Set the fog color to white by moving the Red, Green, and Blue color
sliders all the way to the right, or enter 1.0 in their edit boxes.

Leave the Near Distance set to its default of 0.00 and Far Distance to its default of 1.00. Also,
leave the Near and Far Fog Percentage setting at their default setting of 0.00 and 1.00. Then click
the OK button to return to the Render dialog and render the viewport. The rendering will have a
decidedly foggy appearance, and the fog increases in density with distance from the camera. The
dark green backdrop appears to
be completely white.

Move to a third viewport.
Start the RENDER command,
and again go into the Fog dialog
box. Change the Near Distance
from 0.00 to 0.60, and leave all
of the other settings as they are.
The rendering will be similar to
the previous one, except that
the house will be in the clear.
This is because the fog begins
just beyond the house.

For the rendering in the
fourth viewport, reduce the Far

Fog Percentage to 0.70 and leave all of the other fog settings as they are. Some of the green in the backdrop will appear through the fog in this rendering.

You should experiment on your own to see the results from various settings of fog distance and percentages. You should also see the effects of using black as a fog color. The results will be comparable to those when white is used, except that distant objects in the rendering will become darker rather than whiter.

Command: FOG

Purpose: During renderings, this command enables you to add color to objects that are beyond a specified distance from the back clipping plane. This color can enhance the illusion of distance.

Initiate with:

- On the command line enter FOG.

- From the View pull-down menu, select Render, then Fog.

- Select the Fog button from the Render toolbar.

- Press the button labeled Fog/Depth Cue in the Render or Render Preferences dialog boxes, used by the RENDER and RPREF commands.

Options:

The FOG command uses a dialog box titled Fog/Depth Cue for setting its options.

- Enable Fog

    This toggle button turns fog on and off. Although all other sections of the dialog box will be grayed out when it is turned off, their current settings are retained and will be in effect when the Enable Fog toggle is turned back on.

- Fog Background

    When this toggle is on, the fog settings will also apply to the rendering background.

- Color Controls

    Use the buttons and sliders in this section of the dialog box to set the color of the fog. You can choose between the RGB (Red—Green—Blue) and the HLS (Hue—Lightness—Saturation) color systems, and you can set the individual color components by entering values in the edit boxes or by moving the sliders. If you press the Select Custom Color button, a dialog box with panels showing a wide range of colors will be displayed for you to use in choosing a color. If you press the Select from ACI button, a dialog box showing the 255 standard AutoCAD Color Index colors will be displayed. This is the same dialog box displayed by the DDCOLOR command.

- Near Distance/Far Distance

    These two distances represent the percent of the distance from the camera point to the back clipping plane. The higher the value, the closer the distance to the clipping plane. Near Distance is the distance at which the band of fog begins, and Far Distance is the distance at which it ends.

- Near Fog Percentage/Far Fog Percentage

  The relative effect of the fog at the near and far distances is controlled by these two values. Their value can range from 0 to 1. The higher the value, the more the fog color hides objects.

Notes:

- The camera point and the location of the back clipping plane are established through the DVIEW command. The back clipping plane is perpendicular to the line of sight and is located relative to the target point, which is also established by the DVIEW command.

- While you will want to place a back clipping plane so that you can set the fog start and stop points, you will not want to turn it on. Otherwise, objects behind the clipping plane will not be visible.

- Allow plenty of room between the camera and the back clipping plane. If the distance is too short, the near and far distance settings may not work properly.

The files on the CD-ROM are in three folders

Utility   AutoLISP programs and script files referred to in the book.

Exercises   AutoCAD drawing files for the book's exercises

Bonus   Extra files that are not referred to in the book.

You can either copy all of these files to your computer at one time, or copy them individually to your computer when you are working in the chapter they pertain to. The files will all have their read-only attribute set, since they are from a CD-ROM, and you will not be able to edit or modifiy the files in AutoCAD unless you clear the read-only file attribute.

To clear the read-only attribute of a file, highlight the name of the file in Windowís Explorer. Then press the right-hand button of your pointing device to bring up a shortcut menu. Select Properties from that menu to bring up the Properties dialog box. The attributes of the file will be shown near the bottom of the General tab in this dialog box. Click the read-only attribute check box to clear it.

To make the AutoCAD files on the CD-ROM as compatible with as many AutoCAD versions as possible, they have been saved in AutoCAD Release 14 format. If you are using AutoCAD 2000, you will not notice any difference in the files as you build wireframe, surface, and solid models. However, when you work with rendering materials in Chapters 19 and 20, you may have to adjust the path that AutoCAD uses in finding bitmapped files. Instructions for changing the path to the material files are given in the bookís exercises in which this might happen.

The layers in the AutoCAD files for the exercises all use black as the object color. For many files, you will want to change the layer colors to colors that are appropriate to your computer's screen color.

Utility folder file contents

File	Chapter	Description
Helix_01.scr	5	Script file to draw a simple 3D helix wireframe curve.
Helix_02.scr	5	Script file to draw a complicated 3D helix wirframe curve.
Helix_02.xls	5	MS Excel spreadsheet file that Helix_02.scr is based on.
4_LgR.lsp	4	Makes four model space viewports with preset view directions.
spiral.lsp	5	Draws 3D wireframe helixes and spirals as 3D polylines.
join3dpl.lsp	5	Joins two 3D polylines.
mface.lsp	6	A front end for PFACE.
fplot.lsp	8	Uses 3DMESH to map mathematical functions.
globexyz.lsp	11	Additional location and size parameters for the SOLID command.
ps2ms.lsp	15	Moves objects from paper space to model space and viceversa.

Exercise folder file contents

File	Chapter	Description
mfe02108.dwg	2	Wireframe exercise.
mfe02213.dwg	2	3D Wireframe of a sheet metal part.
mfe04110.dwg	4	3D Wireframe for a house.
mfe04207.dwg	4	3D Wireframe for an automobile oil pan.
mfe05105.dwg	5	3D Wireframe for an automobile oil pan with splines.
mfe05209.dwg	5	3D Wireframe of an airplane propeller blade.
mfe06102.dwg	6	Example of extruded lines.
mfe06203.dwg	6	Three legged table made from extruded polylines.
mfe06315.dwg	6	3D model House partially surfaced with 3D faces.
mfe06402.dwg	6	Oil pan partially surfaced with 3D faces.
mfe06503.dwg	6	Surface model of an air duct made with PFACE.
mfe06601.dwg	6	3D model house with roof completed by PFACE.
mfe07101.dwg	7	3D house with doors & windows for a DVIEW exercise.
mfe07201.dwg	7	A 3D kitchen and dining area for a DVIEW exercise.
mfe08101.dwg	8	Oil pan with extra wireframe curves, ready for surfacing.
mfe08108.dwg	8	Completely surfaced oil pan.
mfe08201.dwg	8	Airplane propeller ready for surfacing. Has wireframes for hub.
mfe08207.dwg	8	Airplane propeller blade completely surfaced.
mfe08208.dwg	8	Threeblade airplane propeller surface model, with center hub.
mfe09101.dwg	9	2D polyline and axis for exercise.
mfe09201.dwg	9	3D mesh for editing practice.
mfe10101.dwg	10	Profile of a spur gear as a region.
mfe10202.dwg	10	Spur gear extruded into a 3D solid.
mfe10303.dwg	10	Helix shaped 3D solid.
mfe10404.dwg	10	Sides of a thick walled pan from extruded profiles.
mfe10503.dwg	10	Two similar profiles revolved about different axes.
mfe10603.dwg	10	Thick walled pan with corners from revolved solids.
mfe11102.dwg	11	Thick walled pan with bottom added.
mfe11201.dwg	11	Exercise in making a wedge.
mfe11302.dwg	11	Thick walled pan with cylinders added flange for holes.
mfe11402.dwg	11	Exercise in making a cone.
mfe11501.dwg	11	Solid spheres made with SPHERE and globexyz.lsp.

APPENDIX A

File	Chapter	Description
mfe12101.dwg	12	Thick walled pan with pieces unioned.
mfe12201.dwg	12	Spur gear solid model with center hole subtracted.
mfe12301.dwg	12	Thick walled pan with holes in flange. Completed model.
mfe12402.dwg	12	Pyramid made with the INTERSECT command.
mfe12505.dwg	12	2D drawing transformed into a 3D solid model with INTERSECT.
mfe12609.dwg	12	Flanged pipe elbow solid model.
mfe12708.dwg	12	Sheet metal part with complex bends. Solid model.
mfe13103.dwg	13	Three solid models for practicing fillets.
mfe13205.dwg	13	Flanged pipe elbow solid model. Completed.
mfe13304.dwg	13	Sheet metal part with fillets and chamfers. Completed.
mfe13501.dwg	13	Solid model of a wrench that is to be shortened.
mfe14102.dwg	14	Model for exercises with INTERFERE and SECTION.
mfe15301.dwg	15	Dimensioned, multiview paper space drawing of the oil pan.
mfe16104.dwg	16	Isometric drawing made from the flanged pipe elbow.
mfe16206.dwg	17	Dimensioned, multiview paper space drawing of the pipe elbow.
mfe17110.dwg	17	Demonstration of rendering features.
mfe18101.dwg	18	Solid model for exercise in installing rendering lights.
mfe18102.dwg	18	Solid model with lights installed.
mfe18201.dwg	18	3D surface model kitchen and dining area for exercise.
mfe18202.dwg	18	Kitchen and dining area with lights installed.
mfe18301.dwg	18	3D surface model house for exercise in installing lights.
mfe18302.dwg	18	3D house with rendering lights installed.
mfe19305.dwg	19	3D house with materials attached.
mfe20101.dwg	20	3D house with landscape objects installed.
mfe20201.dwg	20	3D house with distant sheds for an exercise with FOG.

Bonus folder file contents:

See the file readme.txt for the contents and description of the files in this folder.

INDEX

Page numbers in italics indicate illustrations.

Special Characters and Numbers

. (filter), 19-20
- (minus sign), 3
? option, VPLAYER, 353
@ (relative to), 19
2 option, MVIEW command, 341
2D drafting, 16
2D drawings, multiview. *See* multiview 2D drawings
2D isometric type drawings, 361-68
  hidden profile lines, 366
  layers, 365-66
  SOLPROF command, 362-68
  tangential edges, 363, 367
2D multiview drawings, 346-51
  alignment, 347
  visibility of objects, 352-55
2D polylines
  as paths, 229
  polygon mesh surfaces, 181
  surfaces, 122
2D representations, 330. See also 2D isometric type drawings; 2D multiview drawings; floating viewports; paper space
2D solid surfaces, 122
2D wireframe objects, 60-83
  3D editing commands, 73-81
  3DARRAY command, 73-75, 82
  ALLIGN command, 80-81
  apparent intersection snaps, 63
  arcs, 61
  ARRAY command, 69
  BREAK command, 65-66
  CHAMFER command, 66
  circle, 61
  COPY command, 65
  dimensions, 61-62
  editing, 63-83
  ellipses, 62
  EXTEND command, 66
  FILLET command, 66, *66*
  intersection object snaps, 63
  leaders, 62
  lines, 62
  MIRROR command, 69-71
  MIRROR3D command, 75-77, 83
  mlines, 62
  MOVE command, 65
  mtext, 62
  object snaps, 63-65, *64*
  OFFSET command, 65
  points, 62
  polylines, 2D, 62
  rays, 62
  ROTATE command, 69

ROTATE3D command, 77-79
shapes, 63
STRETCH command, 69
text, 63
TRIM command, 66-68, 72
xlines, 63
3 option, MVIEW command, 341
3D command, 202-6
3D coordinates, entering, 19-26. See also coordinates
3D curves. *See* curves
3D editing commands, 73-81
3D face surfaces, 122, 127-34
3D Objects dialog box, 202, *202*
3D Operation submenu, 73
  3DARRAY, 73-74
  ALLIGN, 80
  MIRROR3D, 75
  ROTATE3D, 77
3D Orbit command (View menu), 168-69
3D Orbit commands, 166-73
  2D wireframe mode, 166
  3DCLIP command, 172-73
  3DCORBIT command, 169
  3DDISTANCE command, 171
  3DPAN command, 170
  3DSWIVEL command, 169
  3DZOOM command, 170
  arcball, 168-69
  CAMERA command, 167, 171
  complexity of models, 166
  cursor, 168-69
  options, 167
  Preset Views option, 167
  projection option, 167
  rotation axis, 168-69
  Saved Views option, 167
  SHADEMODE command, 166
  Shading Modes option, 167
  shortcut menus, *167*
  Visual Aids option, 167
3D Orbit toolbar, 166, *166*
  3D Adjust Distance, 171
  3D Continuous Orbit, 169
  3DPAN command, 170
  3DSWIVEL command, 169
  3DZOOM command, 170
  Adjust Clipping Planes, 172
  Camera, 171
3D polygon mesh surfaces. *See* polygon mesh surfaces
3D polylines, 85-95
  closed, 86
  convert to splines, 86-87, 89
  editing, 90-95
  open, 86
  as paths, 229
  PEDIT command, 90-95
3D solids. *See* solids
3D Studio, 146
3D Surfaces command (Surfaces menu), 202
3D Views submenu, *9*

Plan View, 16
Viewpoint presets, 9
3DARRAY command, 73-75, 82
3DCLIP command, 172-73
3DCORBIT command, 169
3DDISTANCE command, 171
3DFACE command, 127-34, *128*
  edge visibility, 129-30, 132
  surfaces, 122
3DMESH command, 192-96
3DORBIT command, 9, 176-79
  Perspective option, 174, 179
  Projection shortcut menu, 174
3DORBIT shortcut menu, Projection command, 174, 179
3DPOLY command, 85-86, 88
3DSIN command, 146
3DSOUT command, 146
3DSPIRAL command, 90, 230-31
3DSWIVEL command, 169
3DZOOM command, 170
4 option, MVIEW command, 341

A

ACIS Geometric Modeler, 103, 224-25
ACISIN command, 225
ACISOUT command, 225
Acquire From option, SETUV command, 447
active viewports, 338
Adaptive Sampling option, RENDER command, 394
Adjust Bitmap button, 430
Adjust Bitmap option
  RMAT command, 440
  SETUV command, 448-49, 550
Adjust Coordinates option, SETUV command, 447
Adjust Cylindrical Coordinates option, SETUV command, 449
Adjust Planar Coordinates option, SETUV command, 447
Adjust Spherical Coordinates option, SETUV command, 450
Adjust UVW Coordinates option, SETUV command, 451
air duct model, 147-48
AI_SPHERE command, 387
ALIGN command, 80-81
align option, MVSETUP command, 350
aligning objects, 80-81
alignment, 2D multiview drawings, 347
Altitude (light), 388, 404, *416*
ambient color, 421
ambient light, 384, 404
Ambient Light option, LIGHT command, 413
AME (Advanced Modeling Extension), hiding surfaces, 153
analysis, 317-28
angdir system variable, 11, 14, 22, 34-35, 39
angle, principle axis, 320

481

Want More Information

on Working in 3D?

Check out *3D*, the leading magazine for professionals designing and animating in 3D.

- Hard-hitting reviews of new tools
- Step-by-step tutorials that teach beginner to expert-level
- Insightful case studies of innovative 3D projects

Start working in 3D today!
For more information and a free subscription, visit
http://www.3dgate.com/free/

3D **3D**gate **3D** CONFERENCE & eXPO

www.3dgate.com

Get The Latest
In Computer-Aided Design

CAD-Channel
www.cad-channel.com

Log on to CAD-Channel for the latest in computer-aided design.

- CAD Gallery
- CAD discussion groups
- CADShop
- AEC, MCAD & CAD Manager Newsletters
- MCAD Design Contest
- Online Subscription Service
- Headline News
- *CADENCE* magazine feature articles, columns, and departments
- Code Archive, Back Issues & CAD Links